GLOBAL
ENVIRONMENTAL
ISSUES

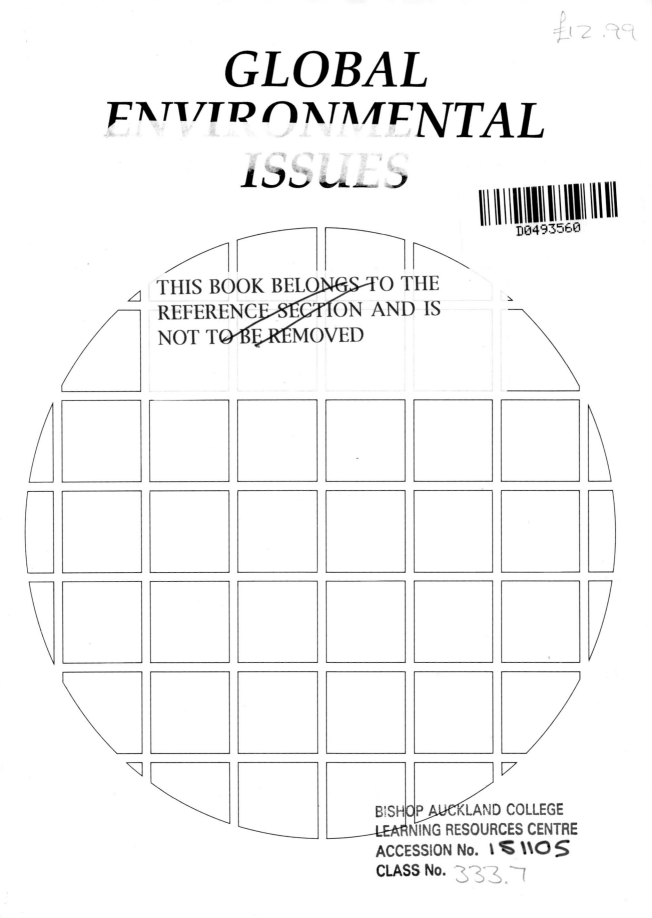

This book is the fourth in a series published by Hodder and Stoughton in association with The Open University.

Environment and Society
edited by Jonathan Silvertown and Philip Sarre

Environment, Population and Development
edited by Philip Sarre

Energy, Resources and Environment
edited by John Blunden and Alan Reddish

Global Environmental Issues
edited by Paul M. Smith and Kiki Warr

The final form of the text is the joint responsibility of chapter authors, book editors and course team commentators.

The books are one component of the Open University course U206 *Environment*. Details of the course are available from the Student Enquiries Office, The Open University, PO Box 71, Milton Keynes MK7 6AG.

GLOBAL ENVIRONMENTAL ISSUES

EDITED BY
PAUL M. SMITH AND KIKI WARR
FOR AN OPEN UNIVERSITY COURSE TEAM

Hodder &
Stoughton

LONDON SYDNEY AUCKLAND TORONTO

IN ASSOCIATION WITH

The Open
University

This book has been printed on non-chlorine bleached paper, produced in Sweden from wood from continuously farmed forests. Independent tests by the Swedish Environmental Research Group confirm that the paper mill concerned, Papyrus Nymölla AB, is the first and so far the only pulp mill producing bleached pulp in which dioxin contaminants do not occur.

British Library Cataloguing in Publication Data

Global environmental issues. – (Environment)
  I. Smith, Paul   II. Warr, Kiki   III. Series
  333.7

  ISBN 0–340–53362–5

First published in the United Kingdom 1991

Designed by the Graphic Design Group of the Open University

Index compiled by Sheila Brown

Typeset by Wearside Tradespools, Fulwell, Sunderland

Printed in the United Kingdom for Hodder and Stoughton Educational, a division of Hodder and Stoughton Ltd., Mill Road, Dunton Green, Sevenoaks, Kent by Butler and Tanner Ltd., Frome, Somerset

Contents

Human societies have long had a major impact on their environment, and their tendency to exploit it as if it were an inexhaustible resource has repeatedly led to disaster. In the past, however, pressures on the environment have typically been localised, leading only to local or regional impoverishment. For example, communities responsible for overgrazing their land or polluting their water supply could often move to new areas. Even if they could not, local hunger and disease did not necessarily affect the continued well-being of societies in neighbouring regions. In the late twentieth century the situation is different. Growth in world population and economy, increased and widespread industrialisation and the development of international trade and society have occurred on such a scale that severe environmental damage and unsustainable exploitation of the Earth's resources are taking place on a global scale.

Examples of such damage and unsustainable exploitation are all too easy to provide. Tropical forests are now being destroyed at an extraordinary rate. Between 1950 and the late 1980s the total area of tropical rainforest halved. If present trends continue, there will only be a few pockets of such forests left by the early twenty-first century, with the extinction of countless plant and animal species and – possibly – major changes to the Earth's climate.

Oil and mineral resources are being consumed rapidly by the industrialised states, irreversibly depleting global reserves at the cost of developing states and future generations. Many of the Earth's seas and oceans are being overfished. Soil degradation and erosion are occurring at an alarming rate in developed and developing regions of the world alike.

Moreover, the dumping of waste-products into the air, sea and land has reached a level at which pollution has become a severe international or global problem. For example, hundreds of millions of tonnes of rubbish are being produced each year by North American and west European states. Shortage of acceptable dumping sites at home has led to large-scale exports of waste, sometimes highly toxic, to third world and east European states desperate for foreign currency earnings. Huge quantities of waste are being dumped into the sea, leading to potentially dangerous concentrations of hazardous chemicals, heavy metals and radioactive materials. Together with sewage and oil spills, this has particularly damaged life in and around semi-enclosed seas and many coastlines and continental shelf areas.

Air pollution is similarly no longer only a local problem. Sulphur dioxide in the exhaust gases from power stations and heavy industry in the United Kingdom has contributed greatly to the problem of 'acid rain' in Scandinavia, which has damaged trees and buildings extensively. The wind and weather do not respect state boundaries. Acid rain, combined with noxious gases from car exhausts, is now a major problem throughout much of Europe, North America and Asia as well as other areas.

Acid rain and many other aspects of pollution are intrinsically transnational problems: they are the result of processes that cross international borders. In recent years scientific evidence has accumulated to show that some air pollutants are also changing the global atmosphere and climate in damaging ways. Depletion of the ozone in the upper atmosphere could dramatically increase the levels of dangerous ultraviolet radiation reaching the Earth's surface. Emissions of carbon dioxide, methane and other gases could lead to an average global warming by several degrees Centigrade by the middle of the next century, with associated coastal flooding, regional climate change and agricultural and ecological devastation.

The issue of how to tackle international environmental problems is therefore now of central importance. Such problems are rarely caused deliberately, as conscious acts of policy. Mostly they are the results of ignorance or the by-products of widely accepted economic and social activities and traditional practices. Thus an increased scientific understanding of our environment, and of human interdependence with it, is essential for any strategy to tackle these problems. An important part of this book, particularly of Chapters 1, 2 and 3, therefore aims to describe and discuss present scientific understanding of the Earth's marine environment, atmosphere and climate, and of the impact of human activities upon these.

However, increased knowledge will not improve the situation unless it is associated with changes in economic and social practices. Much of this book is therefore also concerned with debates regarding policy – about achieving international changes in human activities so as to tackle effectively some key global environmental problems. These are complex issues; researchers are still struggling to develop an adequate conceptual framework for effective analysis. In this Introduction, some key characteristics typical of international environmental problems and approaches to tackling them are discussed and a number of important concepts are introduced. Some necessary historical background is also provided. A careful reading of this material is important for a good understanding of the remainder of the book.

Unfortunately, an appreciation that certain practices are leading to the overexploitation of the atmosphere and oceans, to the ultimate impoverishment of the whole world community, will not automatically bring those practices to an end. This is an old problem, which has come to be known as 'the tragedy of the commons'. It can be illustrated using a hypothetical example of the use of the common fish resources.

Picture a sea or large lake on which many local fishing communities depend as a source of food and income. Naturally, each fisher has an immediate interest in making as large a catch of fish as s/he can sell or eat, in order to improve her or his standard of living. For centuries this arrangement has worked satisfactorily. Human populations have been kept sufficiently low by disease, war or social disruption, and fishing technology has been sufficiently primitive, that there has been no overfishing. Gradually, however, living conditions improve and human populations grow, increasing the number of people fishing and also the demand for fish. At the same time fishing technology improves. Fish begin to be caught at unsustainable levels and the total stock of fish falls.

In spite of this, each individual fisher continues to have an interest in maintaining or improving their catch. Each fisher gains the full extra benefit of catching additional fish, but bears only a small part of the extra cost of fishing a depleted fish stock because this is shared throughout the whole community. Even concerned and environmentally-aware fishers are sorely tempted to continue making large catches: they know that even if they desist, others are likely to continue to try to maximise their own catches while they can.

Thus 'rational' individual actions can lead to 'irrational' collective practices resulting in catastrophic overfishing. Unilateral acts of public-spirited restraint do not tackle the problem. If the rest of the community continues with its old ways, the public-spirited suffer along with the selfish without even having benefited from the 'good times' in the meanwhile.

Many environmental problems of industrial society have a similar structure. In an unregulated society, the owners of a factory have an interest in continuing to produce goods in the cheapest way, even if that involves dispersing untreated pollutants into the rivers or atmosphere. They gain most of the benefits of cheap production, while the pollution costs are uncertain and in any case are shared by the whole community and other species of life. In this way, governments have tended to tolerate sulphur emissions from power-stations in their territory, since the resulting acid rain is dispersed over a number of states. Moreover, the damage caused to buildings and forests typically does not appear in power-generation budgets, whereas the costs of cleaning the emissions would do so. Likewise, an operator of a modern fishing fleet has an interest in maximising fish catches, even beyond sustainable levels, in order to cover immediate maintenance costs and interest repayments. The 'tragedy of the commons' is that this depletion of common resources can continue remorselessly to their destructive conclusion, even if each organisation involved is well-intentioned, well-informed and exercising only its traditional and legal rights.

One response to the problems of overexploitation of common resources is to 'exploit and move on'. This has been the approach taken by 'slash and burn' agricultural communities in the tropical forests, cattle herdsmen in regions of Africa, and many international timber companies. Where the damage is very localised, and the scale of exploitation and population density are low, such practices may be sustainable: the environment has an opportunity to recover. Increasingly, this is no longer the case. The environment cannot recover (or is given insufficient time and space in which to recover), and there are fewer places to move on to.

Another response is 'privatisation'. If the vulnerability of communal resources is largely due to the fact that no-one specifically takes responsibility for managing them sustainably, privatisation is clearly a potential way of tackling the problem. Take, for example, the overgrazing of common land. Each commoner has an immediate interest in increasing the size of their herd kept on common land, even though this may lead to disastrous overgrazing. But if the common grazing land were divided amongst the local people, each herdkeeper would have a direct interest in grazing their own piece of land at sustainable levels.

In principle, this approach could play a significant role in improving land resource management and agricultural practices in many areas of the world. However, the private owners would have to have a clear interest in the long-term management of the resources under their control (rather than just an interest in short-term exploitation), and have the resources and knowledge necessary to their management role. In practice, such conditions would often not be met, as was shown in Book Two of this series. Moreover, a 'privatisation' policy would be hard to apply effectively in our hypothetical example of overfishing: fish would not respect any artificial division of the marine area. There are many such examples of resources or problems (such as atmospheric, river or sea pollution) that by their nature cross boundaries.

A third potential approach is to impose new laws or taxes to prevent unsustainable or damaging practices. In relation to our example of overfishing, the community or state authorities could have imposed limits on the total weight of fish caught in any year, on the minimum size of the mesh of the fishing nets (so that only mature fish were caught), or perhaps on the permitted fishing techniques. Similarly, pollution from a factory could be limited by law, or taxed according to its estimated 'real' costs to the community and environment, in line with the 'polluter pays' principle.

This approach is probably the most generally applicable. But it is clear that any system of regulations and taxes to tackle environmental problems is bound to be controversial. Some of our fishers, for instance, would deny that there is an overfishing problem. Others would dispute the total size of the catch that the lake or sea could sustainably support, and there would probably be genuine uncertainty about this.

Even when this issue was resolved, the details of the regulatory regime would be a source of bitter controversy. To 'freeze' each fisher's annual catch at some fraction of its present size would be to freeze-in existing inequalities: poor fishers would be prevented from catching up with their richer neighbours. A decision to limit each catch to a given – equal – size would challenge existing economic power structures: rich (and influential) owners of large fishing fleets would oppose it. Moreover, such a system would arguably be inequitable: fishers with larger families or who were more dependent on fishing for their livelihood could argue that they needed larger fishing quotas. The regulations would also need to be complex: some might want to catch different types of fish or other marine resources, or use the marine area for other purposes (such as for dumping or transport), and regulations to balance competing demands and needs would be debated. A system to enforce the rules would also be needed.

Such debates are characteristic of all attempts to tackle environmental problems. Ignorance about our complex environment and the effect of human activities upon it means that we are often unaware of the existence of environmental problems. Even as awareness of the potential risks grows, the scientific evidence for environmental damage may be ambiguous and incomplete. Typically the scientists struggle to get a public hearing or to obtain funding amid widespread apathy or scepticism. After all, many problems are the result of an intensification or development of widely accepted practices that do not appear to have caused difficulties in the past. Organisations with a vested interest in the continuation of the status quo seek to undermine arguments for change, and are frequently in a position to lobby powerfully, fund 'alternative' scientific work, or even to suppress relevant data. Thus science and politics tend to be intimately related to debates about environmental problems.

Once the need for action has been established, the debate focuses on the relative benefits and costs of the various strategies for action. Scientific uncertainties tend to provide plenty of scope for dispute. Although the debate is often conducted in technical terms, it is typically really about politics and economic interests: about how the costs and benefits of tackling the problem will be distributed. The outcome of the debate frequently depends more on the lobbying power of interest groups than it does on the scientific merits of the strategies proposed. If the final decision is bound to be controversial, and the risks are long-term, politicians are tempted to postpone action, at least until after the next election.

Establishing regulations or taxes to tackle environmental problems on a local or national level is thus hard enough. But at least there is a state structure for taking decisions and enforcing them on dissenting groups. This is not true at the international or global level. In the absence of a world government, authority for legislation is dispersed amongst some 160 states.

Moreover, the atmosphere and much of the Earth's oceans do not come under the jurisdiction of any one state.

A state cannot legally be forced to obey an international law to which it does not subscribe. In any case, there is no international police force to enforce any environmental laws. Thus international regulations to tackle global environmental or resource problems typically need to be adopted and implemented by consensus amongst a large number of states (although this does not mean that much 'arm-twisting' cannot occur in order to achieve agreement).

The process is further complicated by the significance of large numbers of organisations other than states in international affairs. There are hundreds of international organisations with their own secretariats and agendas, such as the UN agencies and the World Bank. There are tens of thousands of multinational corporations, financial organisations, industrial and commercial conglomerates playing an important role in activities related to the environment and resources. Increasingly transnational environmental, scientific and media groups (such as Greenpeace or the International Council of Scientific Unions) also play an important role in environmental debates.

In view of the weaknesses of international law (relative to domestic law), and the complexity of global society and its decision-making processes, it would be easy to be extremely sceptical about the possibility of establishing international regulations to tackle transnational environmental problems. However, regional organisations such as the European Community are increasingly formulating and enforcing environmental regulations. Furthermore, some progress has been made in establishing international regimes for tackling at least some problems.

The concept of an 'international regime' is an important one. Traditionally, students of international collaboration have tended to divide into three 'schools'. The first (so-called 'realist') school emphasises state autonomy and regards conflict as endemic to an international system of 'sovereign' states, given the existence of real conflicts of interest between them. From this perspective, international collaboration frequently rests on the capacity of a few great powers to coerce lesser states, although on a limited number of issues where their interests coincide (at least temporarily) there is scope for negotiating agreements.

The second school ('idealist', according to its sceptics) tends to believe that international conflict is typically a consequence of misperception, ignorance and irrationality. From this perspective, there is scope for constructing a rational world-order base on international laws founded on a natural harmony of interests.

The concept of international regimes is emphasised in a third school of thought. This 'interdependence' or 'pluralist' perspective argues that states are only one of many important types of organisation in international affairs, and are typically too constrained by interdependencies and interpenetrated by transnational structures to act unilaterally or to make effective use of military or economic coercion. However, this approach does recognise the existence of real conflicts of interest amongst all of the different international actors, and the significance of power and influence in determining the course of events.

From this perspective, therefore, international laws are vulnerable when they clash with the interests of a powerful country (or, for example, with an influential multinational company or bureaucratic institution). But it is possible for laws to be embedded within a regime of internationally recognised principles, norms, regulations and collective decision-making procedures, which have become a part of the fabric of international relations. Any state or organisation tempted to rupture this fabric would then have to take account of the disruption this would cause throughout the whole network of international interdependencies and of the consequent resistance and resentment of the international community on which it depends.

The 'pluralist' perspective on international affairs seems to be well-suited for the study of the politics of global environmental problems. As discussed above, such problems typically arise from activities involving a wide variety of actors, and involve processes for which state borders are of little relevance. Any international laws regulating these activities must be negotiated and agreed by states. But the formulation and implementation of such laws, together with associated principles, norms of behaviour and informal guidelines and rules, must involve a multiplicity of different organisations.

The early international responses to pollution and resource problems were fragmented, leading to bilateral or regional regimes. For example, the Rhine and Danube rivers are two of nine river basins in the world that are shared by six or more countries. Water pollution and water use in one of these states can affect people and organisations in the other states. The international river commissions established for the Rhine and Danube are amongst the oldest of the inter-governmental organisations.

The fact that regimes, once established, are continually under stress and open to revision is illustrated by the continuing debates about tightening environmental controls relating to these two highly polluted rivers. The political complexity of this process is highlighted by the significance in these debates of: transnational environmental organisations such as Friends of the Earth and the European green movement; national environmental groups such as Eco-Glasnost in Bulgaria, and various nature conservancy councils; transnational and national industrial and shipping lobbying organisations; government departments and nationalised industries dealing with water and energy provision; state governments; international organisations such as the European Community and the Council of Europe. Similarly the environmental regulations affecting these rivers include national laws, bilateral agreements, international river commission treaties and European Community law.

International regimes are rarely constructed in one grand agreement; they are built over a period of time and are constantly evolving. As with the river commissions for the Rhine and Danube, many of the international organisations now deeply involved with environmental policy started life primarily to facilitate and regulate international trading and economic activities. For example, the International Maritime Organisation (IMO) was originally formed in 1948 to facilitate international shipping and promote safety and facilitate navigation. It was widely regarded as a 'ship-owners club'. However, the IMO was given responsibility for implementing the 1954 Convention for the Prevention of Pollution of the Sea by Oil – a landmark treaty for marine pollution. Its role in protecting the marine environment intensified as concern grew about maritime pollution in the 1960s, especially in the Mediterranean Sea, North Sea, Red Sea and Persian Gulf. After the *Torrey Canyon* oil spill in 1967, the 1954 convention was widened and toughened in a series of amendments. The London Dumping Convention of 1972 established a framework for restricting the dumping or incineration of toxic wastes at sea. In 1973 a special conference adopted the International Convention for the Prevention of Pollution from Ships

(MARPOL), imposing a system of regulations to reduce discharges of oil. This was further strengthened in 1978 after a series of spills provoked intense concern in the United States.

IMO continues to provide a framework for debates about further regulations to protect the marine environment, although many environmentalists still regard it as unduly influenced by interest groups such as Oil Companies International Marine Forum. At the same time, regional groupings have sought to establish firmer regulations on pollution to protect the Mediterranean and North Seas, for example. Meanwhile, as discussed in Chapter 1, a new Law of the Sea was finalised in 1983, after a decade of negotiations, to provide a framework for the exploitation of ocean resources. However, by 1990 this law had yet to come into force, and in any case many of its requirements for environmental protection are vague and require further development.

International awareness of the need for environmental regulations grew through the 1950s and 1960s. Dissatisfaction with fragmentary responses to environmental problems led to efforts to establish more unified international approaches. In 1968 UNESCO held a conference on the biosphere. Later in that year the UN General Assembly adopted a Swedish resolution to convene the United Nations Conference on the Human Environment, which took place in Stockholm in 1972.

The Stockholm conference marked a turning-point in the establishment of global environmental problems on the international agenda. Shortly afterwards, the United Nations Environment Programme (UNEP) was established, which has since been a focal point for international environmental policy-making.

The Declaration on the Human Environment agreed at the Stockholm conference adopted a number of principles guiding environmental policy. These did not immediately command universal acceptance – for example, the Soviet bloc had boycotted the conference. Moreover, many 'developing' states argued in the Stockholm conference that they should not be equally affected by environmental regulations. Since they were not primarily responsible for global pollution and desperately needed to develop, they argued that regulations should not apply as rigorously to them as to developed states. As will become clear in later chapters, these arguments continue. Nevertheless, the Stockholm principles have since gained in stature. They include:

- harm from pollution should be minimised, but regulations should also take into account economic and social goals;

- the 'sovereign right' of a state not to have its territory polluted as a result of activities in another state takes precedence over the sovereign right of a state to do what it wants within its boundaries;

- the international community should determine limits on the use and abuse of 'global commons', such as the high seas and ocean resources, the atmosphere, outer space, and Antarctica.

The establishment of a consensus about the existence of a problem and broad principles guiding how it should be tackled is, of course, an essential first stage in the establishment of an international regime for managing the global environment. However, there is a great difference between establishing principles and tackling the problems effectively.

As discussed above, modest progress has been made in establishing a framework to regulate marine pollution. However, the problems are still intense, and in many respects, continuing to get worse. In comparison with marine pollution, progress on problems associated with transnational air pollution has been meagre.

In the Partial Test Ban Treaty of 1963, the United States, Soviet Union and United Kingdom agreed to end atmospheric nuclear weapon tests, which had been dispersing large amounts of radioactive material into the atmosphere. Since then, partly due to international and domestic pressures, France and China have both also ceased atmospheric nuclear tests, although they have not signed the treaty (an example of the difference between international law and the broader concept of an international regime).

In 1979 the Treaty on Long-Range Transboundary Air Pollution was accepted by some 31 states (including almost all countries in Europe, North America and the Soviet bloc). This treaty obliges signatories to limit – and if possible reduce – air pollution, to collaborate on relevant research and to employ 'the best available technology that is economically feasible' in order to combat pollution. However, the terms of the agreement are vague and lack any provisions for enforcement.

Since then, some measures to limit sulphur emissions have been agreed in Europe and North America. Progress has been made in achieving international agreements to reduce emissions harmful to ozone in the upper atmosphere, through the Vienna Convention (1985), Montreal Protocol (1987) and the review conferences following on from these agreements, beginning with the London Review Conference (1990). International discussions to formulate regulations to tackle the risk of 'global warming' were given some priority in the late 1980s. A series of international conferences and working groups were convened to prepare for a Second World Climate Conference in November 1990, where it was agreed to start negotiations on an international framework for limiting global warming. However, there is still a long way to go in achieving an effective international regime to tackle the problems of transnational atmospheric pollution.

We are therefore in a transitional period. Environmental problems have intensified in the late twentieth century, as industrialisation, population growth and other processes have increased the exploitation of resources and release of pollutants. Somewhat belatedly, the international community has begun to formulate and implement policies to tackle these problems. The question is whether international environmental regimes will be established quickly enough to avoid disaster.

The chapters that follow examine a number of these global environmental issues in some depth, outlining what is understood about the problems themselves and examining strategies for tackling them. Chapter 1 is concerned with the ocean environment. After describing the marine environment, it discusses the ways in which ocean resources are used and abused. Then the development of the Law of the Sea, which provides an international framework for the exploitation of these resources, is examined, partly in order to outline the new Law of the Sea developed in the 1970s and 1980s and partly to illustrate the politics of developing and changing an international regime. Finally, the management of the ocean is described and discussed.

The following three chapters are concerned with understanding and tackling two major global problems associated with atmospheric pollution: 'global warming' and the depletion of stratospheric ozone. These are not, of course, the only urgent air pollution problems. For example, the problem of 'acid rain' is of great international concern (and is discussed in Book Three of this series). However, at the present time the risks of global warming and ozone depletion are arguably the two most pressing and truly global environmental issues associated with atmospheric pollution.

Chapter 2 introduces the 'greenhouse effect' and its role in determining the Earth's climate, and then examines the scientific basis and results of projections that emissions of 'greenhouse gases' could be leading to substantial climatic changes over the forthcoming decades, involving an average global warming of several degrees. The chapter describes some of the potential consequences of such climate changes for the environment and for human societies, and ends with a brief outline of the choices forced upon us by the risk of these changes.

Chapter 3 introduces present scientific understanding of the natural processes responsible for the maintenance of an ozone 'layer' in the upper atmosphere, and outlines why the emission of certain chemicals threatens to deplete it. It tells the story of how this risk came to be recognised and internationally accepted, and of the measures taken to prevent further damage. This chapter builds directly upon some of the science introduced in Chapter 2. Moreover, international measures to prevent ozone depletion are further advanced than those aiming to tackle the risk of global warming, and may provide valuable lessons for this latter task. Thus, we have chosen to discuss the problem of ozone depletion before proceeding, in Chapter 4, with an examination of the prospects for preventing or reducing global warming.

The task of building an international regime to limit global warming is much more challenging than for preventing the depletion of the ozone layer. Such a regime would involve major changes in the most basic human activities. It would also have to accommodate the pressing need for economic development in the third world. Chapter 4 discusses the possibilities for reducing emissions of greenhouse gases and analyses the problems and prospects for achieving an effective international regime.

The risk of global warming puts into sharp focus an issue raised by all the environmental problems discussed in this book, and in the other three books in this series. It cannot be tackled effectively without fundamental changes in economic activities and in global strategies for economic development. Chapter 5 examines the evolution of present models for economic development, and the challenges to them. It then looks at the political and economic context within which a sustainable form of development might be achieved, that puts environmental management at a premium. The term 'sustainable development' is open to wide interpretation, but here it is taken to mean development that meets the needs of the present without compromising the ability of future generations to meet their own needs. Chapter 5 aims to develop an understanding of this concept by examining the concept itself and by evaluating two case studies of 'environmental mis-use'.

Chapter 6 develops this discussion further. First, it discusses proposals and agendas to move towards more sustainable patterns of development. Then it deepens this analysis by contrasting, ecology-centred, neo-Marxist and market-based approaches to achieving this goal.

Overall, the book aims to examine the key scientific, political and economic factors associated with major global environmental problems and with the construction of international regimes to tackle them. The issues are complex and still inadequately understood, but after completing this book it is hoped that readers will be in a position to understand, assess and contribute to the continuing debate.

1   Introduction

So far this series* has concentrated on the environment most familiar to us, the land environment. However, much more of the Earth is covered by ocean than by land – about 71% – so, in terms of its size at least, the ocean is an important environment on Earth. Up to about a hundred years ago we knew little about the ocean. Coastal-dwellers knew about the tides, and sailors something about currents, as in the days of fairly slow sailing-ships it took much longer to sail against a current. Those who fished also had some knowledge of what fish could be caught and where. But knowledge was generally limited to the surface layers of the ocean. What happened below the surface, and even how deep the ocean was, were unknown. But in spite of the difficulties of researching the ocean, there are many urgent environmental issues which make it necessary to know. Here are two which are current at the time of writing (mid 1990):

● It has been proposed that obsolete nuclear submarines could be disposed of by sinking them in deep water rather than dismantling them and dividing the materials between high-, intermediate- and low-level radioactive waste stores on land.

● Some communities in Iceland and Norway have proposed that there are enough minke whales to allow them to resume whaling.

Such proposals raise a host of questions: are there places in the ocean depths where no one will ever want to go? Can we be sure that ocean circulation will not bring radioactive materials back to the surface? How can we be sure that catching minke whales will not drive them to the verge of extinction as has happened with other species? Who decides about issues like these and who should decide?

To answer such questions, we need a basic knowledge of the main features of the ocean and the processes which occur within it. The features include the size and depth of its different regions and the salinity and chemical content of sea-water. The processes are both physical – the circulation of water both horizontally and vertically – and biological – from photosynthesis by phytoplankton to complex food webs supporting predatory fish and mammals. These are introduced in Section 2.

There are many other uses of the ocean apart from for food and dumping of waste: Section 3 looks at these uses and at how some have developed into abuses. It can be difficult to discern use from abuse, as this requires more than knowledge; it also depends on values. Competition for ocean resources has led to examination of these values and attempts to establish international laws for the ocean, an issue studied in Section 4.

So, finally, the important questions about the ocean depend on knowledge, values and the law of the sea. These are brought together in Section 5 which looks at the management of key issues, such as fishing stocks, pollution and whaling, and attempts to answer the questions outlined above.

*This is the fourth in a series: the other titles are printed at the front of the book and on the back cover.

2   The marine environment

2.1   The oceans and features of the ocean floor

The Earth has three major oceans – the Pacific, the Atlantic and the Indian Oceans (shown in Figure 1.1). The Pacific, which is the largest, is 170 million square kilometres in area, about the same size as the Atlantic and the Indian Oceans combined. It covers more than a third of the surface of the Earth and stretches almost half-way around it from east to west. It is so large that all the dry land of the Earth's surface could fit within its borders. The Arctic Ocean is much smaller than the major three and is covered almost entirely with ice. The smaller water-covered areas on the Earth are calles *seas*, such as the Mediterranean and the Caribbean. Seas may be part of an ocean – the Caribbean, for example, is part of the Atlantic – or they may be nearly separated, like the Mediterranean.

This division of the ocean into named parts is not as precise as the division of the land into continents. Whereas, for example, it is easy to see the difference between the Australian continent and the South American continent, it is not so obvious where the Pacific Ocean ends and the Atlantic Ocean starts. This is because the continents are separated (or mostly separated), whereas the oceans are all interconnected, and water flows between them: there is really only one world ocean.

Q   What is the implication of this for pollutants dumped in the ocean?

A   It may be that a pollutant dumped in one ocean may be found anywhere in the other oceans.

In practice this does not always happen, and it is possible to estimate where a pollutant can travel from knowledge of water movement. For

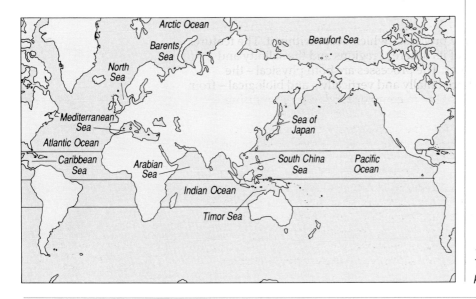

◀   *Figure 1.1*
The oceans and some of the principal seas of the Earth.

example, floating pollutants, such as plastics, in the Mediterranean Sea will remain there, as there is no flow of surface sea-water to take them out of the Mediterranean, whereas a pollutant that dissolves and sinks can flow into the Atlantic and the world ocean with a current that travels out of the Mediterranean below the surface at the Straits of Gibraltar.

How deep is the ocean? Does it get gradually deeper the further from land with its greatest depth in the middle of the oceans? If we think of the land, it does not necessarily get higher the further from the ocean, so perhaps we should not expect the ocean to get deeper further from the shore. The discovery that the ocean floor is as varied and rugged as the land – and not a flat, empty plain – is one of the most striking that oceanographers have made in the last hundred years: see Figure 1.2. The ocean floor has a number of major features, called continental margins, the deep ocean floor, ocean ridges and ocean trenches. Their position in the ocean in most cases falls into a simpler pattern than the position of features on land.

Continental margins border the land and have three distinct parts. The part closest to land and shallowest, the **continental shelf**, is generally only about 100 metres under the water and is relatively flat. At the outer edge of the continental shelf, called the *shelf break*, the steeper *continental slope* begins. The deepest part of the margin is the *continental rise*.

The continental shelf is the best known and most used part of the ocean. In width, the continental shelf ranges from almost nothing to 1500 kilometres, with an average of about 70 kilometres. It is widest where it borders low-lying land that was once covered by glaciers, or where large rivers empty into the sea (see Figure 1.3). The coast of Britain, and land around the Arctic Ocean, for example, have wide shelves. Where the land bordering the ocean is mountainous, as along the west coasts of North and South America, the continental shelf is narrow.

Although the continental shelf is covered by water, it is actually part of the coastal land. The edge of the ocean has moved back and forth over it as the sea-level has risen and fallen over geological time. At the maximum of the last glacial period when the sea-level was 130 metres lower than it is now, the shoreline must have been at the shelf break with the whole continental shelf above water.

Beyond the continental margin are the deep ocean basins. Because they are deep and flat, they are often called **abyssal** (from abyss) **plains**. They tend to lie at a depth of between four and six kilometres below sea-level. The flatness of abyssal plains is caused by a cover of sediments.

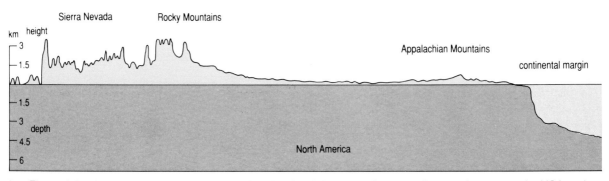

▲ *Figure 1.2   A comparison of the features of the land and the ocean floor on a line running across the USA and*

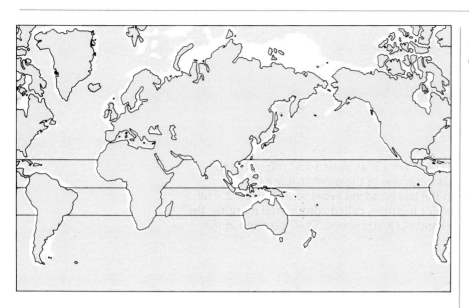

◀   Figure 1.3
The continental shelves
of the world.

Rising from the abyssal plains are enormous undersea mountain chains called **ocean ridges**. The tops of most are between two and three kilometres below sea-level. A few rise above sea-level: Iceland, for example, is the top of an ocean ridge. Ocean ridges have steep, rough sides and are similar in size and shape to mountain chains on land (look again at Figure 1.2), but they are much longer. The ridge in the Atlantic Ocean, for example, is longer than the Rocky Mountains, the Andes or the Himalayas. It runs the length of the Atlantic Ocean, and joins a ridge in the Indian Ocean which continues into the Pacific. In some oceans, including the Atlantic and the Indian Oceans, the ridges are central or mid-ocean, dividing the ocean basin roughly into two equal halves. In the Pacific, however, the ridge is closer to the eastern side of the ocean.

Dissecting the abyssal plains are **ocean trenches**, the deepest parts of the ocean, usually between seven and nine kilometres deep but descending to over 11 kilometres in some places. They are long, narrow and usually curved: they are about 100 kilometres wide and often thousands of kilometres long. There are no major trenches in the Atlantic Ocean. In the Pacific they run along the west, north and east sides, occurring just off the coast of western South America. There is a trench on the north-east side of the Indian Ocean.

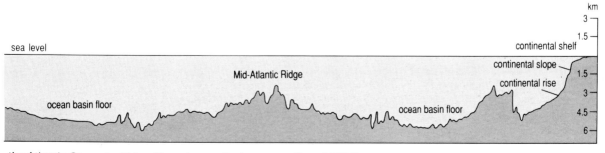

the Atlantic Ocean to Africa. There is a vertical exaggeration of 100 times.

The answers to Activities are given at the end of each chapter.

Activity 1

How deep is the North Sea?

How deep is the middle of the Atlantic Ocean?

Is the greatest depth in the middle of the oceans?

2.2   Sea-water

In Book One of this series (*Silvertown and Sarre** (eds) 1990) we learnt that the Earth's surface was covered with about 1380 million cubic kilometres of water, most of which – around 98% – is in the oceans. Sea-water has gases and solid substances dissolved in it. Although almost all the elements are present (in ion or compound form), the two most abundant are sodium and chlorine, the ingredients of common salt. These and four other elements – magnesium, sulphur, calcium and potassium – make up more than 90% in weight of the chemical elements dissolved in sea-water: see Table 1.1. The other elements are present only in extremely small quantities.

Table 1.1   The concentration of chemical elements in sea-water. The other elements are present in less than 1 part per million

Element	Parts per million by mass
chlorine	19 500
sodium	10 770
magnesium	1 290
sulphur	905
calcium	412
potassium	380
bromine	67
carbon	28
nitrogen	11
strontium	8
oxygen	6
boron	4
silicon	2
fluorine	1

The **salinity** of sea-water is the amount of these chemical elements dissolved in the sea-water. In the open ocean, the salinity at the surface ranges from 3.3 to 3.7% (that is, 3.3 to 3.7 kg of elements in 100 kg of sea-water), with an average of 3.5%. Higher percentages occur where evaporation removes much of the pure water, thus concentrating the remaining sea-water, and where water is enclosed and cannot mix with the open ocean. The Red Sea, for example, which is partly enclosed in a hot, dry area, has higher than average salinity. Lower than average salinity occurs in coastal areas where large rivers of freshwater empty into the sea,

*Authors' names in italics indicates that this is another book, or a chapter in another book, in the series.

and in polar regions where melting ice dilutes the sea-water. At depth in the oceans there is little variation in salinity, and it remains constant at about 3.5%.

Although salinity varies from one area of open ocean to another, the relative amounts of the six most abundant elements, shown in Table 1.1, and bromine, strontium and boron remain the same. By contrast the relative amounts of some of the less abundant elements in sea-water vary because marine plants use them and can deplete the supply. The most important of these elements are carbon and dissolved oxygen, but plants also need small amounts of other chemical substances, called **nutrients**, such as nitrogen and phosphorus, and although these are only present in almost undetectable amounts they are essential for life in the ocean.

Because of the dissolved substances in it, sea-water is colder than pure water when it freezes. While pure water freezes at 0°C, the temperature of sea-water must drop to about -2°C to freeze. (This principle is used when antifreeze is added to the water in a car radiator: the antifreeze lowers the freezing-point of the water.) When ice begins to form on sea-water, the dissolved substances in it remain in solution. Sea ice, therefore, is made of nearly pure water. Icebergs are not made of sea ice, but are huge chunks of glaciers on the Antarctic continent or the land around the Arctic Ocean which have broken off at the point where these glaciers meet the ocean. Winds and currents carry them out to sea. Icebergs can be dangerous to shipping and oil rigs: in 1912 the luxury liner *Titanic* sank after it hit a relatively small iceberg in the North Atlantic.

Activity 2

Q1 The average concentration of gold in sea-water is 4×10^{-6} parts per million. Taking the density of sea-water as around 10^3 kg m^{-3} how much gold is there in a cubic kilometre of sea-water?

Q2 The price of gold is around £10 000 a kilogram. What is the value of gold in a cubic kilometre of sea-water?

Given the value of the gold in only one cubic kilometre of sea-water, and considering how many cubic kilometres of sea-water there are in the oceans might justifiably make you wonder why we do not extract gold from sea-water. The answer is the cost of extraction: at the moment it is not economic as the cost of separating the gold, present in a relatively minute proportion by comparison with the other elements, would be higher than its value. Sea-water is an economic resource only for common salt, magnesium and bromine, all of which are present in much higher concentrations than gold.

2.3   Water movement

Sea-water is rarely still: usually it is in motion with waves, tides or currents.

Waves

Waves range in size from ripples to towering masses of water over fifteen metres high. They are described by their *wavelength*, which is the distance between two crests, and their *wave height*, which is the distance between the bottom of the wave trough and the top of the crest. The highest open sea wave ever measured had a wave height of 34 metres.

The main cause of waves is wind blowing across the surface of the ocean. The speed of the wind, the length of time it has been blowing, and the distance it has travelled across the open ocean influence the height of the wave. Waves are the result of the water surface changing shape, not of water flowing with the wind. The water involved in this movement is only surface water: at depths greater than half the wavelength, the water moves very little, and there is no wave motion.

Tides

Tides are caused by the gravitational pull of the Moon and the Sun on the Earth and modified by the rotation of the Earth. The pull is greatest on the side of the Earth facing the Moon, causing a high tide. On the side away from the Moon, where its pull is weakest, the water bulges away from the Moon, causing a corresponding high tide (Figure 1.4).

The Earth rotates once every twenty-four hours, and the Moon orbits around the Earth once in every twenty-eight days, so it takes longer than twenty-four hours (twenty-four hours and fifty minutes) for the Earth to rotate in relation to the Moon. During this time a place on Earth faces the Moon once and faces away from the Moon once and therefore most places have two high tides. Although most parts of the Earth have two high and two low tides every twenty-four hours and fifty minutes, a few areas have only one high and one low and some have a mixture of the two, with one high tide being much higher than the other. These differences are due to latitude, the effect of different depths of the ocean, the shape of a coastline, and the angles of the Moon and Sun relative to the Equator.

The Sun is much further away so its effect on the ocean is less than half that of the Moon. When both the Sun and Moon face the same side of the Earth at the same time, their pull is then combined and very high tides, called *spring tides*, result (Figure 1.4a). These occur every 14 days. When the Sun and Moon form a right-angle with the Earth, the gravitational pulls are in different directions, causing weaker tides, called *neap tides* (Figure 1.4b). Like the spring tides, neap tides also occur every fourteen days.

The difference between the high water level and the low water level of a tide is known as the *tidal range*, which varies from time to time and from place to place. The greatest tidal range in the world is at the head of the Bay of Fundy on the east coast of Canada, where it is up to 18 metres. The

(a)   (b)

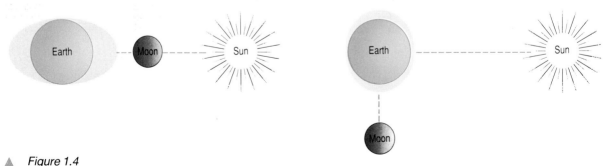

▲   *Figure 1.4*
Tides are caused by the gravitational pull of the Moon and Sun on the Earth. (a) Spring tides. (b) Neap tides.

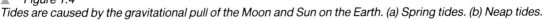

Mediterranean, by contrast, has a very small tidal range. In the English Channel, the range in most places is about two metres, while in the Bristol Channel it can be 12 metres.

Surface currents

Q   What is the main cause of the surface currents in the oceans? (This was introduced in Chapter 2 of Book One (*Silvertown*, 1990a).)

A   The winds.

Winds drive surface currents in the oceans, as well as creating waves. Winds create waves by pushing the sea surface up and down, and currents by dragging the water along with the wind. Currents do not flow directly downwind, but are deflected to the right or the left by the rotation of the Earth, depending on whether the currents are in the northern or southern hemisphere. The prevailing winds and the Earth's rotation, combined with the land masses which act as giant breakwaters on the currents, produce a pattern of rings of currents circulating in the open oceans called **gyres**: see Figure 1.5. These usually flow clockwise in the northern hemisphere and anticlockwise in the southern hemisphere.

The currents in each gyre that carry water from the Equator towards the poles, such as the Gulf Stream and the Kuroshio in the northern hemisphere, are warm. They gradually lose their heat in higher latitudes.

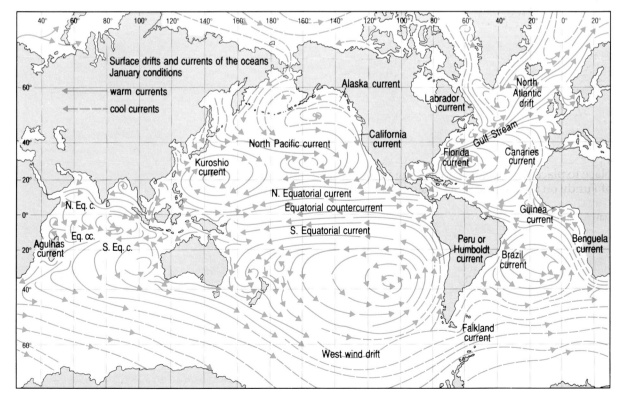

▲   Figure 1.5   The surface currents in the ocean.

The currents that return the water to the Equator are cooler. Because of this the surface currents moderate our climate, warming cool regions and cooling hot ones.

Currents are fairly weak over most of the ocean surface. Currents on the eastern side of the oceans may reach a speed of 2 kilometres per hour, while those on the western side, such as the Gulf Stream, are stronger and may reach as much as 8 km per hour. While most wind-driven currents are no more than 100 metres deep, the major currents transport enormous volumes of water. At any given moment the Gulf Stream alone is transporting more than 100 times as much water as all the rivers on Earth combined.

There is one major difference in the current systems in the northern and southern hemispheres: that is the presence of a current in the southern hemisphere which does not travel in a gyre but circulates around the world – the Antarctic Circumpolar current or West wind drift. This occurs because there are no land masses at these latitudes to deflect the current, which is driven by westerly winds.

Q   The Arctic region is generally less cold than the Antarctic region. This is due mainly to the surface current patterns in the ocean. Examine Figure 1.5 and consider the reason for this.

A   A major warm ocean current, the North Atlantic Drift, penetrates into the Arctic Ocean, bringing warm water and warming the Arctic region. There is no similar warm current reaching the Antarctic, as the Antarctic Circumpolar current prevents any warm current reaching the land area of Antarctica.

2.4   Vertical circulation, upwelling and mixing

In the last section we looked at currents in the surface water of the oceans. In this section we will examine the motion of water in the deep ocean, and the transfer of water between the shallow and deep ocean.

Deep ocean currents cannot be driven by winds as are the surface currents. Instead they are driven by density differences in the water. Colder water and water with greater salinity are denser than warmer or less saline water, and tend to sink. However, this occurs in very few places in the oceans as usually the warmest water is at the surface (Figure 1.6). The top 100 metres or so of the oceans are heated by solar radiation and are fairly warm (apart from in the polar regions), at about 10–15°C in middle latitudes and over 20°C in the tropics. The temperature decreases sharply below this depth, in a temperature gradient called a **thermocline**. Below about 1000 metres the temperature is constant at a few degrees, and this is independent of latitude: the deep waters of the tropics are at about the same temperature as the deep waters of the polar regions (Figure 1.6). The only area in the oceans where the temperatures are similar at all depths, and where the surface water might sink, is the polar regions. Here wind blowing off the ice-caps cools the surface water. When the water freezes, forming ice, this leaves the unfrozen water with a greater salinity, and therefore greater density, so this surface water sinks and flows along the ocean bottom to other parts of the oceans, even to the tropics. This water sinking in parts of the polar regions carries with it a good supply of oxygen and nutrients.

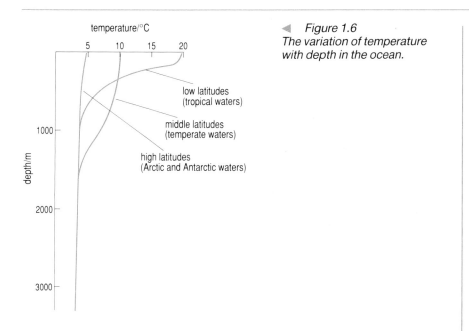

◀   *Figure 1.6*
The variation of temperature
with depth in the ocean.

How does water in the deep oceans return to the surface? One way this occurs is by **upwelling** (*Silvertown*, 1990a). Surface water may be driven offshore by an offshore or along-shore wind (Figure 1.7). This water is replaced by cold, deep water. Main areas of upwelling are the western coasts of North and South America and the western coast of Africa.

Q   Why are upwelling areas important?

A   They support major fisheries. The upwelling water is rich in nutrients, which allows the growth of phytoplankton. These are fed upon by zooplankton, which are the food for fish.

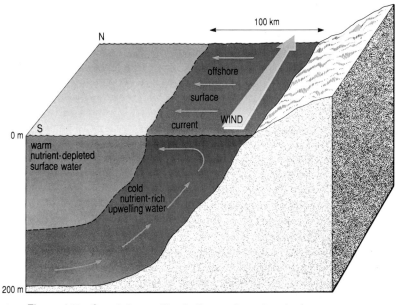

▲   Figure 1.7   Coastal upwelling in the southern hemisphere.

Upwelling can also occur in the open ocean, where wind patterns cause surface waters to move apart. This happens in parts of the Antarctic, the North Pacific and equatorial regions, and again produces areas of high productivity.

But how fast does water circulate vertically in the oceans? In particular, on average how long will it take for water at the surface of the ocean to reach the deep ocean and, with it, any pollutant we introduce to the ocean? This can be calculated from measurements of the ratio of two carbon isotopes in sea-water. The technique can be used to calculate the 'age' (time out of contact with the atmosphere) of the water. Measured ratios suggest that deep waters are between 200 and 1000 years old, that is, on average, water will spend 200–1000 years in the deep sea before returning to the surface.

Q   In Chapter 2 of Book One (*Silvertown*, 1990a) the *residence time*, the average amount of time water spends in the ocean before evaporation to the atmosphere, was calculated. How does this compare with the rate of vertical circulation in the ocean?

A   The residence time of sea-water is about 4000 years. During this time it could circulate vertically 4–20 times.

The rate of vertical circulation has implications for the deep ocean disposal of radioactive waste. One of the questions asked in the introduction to this chapter was whether radioactive waste, which remains radioactive for thousands of years, could be safely dumped in the deep ocean. With a vertical circulation rate of a few hundred years any leakage of waste from canisters in the deep sea would return to the surface ocean in a similar time while it was still radioactive. The deep ocean is not an isolated environment suitable as the ultimate garbage disposal for our most dangerous waste: anything dumped there may be out of sight only for a few hundred years.

2.5   *Marine life*

Marine organisms can be divided into **pelagic organisms**, which live and feed in the body of the sea, and **benthic organisms**, those associated with the seabed.* Plants in the oceans have to live in the **photic zone**, the top hundred metres or so of the surface waters where there is light for photosynthesis. This means that benthic plants can only grow in the shallowest parts of the ocean, on the continental shelves. The deeper ocean has no benthic plants – here plants are all planktonic, unattached and floating in the surface layers as plankton.

Q   What are the major differences between terrestrial and marine plants?

A   Terrestrial plants are large, often trees and other long-lived plants. The main marine plants are microscopic, floating **phytoplankton**, which unlike terrestrial plants have brief lives, multiply very fast and decompose very quickly when they die.

Marine plants live in a very different environment from plants on land. They derive gases for photosynthesis and respiration, and their nutrient supply, directly from the water surrounding them rather than through special structures such as leaves and roots. Consequently, the ratio of

*Life in the oceans was introduced in Chapters 3 and 4 of Book One, where marine habitats and ecosystems were discussed.

surface area to volume of a marine plant must be large, so they must be very small (e.g. phytoplankton) or have many filaments or fronds (seaweeds). They must also have a mechanism for staying in the photic zone, either attached to a shallow sea bottom or able to control their buoyancy. Unicellular plants control their buoyancy by producing oils within their cells and floating seaweeds have small gas-filled bladders on their fronds.

Phytoplankton have a very high potential rate of population increase when conditions are right. They require light and a good nutrient supply and under these conditions have a high **productivity**.

Q   Which marine ecosystem has the highest and which the lowest **primary productivity** per unit area?

A   If you have read Table 4.1 in Chapter 4 of Book One (*Silvertown*, 1990c) you will know – but you should also have been able to work out – that the highest productivity occurs in algal beds and coral reefs, and the lowest productivity occurs in the open ocean.

Algal beds and coral reefs are very productive because nutrients are recycled within the community by animals and plants. Estuaries are also highly productive, because of the supply of nutrients from land. Continental shelves are fairly productive for the same reason. Upwelling zones are usually slightly more productive than continental shelves. (This can be seen in Plate 1.) The continental shelves (such as those around Britain) have high productivity, and so do coral reefs (look around the Bahamas) and upwelling areas (the coast of Peru). The high productivity in parts of the polar regions in spring is also visible.

Marine animals, like marine plants, are also adapted to a different environment from that of land animals. For example, an animal on land, if fixed in one place, would starve, as it would not be able to search for food. However, in the oceans there are animals that live fixed in position on the seabed, with a constant supply of food brought to them in the water, without any effort on their part, by currents, tides and organic debris falling from overlying waters. Animals that live in the open ocean may be very fragile, such as jellyfish, as they can rely on the sea for support.

The abundance and distribution of marine animals depends on that of the marine plants, which are their ultimate food source, so continental shelves and upwelling areas have large quantities of animals and the open ocean very few. In an upwelling area the phytoplankton are so dense that fish can feed directly on them (a two-stage **food chain**) and even some types of whales have only three stages in their food chain (phytoplankton – krill – whales). In the open ocean, where phytoplankton are widely scattered, food chains tend to be longer.

The deep ocean floor has relatively few animals because of the poor supply of food. The animals are mainly invertebrates, crustaceans and fish which feed on the remains of dead animals falling from the waters above, or on each other. The animals are small, and grow slowly.

2.6   Summary

The major oceans, although they have different names, are interconnected.
The ocean floor is as varied as the land surface. Its main features are
continental margins, abyssal plains, ocean ridges and trenches.

About 3.5% of sea-water is dissolved gases and solid substances. The
most abundant of these substances are sodium and chlorine. Plant life in
the oceans needs dissolved carbon, oxygen and nutrients such as nitrogen
and phosphorus.

Sea-water moves in waves, tides and currents. Waves and surface
currents are driven by winds. Tides are caused by the gravitational pull of
the Moon and Sun. Deep currents are due to density differences in the
water. Upwelling systems are driven by winds. It takes around 200–1000
years for water to circulate between the surface ocean and the deep ocean.
Plants live in the surface waters of the ocean. The productivity of the
oceans varies, the most productive regions being algal beds and coral reefs,
estuaries and upwelling areas. Both marine plants and animals are very
different to land organisms.

3   Uses and abuses of the ocean

3.1   Introduction

Today we use the ocean in many more ways than a century ago, when
shipping and fishing were the only human activities associated with the
oceans. Even these uses have now changed: ships have become larger and
larger and fishing has increased to the extent that some species of fish are
threatened by overfishing.

Many of our present uses of the ocean are harmless, or fairly harmless,
but many are damaging. In considering the uses of the oceans, it is useful
to distinguish between the uses which do not remove anything from the
ocean (*non-extractive use*) and those which do (an *extractive use*, or resource).

The obvious non-extractive use of the ocean is as a separator or buffer
between countries, a use that has been of great importance to the United
Kingdom in particular. Another very important use is for transportation,
both coastal and intercontinental. Transportation is, or can be, a relatively
benign use of the ocean, except for the development of port facilities,
frequently at the expense of estuaries and other important coastal habitats,
and the pollution associated with transportation.

Other non-extractive uses of the ocean include seabed cables and oil
pipelines, the former generally harmless but the latter potentially less so.
The ocean is also used for a variety of recreational activities, most of which
are relatively harmless. However, uses of the ocean that add material to it,
such as building harbours and dumping of waste, are among the most
detrimental uses.

The extractable resources of the ocean are of two main types, the living
resources and the non-living energy and mineral resources. About 3
million tonnes of marine plants are harvested each year, mainly giant kelp
and other large seaweed. This is used for fertiliser, food, animal feed and as

a source of chemicals. About 70 million tonnes of marine fish are caught each year, and also shellfish and marine mammals such as whales and seals. In some countries the marine fishery provides a large proportion of the human protein intake, for example about 50% in Japan and about 20% in the USSR, although only about 3% in the United States.

After food, petroleum is the most valuable resource extracted from the ocean. About 27% of crude oil now comes from offshore production platforms, and about 20% of natural gas. The UK is one of the world's greatest producers of offshore oil: the only other nation with a comparable offshore production is Saudi Arabia. Extraction of this wealth from the ocean comes at a price, as accidents during production (oil-rig blow-outs) and transportation (tanker spills) can cause major disasters for coastal habitats, although on a relatively local scale.

The mineral resources of the ocean are also valuable, but overall only a small proportion of the minerals we use come from the sea (a few per cent). There are two main sources of minerals, those that are extracted from sea-water, such as salt and bromine, and those that are mined from sediments on the seabed, such as tin. Extraction from sea-water has relatively minor effects on the ocean environment, but seabed mining can be very disruptive and harmful to the local marine life.

3.2   Shipping

The main commercial uses of ships are to transport passengers and cargo, and for fishing. Intercontinental passenger traffic by sea has generally declined over the last 50 years as travel by air became faster and cheaper, but shorter distances are still often travelled by ship, for example across the English Channel.

The rise of air travel has had little effect on cargo transport, as the size and weight of most cargo make air transport prohibitively expensive. There are three broad categories of cargo: bulk liquids, bulk dry cargo and liner cargo. Bulk liquids consist mainly of petroleum, which accounts for just

▲   A very large crude carrier (VLCC), here unloading crude oil at the oilport at Teesside, north-east England.

Table 1.2   *World commercial shipping tonnages, 1983*

Vessel	Tonnage/million gross registered tonnes
Oil tankers	160
Liquified gas carriers	9
Chemical carriers	3
Miscellaneous tankers	0.3
Bulk/oil carriers	26
Ore and bulk carriers	100
General cargo	81
Container ships	14
Vehicle carriers	3
Fishing factories, carriers and trawlers	13
Ferries and other passenger vessels	8
All other vessels	11

Source: *Lloyd's Register of Shipping Statistical Tables*

over a half of the world's cargo movements. Bulk dry cargoes consist largely of iron ore, coal, bauxite (an aluminium ore), phosphate (for fertiliser) and grain. Liquid and dry bulk cargoes form about 80% of world cargoes. The rest is shipped in mixed cargoes of small consignments of various items, carried on liner vessels and container ships instead of bulk carriers. The relative importance of the different ships and cargoes can be interpreted from Table 1.2.

Oil tankers have the greatest tonnage of all shipping on the ocean. The largest individual ships are also oil tankers. The first ships specifically built as tankers were small, carrying around 5000 tonnes of oil, but the decision of the British Navy to switch to oil from coal in its ships in 1912, a policy rapidly followed by other navies, led to the building of larger tankers, up to 15 000 tonnes. A further growth in the use of oil in vehicles and in boilers between the two World Wars led to a large growth in tanker tonnage, and the building of supertankers. Much of the oil was transported between the Middle East oilfields and western Europe and the tanker size was largely limited by the size of the Suez Canal. Closure of the canal following the Anglo–French attack on Egypt in 1956 and after the Arab–Israeli war in 1967, and a growing demand for oil, led to the building of even larger tankers, known as **very large crude carriers (VLCC)** of around 250 000 tonnes, and now the even larger **ultra large crude carriers (ULCC)** of over 400 000 tonnes. The VLCCs and ULCCs have their own problems of draught, limitation to deep water, manoeuvrability and stopping distance.

Q   From Figure 1.8, what are the two main oil transport routes?

A   From the Middle East to western Europe by the South Atlantic, and from the Middle East to Japan.

The Suez Canal, although open and offering a much shorter route to western Europe, is used much less than the South Atlantic route because of tanker size.

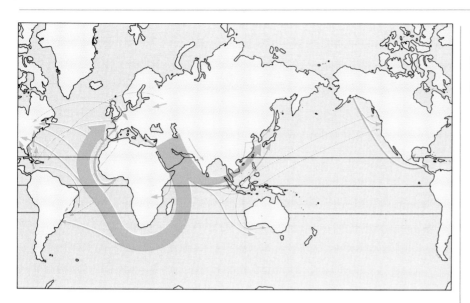

Figure 1.8
The main oil transport
routes by sea in 1980.
The arrow width
represents the tonnage.

How safe is shipping? Over a million tonnes of shipping is lost at sea
each year, and a far greater amount is damaged, often leaking cargo into
the sea. Loss and damage is due to insufficient charting of the seabed, bad
weather, collisions or human error. Insufficient charting may seem
surprising for present-day ships, but many areas are daily navigated by
ships whose charts have not been updated since the days of steam. For
example, the $25 million ore-carrier *Igara* was holed on an uncharted rock
near Singapore in 1975: the most recent surveys of this area were done in
1907.

The greater size of present ships does not make them invulnerable to
bad weather: in some cases their length makes them more vulnerable.
Immense freak waves, for example, are known to occur at times in various
areas of the oceans, particularly in the southern Indian Ocean off the east
coast of Africa. Here the ships use the southerly Agulhas current
(Figure 1.5) on passage to the Atlantic. When this current meets storm
waves from Antarctic waters, very high waves can form, over 30 metres
high. A small ship may ride over one wave, but two or more waves may hit
a larger ship at the same time, raising each end of the ship but not
supporting the middle section, causing the ship to break in two. Many
ships have vanished totally in the Agulhas current but the route continues
to be used, as it is the fastest and therefore most economic route around
Africa.

Many ship casualties arise from human error of the 'dangerous driving'
kind. The busiest shipping lane in the world, the English Channel, has had
many of these. An example is the *Texas Caribbean*, a tanker which ran
aground on Varne Bank in 1971. The same day, another ship, the
Brandenburg, collided with the grounded tanker and sank, taking the
further holed *Texas Caribbean* with her. A few days later a third ship, the
Niki, hit the uncharted wrecks.

It is the loss and damage of ships that produces the greatest damage to
the marine environment by shipping, through the loss of their cargo, and
coastal states now usually have emergency action plans for coping with
large oil spills, but they do not always work. The relatively small spill of

37 000 tonnes of oil from the VLCC *Exxon Valdez* in Alaska in 1989 was an environmental disaster, despite an emergency clean-up operation costing $1000 million. Twice the English Channel has had greater spills: 100 000 tonnes in 1967 from the supertanker *Torrey Canyon* (at this time there was no emergency action plan in existence) and 230 000 tonnes in 1978 from the VLCC *Amoco Cadiz*. These spills have highlighted the question of whether VLCCs and now ULCCs should be allowed passage in busy shipping lanes or in environmentally important areas and, if not, how to legislate to prevent their passage.

3.3   *Military use*

The military use of the ocean is generally to support a nation's land interests, but is also increasingly in support of its marine interests. The traditional purpose of a navy is the protection of the nation's shores, the safeguarding of its merchant fleet and the intimidation of smaller nations by a naval presence ('gunboat diplomacy'). More recently navies have been used to protect national interests in marine resources. The 1970s 'Cod War' between Britain and Iceland was an example of this, and less obviously the war between Britain and Argentina over the Falklands in 1982, since sovereignty of the islands confers the right to exploit the ocean resources around them and this area may have large petroleum reserves. The strategic use of navies has also become very important. Nuclear-powered submarines with intercontinental nuclear missiles are essential parts of the major navies, together with the associated anti-submarine warfare capabilities, which involves other nuclear submarines.

Military activities have similar pollution effects as civil shipping, and in addition are the main cause of radioactivity entering the ocean. Up to 1963,

▲   *The underwater atom bomb explosion in Bikini lagoon, 27 July 1946. Atmospheric fall-out from the explosion released radioactive isotopes into the ocean over a large area of the Pacific.*

when the Partial Test Ban Treaty came into force, nuclear weapon tests were carried out in the ocean, which had lethal effects locally but also released radioactive isotopes into the ocean, which have had much wider effects. Radioactivity still enters the ocean from atmospheric nuclear test fall-out. Accidents involving nuclear weapons can also lead to contamination: for example, about 390 grams of plutonium were released into the Atlantic Ocean off Greenland in 1968 as a result of an accident involving four nuclear bombs, killing or contaminating marine organisms over a considerable area. Nuclear-powered submarines have also been lost: two at least from the USA, the *Thresher* in the western Atlantic in 1963 and the *Scorpion* in the central Atlantic in 1968, and at least six from the USSR. Leakage of radioactive isotopes from the break-up of the submarines' reactor power plants, as well as from nuclear missiles, is of concern.

Military activities also have the occasional local beneficial effect on the ocean. The prevention of fishing in large areas of the ocean owing to wartime activities permits the building of fish populations. Fish catches on the Atlantic continental shelf of Europe were remarkably better when fishing recommenced after the Second World War than before it. As a fish conservation plan, however, wars are a drastic solution.

3.4   Food resources

In Section 3.1 the living resources of the oceans were introduced as the most valuable resource we extract from the ocean, most of it as fish, with smaller amounts of other marine animals and plants.

Q   What is the general difference between the main type of food obtained from the ocean and that from the land?

A   The main foods produced on land are plants, cereals and root crops (*Grigg*, 1991), which provides mainly carbohydrates. The main food from the ocean is fish, which provides protein.

Protein is an essential part of the human diet, but is supplied only in small quantities by cereals and root crops, so that many people in developing countries suffer from a protein shortage. Later in this section we will consider whether the ocean could supply more protein than at present, to alleviate this protein deficiency.

Activity 3

This activity relates to the distribution of fish and other animals in the ocean. Use earlier sections of this chapter (and *Silvertown*, 1990c) to list the factors that will influence the distribution of animals in the ocean, in terms of both location and depth.

Thus the food resources of the ocean are not distributed evenly throughout the ocean, but are concentrated in the surface layers of the ocean near to land (continental shelf areas) and upwelling areas. This uneven distribution influences the way that we get food from the ocean, in comparison to how it is done on land. Food gathering on land is almost entirely by farming, by planting crops and keeping domestic animals. In the ocean, food is mainly gathered by hunting, and this is easier in the areas where the animal populations are densest.

There are three main methods of catching fish, with the choice of method depending on the behaviour of the fish being hunted. **Demersal (bottom-living) fish,** such as cod, haddock and plaice, feed on the benthic fauna of continental shelves. These are caught by a bottom trawl (Figure 1.9a). Pelagic fish such as herring, anchoveta and sardines, which feed on the good supply of planktonic organisms over the continental shelves are caught by a drift net (Figure 1.9b), or a mid-water trawl. Fish that live in the upper parts of the deep oceans are much less abundant, and do not form shoals. These include tuna, bonito and shark. They are caught by a number of methods, including long lines (Figure 1.9c), rod and line, and nets.

The north Atlantic, the south-east Pacific (off Peru) and the north-west Pacific (near Japan) produce the highest catches of fish. The oldest fisheries are in the north Atlantic, catching herring, haddock, cod, plaice, mackerel

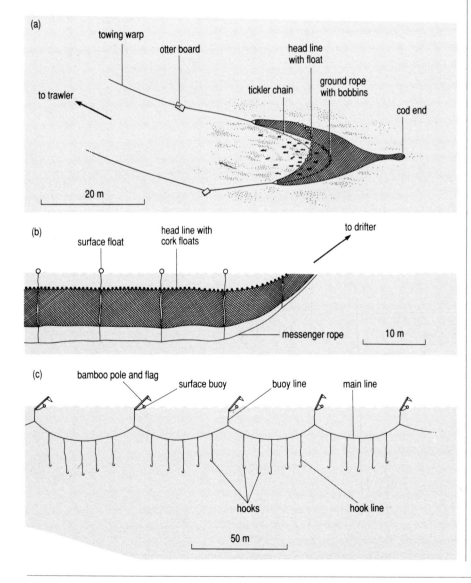

◀ *Figure 1.9 Commercial methods of catching fish.*

(a) A bottom trawl, used on continental shelves for demersal fish.

(b) A drift net, used over continental shelves for pelagic fish.

(c) A long line, used over the deep ocean areas for pelagic fish.

and sardine mainly on and over the continental shelves of Europe and
North America: see Figure 1.10. Nearer the Equator, pelagic fish such as
sardine, menhaden and mackerel are fished, and demersal fish become
unimportant. Many other pelagic species, such as hake and tuna, are
fished in the tropical Atlantic. The south Atlantic produces smaller
quantities of fish, mainly hake (often in the shallow waters around the
Falklands), pilchards (near Africa) and horse mackerel.

In the Pacific, the Peru fishery catches just one fish, the anchoveta.
The Japanese fishery catches anchovy, mackerel, saury, and also an animal
which is not a fish – squid. Pollack, herring and cod are also important in
the North Pacific, and salmon and shellfish off the west coast of North
America.

The Peru anchoveta fishery is, or can be in some years, the largest
fishery in the world ocean, catching over 12 million tonnes in 1970 and
providing a third of Peru's export earnings. However, the catch is very
variable: in 1972 it fell to 4.5 million tonnes and 1973, 1.8 million tonnes,
with disastrous effects on the Peruvian economy. This was due to
large-scale atmospheric and oceanographic variations. The anchoveta eat
phytoplankton, which grow in large populations in the upwelling waters
off Peru. The upwelling is driven by the south-east Trade winds which
drive surface water off the coast of Peru. If these winds blow less strongly,
the upwelling is less and fewer phytoplankton grow, providing less food
for the anchoveta, a situation called 'el Niño'.

Fish catches can also decline because of overfishing. This occurs when
fewer fish are caught even though the fishing effort is increased by more

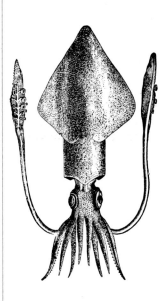

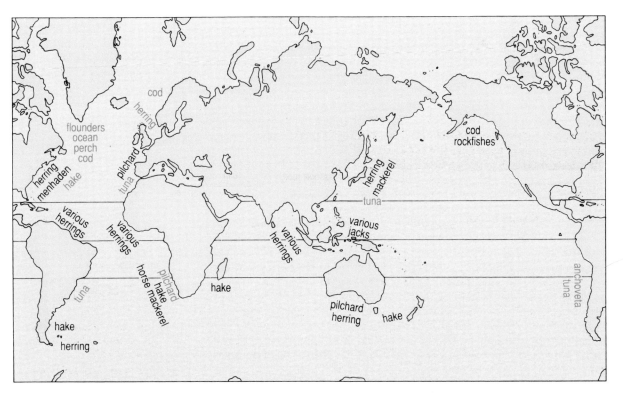

▲   Figure 1.10   Major world fisheries. Those in green have been overfished, or are in danger of overfishing.

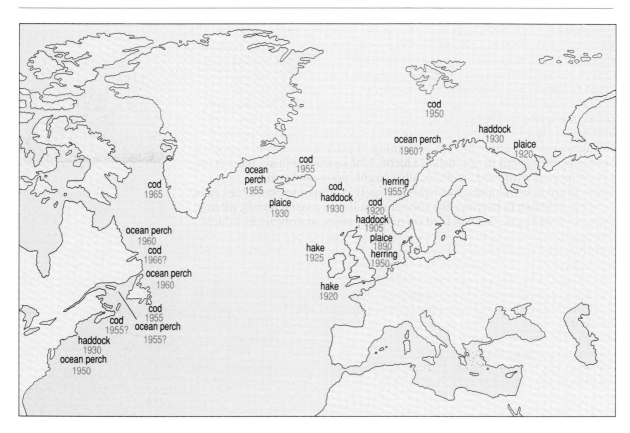

boats or better fishing gear. Ideally a fishery should be regulated to produce a maximum catch with the minimum of fishing effort (fisheries management will be discussed in Section 5.2), but this is difficult to achieve, often for political reasons, such as individual countries setting their own limits on how many fish can be caught, when in combination the limits may result in overfishing, or for economic reasons: what is worse, overfishing or laid-up fishing boats and unemployed fishers? An example is the north Atlantic fishery, where overfishing began as long ago as the last century in the North Sea (shown in Figure 1.11). The overfishing of plaice was followed by cod and haddock by 1920. By the 1950s the same had happened to North Sea herring, hake to the west of Britain and cod, haddock and plaice off Norway and off Iceland. Between 1955 and 1966 cod, perch and haddock off the North American coast were also overfished.

▲ *Figure 1.11*
The North Atlantic fishery, with the dates of the beginning of overfishing for each fish population.

Another problem affecting marine food resources is that of pollution. Coastal areas and estuaries in particular are subject to pollution from land, and the many fish, clams, mussels, crabs and other shellfish which breed in these areas are particularly vulnerable to pollution. These animals may concentrate pollutants in their bodies and even if they survive the pollution, they may be unsafe for human consumption. In the Minamata Bay area of Japan mercury compounds were discharged into the sea as waste products from a chemical factory. The mercury in the water was concentrated by shellfish, which were collected by fishers in the area. In 1963 it was discovered that the shellfish were the cause of mercury poisoning of the local people, causing 45 deaths.

As well as hunting food in the ocean, it is also possible to farm it, to harvest enclosed populations of fish and shellfish, a process called

mariculture. The shortage of food in the developing countries and the value of some types of fish and shellfish in developed countries has led to a recent expansion in mariculture. In principle it is more efficient than conventional fishing, as the fish do not have to be hunted, and could provide continuous, not seasonal, supplies.

Shellfish (oysters, mussels and clams) are successfully cultivated on farms in Europe and America. They feed directly on phytoplankton carried to them by water currents, and so are most suited to coastal areas with strong tidal water movement. The farming of salmon, trout and lobsters is becoming important in Scottish sea lochs. Unlike the shellfish, these have to be supplied with food, often locally caught, poor-quality fish. Mariculture in developing countries is largely confined to South East Asia, farming milk fish (a herring-like fish) and mullet in coastal ponds, often in mangrove swamps. The fish feed on marine plants, mainly algae, which grow in the ponds. Although mariculture has many advantages of cost and supply over conventional fishing, it produces other problems, particularly to the local environment, such as the effect of uneaten fish food and fish wastes and chemical pesticides used for disease control in the fish, which can deoxygenate the local waters and upset the natural ecology of the area.

Can the supply of food from the oceans be increased by a large enough amount to make a significant contribution to world food shortages and protein deficiency? There is little hope of increasing the catch of the conventional fisheries in many regions of the world, but some areas are under-exploited (they could produce a larger catch), particulary the south Atlantic, west-central Pacific and the Indian Ocean, although none of these regions seems to have the productive capacity of the existing main fishing areas. There is also the possibility of greater use of non-fish species, which are underexploited in many areas. Squid, for example, have a large market only in Japan. Krill, a small shrimp-like animal, is abundant in Antarctic waters in summer and is the main food of some whales, but is not yet harvested in large quantities. Much of any new catch that is not directly attractive to human beings may be converted into fish-meal, a protein-rich powder that can be stored without refrigeration. This could provide a protein supplement in developing countries but at the moment is mainly used as animal feed (for most British chickens, for example). Most of the Peruvian anchoveta and other small fish are converted into fish-meal.

The marine catch by country is given in Table 1.3.

Q   Is the catch by country related to the population size?

A   Partly: four of the countries in the top eight have large populations (Soviet Union, China, United States, India).

Q   Is the leading fishing nation a great consumer of fish?

A   Yes: marine protein is very important in the Japanese diet, about 50% of the protein intake (Section 3.1).

Q   Why do the low-population countries Peru, Chile and Iceland have large marine catches?

A   For Peru and Chile this is because of the large anchoveta fishery in their coastal waters. Iceland also has a high catch, partly because of availability of fish, but mainly because fishing is the traditional and main industry of the country. (Most of the catch from each of these countries is exported.)

Table 1.3   *The marine catch in 1986, for countries with catches over 1 million tonnes*

Country	Catch/ million tonnes
Japan	11.73
Soviet Union	11.03
China	7.84
Peru	5.50
Chile	5.46
United States	4.84
South Korea	3.03
India	2.87
Indonesia	2.47
Thailand	2.08
Philippines	1.88
Norway	1.86
Denmark	1.83
North Korea	1.67
Iceland	1.63
Canada	1.44
Mexico	1.27
Spain	1.27
Taiwan	1.18
Ecuador	1.00

Notes: The UK catch was 0.86 million tonnes. Other countries with catches between ½ million and 1 million tonnes were France, Brazil, South Africa/Namibia, Vietnam, Bangladesh, Poland, Myanmar (Burma), Malaysia, Morocco, Turkey and Italy. The catch includes all animal and plant products and includes mariculture.

3.5   *Energy resources*

The ocean can be used as a supply of two main types of energy: energy
from motion of the sea-water in waves and tides and energy from
petroleum, stored in the rocks beneath the ocean floor.

The energy in waves comes from winds, and so ultimately from solar
power. The energy in a wave depends on the height and speed of the
wave, so potential wave-power sites need a reasonably constant supply of
high and fast waves.

Q   What factors determine wave height?

A   Wind speed, length of time it has been blowing, and distance travelled
across the open ocean (Section 2.3).

Some of the highest global wave energies occur in the North Pacific
(a power 10^5 W per metre) and to the north-west and north-east of Scotland
(5–7×10^4 W per metre). About 5×10^9 W of wave power could be supplied
by the ocean around Britain, about 20% of Britain's requirements. Waves
could also supply the same power for Norway (about 50% of Norway's
requirements) and 2×10^{10} W for the USA (about 7% of the United States'
requirements).

The energy in tides is gravitational, from the Moon and Sun. A high
tide is trapped behind a dam in an estuary, and the difference in
water-level used to turn a turbine to generate electricity. The power
generated depends on the difference in water-level on opposite sides of the
dam (the tidal range) and the volume of water trapped behind the dam, so
a large volume estuary (but with a narrow neck to minimise the dam
construction cost) is necessary for a tidal power site. There are many
estuaries with large tidal ranges that are suitable, particularly in the English
Channel, Siberia, Alaska and Canada. A proposed tidal power station in
the Severn Estuary could supply about 1.5×10^9 W, about 6% of Britain's
requirements.

As well as being able to supply a significant proportion of the world's
energy requirements, wave and tidal energy have the advantage that they
are renewable energy sources. They are also non-polluting, with no acid
rain, greenhouse gas generation or radioactive waste disposal problems.
However, despite these advantages there is only one wave or tidal power
station of significant size in operation, the 2.4×10^8 W tidal power station
on the Rance estuary in Brittany.

There are two main reasons for this, the most influential one being the
cost. Electricity generated by tides or waves is more expensive than that
from conventional power stations, because of extremely high capital costs:
the Severn proposal has been estimated at about £8500 million, even
though the long projected life of the power station, about 100 years, would
make it competitive in the longer term. The Rance power station has been
in operation since 1966 and will continue whereas conventional power
stations of equivalent age have been closed down or are reaching the end
of their life.

The second reason is the effect on the environment. Environmental
effects involve changes to the estuary behind a dam or the ocean on
offshore wave power barrages involving current and sediment movement
and the build-up of pollutants. Locally, these effects will be substantial, but
because they are local it is difficult to compare them with the national or
global environmental side-effects of conventional power stations. Which

◄   *The tidal barrage and power station across the Rance estuary uses the rise and fall of the tides to generate electricity. This has been in operation since 1966, but is still the only large tidal power station in existence.*

are the most environmentally damaging? Would you prefer to live next to a tidal power station or a coal or nuclear one? If your answer is 'tidal', would you also be willing to pay a higher price for your electricity?

Petroleum can occur beneath the ocean floor of the continental margins, the parts of the oceans which are geologically similar to the land. While petroleum was easily available and plentiful from sources on land there was little incentive to extract it from rocks under the ocean, as this requires working in a more difficult environment with more complex and expensive technology, leading to a higher petroleum price. However, increasing demand and the OPEC price rises in 1973 led to the development of offshore petroleum fields. The major offshore petroleum-producing countries are Saudi Arabia and the UK, but Abu Dhabi, the USSR, the USA and Venezuela are also important producers. About 27% of crude oil and 20% of natural gas now comes from offshore.

Offshore exploration and production of petroleum produces environmental effects that can be more damaging than from land-based exploration and production, because of the ease with which any oil spill can spread over the ocean surface and be moved over large distances by tides and currents. In Section 5.4 we will examine oil pollution in more detail. Estimates of the contribution to oil released in the ocean by offshore production are around 0.1 million tonnes a year, which although large is only a small proportion, about a few per cent, of the total amount of oil that reaches the ocean.

3.6   *Mineral resources*

The mineral resources of the ocean can be divided into four main categories:

- the non-metallic aggregates (sand and gravel, calcium carbonate)
- minerals obtained from sea-water
- placers (shallow water metallic minerals)
- deep ocean metallic minerals.

Aggregates are the most important mineral resource extracted from the ocean. Sand and gravel are found on beaches, from cliff erosion, and on parts of continental shelves where they have been carried by rivers or are ancient beach sediments from times of lower sea-level. They are extracted by dredging. The cost of recovery is generally more expensive than on land and increases with water depth, so most aggregates are extracted from shallow water, less than 30 m deep. However, the final cost of marine sand and gravel may be cheaper than from land sources if it is used in coastal areas and shipped. The USA, Japan and the UK use large quantities of marine sand and gravel (the Channel Tunnel alone used $2\frac{1}{4}$ million tonnes) but on a global scale the marine supply is only a few per cent of the total.

Calcium carbonate is the other main aggregate mineral, and is used to make cement. In countries without limestone rocks on land, particularly in tropical countries, calcium carbonate offshore sands, formed from the shells of marine organisms, are mined.

Although sea-water is a gigantic store of many minerals, most are present in very low concentrations (Section 2.2) and only common salt, magnesium and bromine are extracted in significant quantities. Salt is produced in the coastal areas of hot countries by solar evaporation of water in shallow evaporating ponds. Magnesium and bromine compounds are precipitated directly out of sea-water by treating sea-water with other substances.

Placers are metallic minerals in beach and continental shelf sediments, mainly minerals of tin, iron and titanium. They have been eroded from ore bodies on land and carried to the ocean by rivers, like sand and gravel, and are separated by the movement of sea-water from the less dense sand and gravel. They are extracted by dredging, generally from shallow water, less than 50 m deep. The main mining areas are Indonesia and Malaysia for tin, Japan for iron and Florida, Sri Lanka and Brazil for titanium. The marine production of these metals is, however, only a small proportion of the world production: 5–10% for tin and titanium and less than 1% for iron.

There are also *metallic minerals* in the deep ocean, polymetallic (or manganese) nodules on the abyssal plains, and metalliferous sediments and crusts on ocean ridges. The main metals in the nodules and sediments are manganese and iron, but their main value lies in the smaller quantities of nickel, copper and cobalt. They exist in vast quantities, but are not being commercially exploited for two main reasons. The first is that the cost of mining in the deep ocean, involving raising the minerals 3–5 km from the ocean floor, is higher than mining on land. The second is the lack of agreement between nations on the rights and profits from mining in an international area: this problem is considered in detail in Section 4.

Extraction of minerals from the ocean can have considerable environmental effects. Dredging is damaging and often lethal to benthic organisms and also affects pelagic organisms by stirring up large quantities of sediment into the sea-water. Nearshore dredging can often lead to beach and coastal erosion as the dredged material may be part of a seasonal beach sediment cycle. Deep ocean mining would bring deep sea-water to the surface which would be colder, have a different salinity, and probably a higher nutrient content.

Comparing these environmental effects with the effects of land mining is difficult, as was the comparison between the effects of land and marine power stations. If done with care, marine mining is probably less environmentally destructive than that on land, but less is known about the long-term effects on the marine environment, especially for the deep ocean, so marine mining could have unexpected side-effects.

3.7   Waste disposal

Human society produces large amounts of waste. Disposal of this waste can be on land, to the atmosphere (mostly by incineration) or in the ocean.

There are two opposite and extreme views on waste disposal in the ocean. The earlier was that the ocean is so vast that any waste we add to it will be made more or less harmless by dilution and have no effect on the ocean as a whole. The opposite view is that the ocean is damaged by any introduction of materials from land alien to the environment of marine plants and animals. The reality lies somewhere between these extreme views: the oceans can accommodate a substantial, but not unlimited, part of our waste production and in doing so can protect valuable resources on land, such as space and the quality of the water we drink. Waste disposal to the ocean is also often the cheapest option.

The main questions of ocean disposal are what *kinds* and how *much* waste the ocean can take. The oceans are not naturally 'pure': they already contain large amounts of most substances, although at lower concentrations, and can tolerate more, but how much more can be tolerated without damage? Most ocean waste disposal takes place in coastal or continental shelf waters, with some local areas having heavy and continuous use, and where these are partially isolated from the rest of the ocean and not dispersed the waste can have undesirable effects. These effects include covering up of benthic habitats, stimulating the growth and death of plants (which uses up the dissolved oxygen necessary for other marine organisms) and toxicity.

The main wastes dumped in the ocean are:

- dredged sediments from rivers and harbours
- rock from land excavations
- sewage in raw form or as treated effluent or sludge
- various industrial wastes and heated water.

The waste may be discharged from land by a pipeline (sewage effluent and heated water) or loaded onto a ship and taken further offshore for dumping (dredged sediments and sewage sludge).

Dredged sediments are a natural substance of the marine environment, but by being moved elsewhere cause turbidity in the water (reducing photosynthesis) and can bury benthic communities. Unless the dumping is continuous these effects are short-lived. *Sewage* contains a number of substances, with different effects on the ocean. The effects of raw sewage on beaches and of disease organisms in sewage are obviously damaging. Sewage contains the plant nutrients nitrogen and phosphorus, and these may be beneficial or damaging: generally the ocean is poor in nutrients and their addition to the oceans in sewage disposal may benefit plant and animal communities in the same way as do nutrients in upwelling waters. The fish catch in many east coastal areas of England is greater than that in the rest of the North Sea, probably because of sewage disposal into the sea. However, it is possible to overwhelm a local area of the ocean with nutrients, producing excessive algal growths or phytoplankton blooms that poison marine animals. Sewage also contains organic matter which uses dissolved oxygen as it decomposes, and in large quantities may deplete an area of the oxygen necessary for marine plants and animals.

Many types of *industrial waste* are dumped in the ocean. Up until 1973 wastes from the china clay industry were dumped into the ocean off Cornwall. Waste from coal mining and slag from iron smelting have been dumped on beaches in northern England. (See Plate 7.) These wastes have severely disrupted the ecology of the areas, reducing and changing the numbers and types of organisms, and are examples of disposal of waste in the ocean with little thought for the consequences.

Substances of potentially greater damage to the oceans are compounds of the heavy metals, such as mercury, cadmium and copper, which are waste-products from chemical, mining and other industries. These are toxic, and disposal on land is inadvisable as they can be dissolved in groundwaters and affect water supplies. Because of this, heavy metal waste has often been dumped in the ocean. Some marine plants and animals can build up high concentrations of these metals from sea-water with no apparent harm, but they are poisonous to other animals and humans that eat them: the problems with mercury in Minamata Bay (Section 3.4) were an example. This does not necessarily mean that no heavy metals should be dumped in the ocean, but does mean that we still need to investigate the effects and pathways of heavy metals in the ocean and that any dumping must be strictly controlled. For example, some heavy metals are essential in small quantities for life in the ocean, but how much more heavy metals can we dump in the ocean without causing problems?

The ocean may also be used for the disposal of *radioactive waste*. For example, nuclear fuel reprocessing at Sellafield discharges radioactive materials into the Irish Sea (*Sarre*, 1990). These include caesium-137 and plutonium which are discharged in liquid form through a pipeline. Radioactive materials may adversely affect all organisms. Although emissions from Sellafield and plants in other countries are limited by the International Commission on Radiological Protection (ICRP), the Sellafield experience has shown that radioactive disposal in shallow coastal waters can lead to human exposure, through consumption of marine shellfish and by accumulation of radioactive particles in beach sediments. The deep ocean floor has also been considered for the disposal of high-level

◀ *Industrial effluent being discharged into the North Sea at Hartlepool, Cleveland. The outfall comes from the Steetley Refractories chemical plant which is visible in the background.*

radioactive waste in containers, the assumption being that containers could be built that would not leak, at least during the active lifetime of the waste, or if leakage occurred, that the deep oceans are sufficiently isolated for the leaked waste not to return to the surface ocean. We have seen that this last assumption is false (Section 2.4) and many countries, including the UK, have now abandoned plans for deep ocean radioactive waste disposal.

The ocean is also used as a repository for a completely different type of waste – *thermal waste*, hot water resulting from the use of sea-water for cooling in power stations or industrial processes. These plants are situated near a source of water, sometimes rivers and lakes, but often the ocean. In Britain, for example, all but one of the nuclear power stations are on the coast in order to use sea-water for cooling. The water is returned to the ocean about 10°C warmer than its original temperature. This temperature rise can have both beneficial and detrimental effects on the marine environment. The temperature difference is within the range of natural temperature variations in the oceans (except in tropical and polar regions) and is not harmful to many adult marine animals. An increase in temperature increases their metabolic rate and can be used in mariculture to increase growth rates. However, a temperature rise also decreases the solubility of oxygen in the sea-water and this, combined with increased metabolic rates, can lead to oxygen deprivation. Plankton and the small eggs and larvae of marine animals can be sucked into the power plant with the cooling water, and the sudden rise in temperature can be fatal.

Overall, our disposal of waste in the ocean has had little effect on it. Locally, however, some estuaries, coastal regions and semi-isolated seas have not fared very well. Some hazardous materials should perhaps not be discharged into the ocean at all, and there are some international agreements on this, such as the London Convention for the Prevention of Marine Pollution by Dumping of Wastes and Other Matter in 1972 (the **London Dumping Convention**). In all cases, waste disposal in the oceans should be compared with disposal on land and incineration to the atmosphere on environmental, technical and economic criteria. After all, we have to do something with our waste: we cannot just ignore it, but neither is the old idea of 'out of sight, out of mind – dump it in the ocean' necessarily valid.

Activity 4

List the advantages and disadvantages of disposal (a) on land and (b) in the North Sea of excavated material from the site of the National Gallery extension in London. The excavated material is a mixture of soil, rock and building rubble.

3.8   A need for legislation?

Many of our uses of the ocean are relatively harmless and exploit the vast resources of the ocean to the benefit of humankind. However, in some cases, overexploitation, such as overfishing, or inappropriate use, as in the disposal of certain wastes, has led to damage to the marine environment. There have also been disputes between states over which state has the right to use which bit of ocean; should the USA dump radioactive waste, for example, in the ocean at all, and if so, in its coastal waters, where they are a potential problem just for the USA, or in the deep ocean, where they become a lesser problem, but shared by other states? Issues such as these have led to attempts to establish an international legal regime for the ocean, which we will examine in the next section.

3.9 Summary

The traditional uses of the ocean were shipping and fishing, but we now use the ocean in many more ways. Some of these are non-extractive uses, and some are extractive uses, or resources.

The main non-extractive use is shipping. Extractive resources are of two main types, the living resources and the non-living energy and mineral resources, and as a repository for waste disposal.

Our more extensive uses of the ocean have led to abuses of this environment, by over-use or inappropriate use. For this reason, and because of disagreements about resource exploitation between states, it is necessary to have an international agreement on the legal regime of the oceans.

4   The new Law of the Sea

4.1   Introduction

Before 1945 the regime governing the use of the oceans was based on the principle of 'freedom of the seas'. Coastal states' territorial waters, where they had full sovereign power, generally extended three miles* from the coast – approximately the range of the first coastal artillery. Beyond that distance, the 'high seas' belonged to no-one. In these areas, according to common law, shipping and fishing could proceed unhindered. This customary law was enforced by the great naval powers, particularly Britain. These powers had a national interest in maximising their freedom of operations at sea, although in practice they did not shrink from interfering with other states' ships during international conflicts.

After 1945 this regime began to erode. Since the late 1960s the fundamental principles of the old law of the sea have been widely challenged. The demise of the old regime has been so rapid that three United Nations Conferences have been held to attempt to codify new rules. The first of these was held in 1958, closely followed by a second in 1960. The **Third United Nations Conference on the Law of the Sea (UNCLOS III)** met from 1973 to 1982, and culminated in the UN Convention on the Law of the Sea which was signed by 119 states on 10 December 1982. This gigantic treaty – 320 articles and 9 annexes – has been called a constitution for the oceans, and must rank as one of the most important pieces of written international law of this century.

It provides for a massive extension of coastal state jurisdiction over adjacent ocean space. Beyond that, its clear message is that the resources of the high seas must be managed internationally, with the notion that the

*It is traditional to use (nautical) miles, rather than kilometres, when referring to maritime limits and regulations, and we follow this convention in this book.

oceans are a 'Common Heritage of Mankind' joining that of 'Freedom of the High Seas' as the founding principles of international law.

The new Law of the Sea has yet to come into force. For that to happen, it must be ratified by 60 states. By 1990 the United States, United Kingdom and West Germany had not even signed it. Most of the states that did sign the Convention have yet to ratify it – that is, the states' legislatures have yet to confirm their agreement in a constitutionally binding manner. Nor is such ratification automatic: a number of key developed states besides the three mentioned above have major reservations about aspects of the Convention. So the framework for the exploitation of ocean resources is still hotly contested.

This section examines the politics of the development of the new Law of the Sea, and outlines its main provisions. This provides a basis for the discussion of ocean management in Section 5. It also provides an important illustration of the issues and problems, as introduced in the Introduction to this book, relating to the establishment of new international regimes to manage global resources.

4.2   The erosion of the old regime

To its later regret, it was the United States that made the first direct challenge to the 'old' Law of the Sea after World War II. The Truman declarations of 1945 claimed US jurisdiction over certain high seas fisheries within 200 miles of the North American coastline, and over the resources of the continental shelf to a depth of 200 metres. The declarations were deliberately formulated ambiguously, in an attempt to avoid damaging the overall regime – which it was in the United States' interest to preserve.

However, the process quickly spread to Latin America. In 1947 Chile claimed rights over both fishing and the continental shelf along its ocean border, followed by Ecuador and then by Peru in 1953, which defined its economic jurisdiction at 200 nautical miles from its coast – the estimated breadth of the Peru current. By 1970 a total of 11 countries had claimed jurisdiction over about 1 900 000 square nautical miles of ocean. At the same time, there was a more widespread trend to extend territorial waters from 3 to 6 or 12 miles.

There were a number of powerful underlying processes eroding the old regime. After 1945 the oceans ceased to be regarded as an inexhaustible resource. Instead they became an area of intense competition for the extraction of potentially scarce goods. This was reinforced by advances in technology, which greatly increased the scale and efficiency of fishing and made it more feasible economically to extract oil and mineral resources from the seabed. Meanwhile, non-extractive uses of the ocean intensified. The density of shipping traffic in many areas made navigation complex and dangerous, and oil tankers and other vessels threatened to pollute coastal states. This generated pressures to redefine **innocent passage** (whereby vessels were allowed to pass through a state's **territorial waters** provided that they intended no harm to that state), and to limit freedom of the seas.

At the same time, the dissolution of the old European empires led to a rapid increase in the number of states: from about 40 to some 150 between 1948 and 1976. Many of these new states have sea coasts, and nearly all are developing countries. These typically had no stake in the old law of the sea, dominated as it was by the developed maritime powers. At first the more established ex-colonial states in Latin America took the lead in challenging the domination of the developed 'North' (as they saw it), but these were joined by newer states in the 1960s. Thus ocean politics became enmeshed in the highly-charged debates between the developed and developing states.

Differences of interest also existed within each of these groups. Developing states broadly divided between inland countries and those that had sea coasts. In the United States, United Kingdom and other maritime developed states, divisions developed between groups such as fishing communities and oil companies, most concerned with the exploitation of coastal resources, and those that wanted to preserve the freedom of the seas for global shipping and naval operations, and for fishing in distant areas.

In this context, revision of the old law of the sea became inevitable. Unregulated claims to ocean resources, and widespread attempts to impose unilateral restrictions on rights of passage or mineral extraction or fishing would lead to chaos and conflict. However, the increasing complexity of the political and economic issues and alignments ensured that the reform process would be difficult and contentious.

The First UN Conference on the Law of the Sea was held in Geneva in 1958, and was attended by 86 states. The agenda was set by the major maritime powers, who aimed to limit the erosion of the old regime. Four conventions were signed, relating to freedom of the high seas, conservation of fisheries, limits on territorial seas and fisheries jurisdiction, and economic rights over the continental shelf. In the first two of these, the principles of the old regime were bolstered fairly successfully and a framework for conservation policy and dispute settlement was agreed. The third and fourth issues proved more difficult, and the wording of the conventions had to be fudged pending the second conference that was reconvened in Geneva two years later.

The second conference came within a whisker of success. A compromise proposal to agree to 6-mile territorial limits and a 12-mile area of jurisdiction over fishing only just failed to obtain the necessary two-thirds majority. On the question of economic jurisdiction over the continental shelf, states had to be satisfied with an agreement to 'sovereign rights' (a fudge between full sovereignty and vague 'rights') out to either 200 metres depth or to 'exploitable' limits (a similarly vague formulation).

Although the North–South issues were already apparent in these conferences, the dominant political divisions ran along East–West lines. In retrospect, the 1960 conference represented a high point in international agreement. Between 1963 and 1966, the four conventions came into force. But as the 1960s progressed, the fragmentary process of unilateral claims and bilateral or regional agreements continued, and the exploitation of ocean resources intensified. The two conferences could not halt the demise of the old regime.

4.3   Setting the agenda for UNCLOS III

In the mid 1960s, as East–West relations improved, the USA and USSR agreed amongst themselves that a Third UN Conference on the Law of the Sea (UNCLOS III) should be called to update and further codify the customary laws of the sea. They were concerned that the extensions of territorial waters and areas of economic jurisdiction were eroding their rights of passage, and thus the areas of operation for their naval forces. Unless these customary rights were reaffirmed and defined in international law, the rights of innocent passage for their naval and commercial vessels

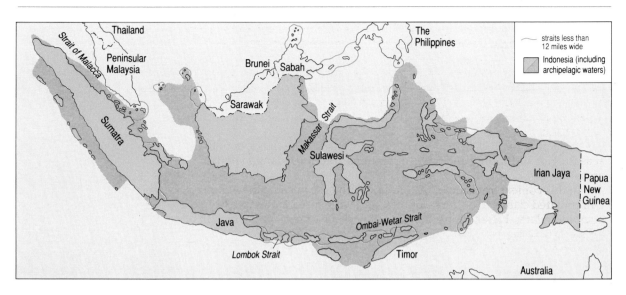

▲   *Figure 1.12   The seas around South East Asia: these waters include important international navigation routes, several of which have been threatened by an extension of territorial waters to 12 miles unless rights of innocent passage have been reaffirmed (as illustrated on the map).*

might be limited. This was particularly worrying in relation to international straits – without clear transit rights, the extension of territorial seas to 12 miles could close some 125 straits of potential importance (such as the Bering, Gibraltar and Malacca Straits, and passage through the seas around Indonesia and the Philippines: see Figure 1.12).

In 1966 the USA and USSR worked out a skeletal Law of the Sea treaty comprising only three articles. On the first two they were in complete agreement: a maximum 12-mile territorial limit and free passage through international straits. The USSR had reservations about the third article, providing for preferential fishing rights in adjacent seas. The USA proposed this in order to win support from coastal states. To the United States it seemed worthwhile to accept extended jurisdiction over fishing and resource exploitation in coastal waters if this could ensure the freedom of the seas for naval forces.

However, the agenda of the conference broadened in a way that was unwelcome to the superpowers. In November 1967 a Maltese minister, Arvid Pardo, made a historic speech at the UN General Assembly. He noted that advances in technology were opening up the possibility of the extraction of resources on or below the deep seabed. The potential wealth of these resources was staggering. In addition to sunken treasures, many analysts at the time estimated that 'manganese nodules' (containing manganese, nickel, copper and cobalt) lying on the ocean floor could be worth trillions of dollars. The possibility of deep-sea oil-wells, and mining of polymetallic sulphides and cobalt-, manganese- and nickel-bearing crusts under the seabed further emphasised the great value of the resources under the high seas.

Arvid Pardo argued that the wealth of the deep seabed should be declared to be part of the 'Common Heritage of Mankind', and that the Law of the Sea should be revised to ensure that it was shared by all members of the international community. To this end, he proposed that an International Seabed Authority should be established to manage deep

You call it the common heritage of mankind—what about us fish?

seabed mining. This position was soon incorporated in resolutions of the UN General Assembly. Third world states, co-ordinated through the **'Group of 77'** (a group of developing countries, originally 77, that operates mainly in the United Nations), adopted this proposal as an element in their campaign for a New International Economic Order and promoted it consistently thereafter.

Q Consider the interests of the developed maritime states on this matter. How were they likely to regard such a proposal?

A The USA, the UK and other developed states have an interest in a minimal framework to assure orderly seabed mining, but not in a supranational management authority and a scheme to redistribute wealth to developing nations. After all, it is the developed states, and the large mining consortia based in them, that actually possess the capital and technology to mine the deep seabed. However, the notion of an area to be administered as the 'common heritage of mankind' was at least better than a national enclosure movement, where claims to exclusive rights over the seabed and fisheries extended even beyond 200 miles. Moreover, the maritime powers wanted to get the negotiations under way, in order to establish rights of passage. So the proposal for an International Seabed Authority was not rejected out of hand.

Pardo and others (such as Alva Myrdal of Sweden) also broadened the conference agenda in other ways. They foresaw that nuclear missiles or anti-ballistic missile systems might be based on the seabed, and argued for a ban on the use of the deep ocean floor for military purpose. Furthermore, they drew attention to inadequate controls over the dumping of radioactive and toxic wastes in the high seas, and over other sources of pollution such as oil spills. These issues were also taken up in General Assembly resolutions. Thus the major naval powers lost control of the conference agenda.

4.4   The Third UN Convention on the Law of the Sea

In formal terms, UNCLOS III began in 1973. In fact, however, the discussions really began in December 1967, when the General Assembly voted to establish the Ad Hoc Committee to study the peaceful uses of the seabed. After much debate, this resulted in a treaty forbidding the emplacement of weapons of mass destruction on or under the seabed in the high seas. This implicitly involved an agreement that the limits of territorial waters would be set at 12 miles from the coast. The treaty was signed in 1971 and, having received sufficient ratifications, came into force in 1972. For the superpowers, which in any case had no plans to place their nuclear weapons on or under the deep seabed, it seemed to be a small price to pay if it would clear the way to negotiations for a treaty to recognise naval rights of passage.

The negotiations for UNCLOS III began in earnest in 1974 and lasted until 1982. They were often bafflingly complex, involving thousands of delegates and experts. Aware that the major powers were really most interested in establishing rights of passage, the majority of states agreed that the new regime would be negotiated as a 'package'. It would be regulated according to one single convention, which states would have to accept or reject as a whole: they could not sign up only to the parts that they liked.

Q   Consider the consequences of this approach for the negotiating process.

A   One consequence of this was that the negotiation process became very complex and prone to delay, as trade-offs were made. For example, inland states with no direct interest in regulations over fishing jurisdiction could obstruct the negotiations on this issue unless their own concerns about an entirely different article of the treaty were taken into account.

As the negotiating agenda became clear, states rushed to establish their claims. In the early 1970s, the notion of an **Exclusive Economic Zone (EEZ)** gained popularity, as an increasing number of states extended their claims to jurisdiction over sea and seabed resources within 200 nautical miles of their coast (see Figure 1.13). Between 1970 and 1977 the ocean area claimed by coastal states increased from 1.9 million to almost 20 million square

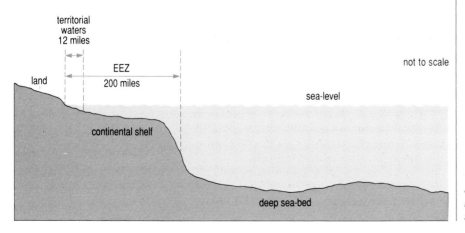

◀   Figure 1.13
Simplified sea-bed profile, illustrating areas of coastal states' jurisdiction.

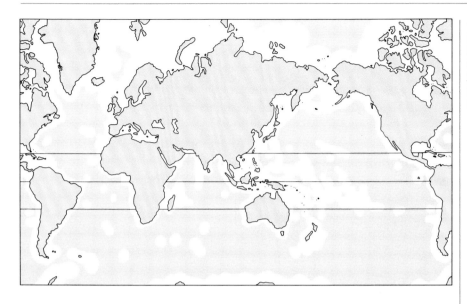

Map indicating the areas of
Exclusive Economic Zones.
If all coastal states claimed
200-nautical-mile EEZs,
they would cover 36% of
the area of the oceans.

nautical miles. Part V of the 1982 UN Convention recognised such claims, implying that a total of about 28.5 million square nautical miles of the Earth's global commons were transferred to the jurisdiction of coastal states – a figure that exceeds the combined land area of Australia, Europe, Africa and North and South America (see Figure 1.14). For many island states, the areas of their EEZs greatly exceeded that of their land territory (shown in Figure 1.15).

This transfer was achieved more or less peacefully. One of the great successes of the 1982 Convention is that it lays out procedures for settling disputes, which become binding once it comes into force. Provision is made for an International Tribunal for the Law of the Sea, as well as a number of other conflict resolution and adjudication bodies. Governments, companies and individuals will all have standing in these dispute settlement procedures.

In its Exclusive Economic Zone a coastal state would have sovereign rights over the resources of the zone, to exploit the minerals and to conserve and manage the fisheries. They would also have jurisdiction over marine research and any installations such as oil rigs, and over the protection of the environment. Further, they have a duty to protect the marine environment in this area, although their right to impose more stringent regulations than the 'generally accepted international rules and standards' is very limited unless they can persuade the **International Maritime Organisation** of their case. An exception to this is in the Arctic Ocean, where Canada and other states bordering the Arctic Ocean won greater rights to regulate potentially polluting activities in ice-covered areas.

Parts II and III of the 1982 Convention establish the right of innocent passage of all naval and commercial vessels through the waters of an EEZ, and also of overflight by aircraft. Further, they provide for the right of innocent passage through the territorial waters of another state. The Convention also establishes the right of all ships (and submarines) to 'transit passage' through international straits, except in the case of 'historical straits' such as the Dardenelles where a separate regime in international law has long been established.

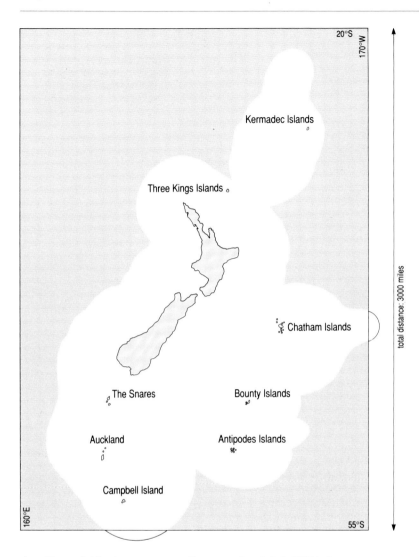

20°S
170°W

Kermadec Islands

Three Kings Islands

Chatham Islands

total distance: 3000 miles

The Snares   Bounty Islands

Auckland   Antipodes Islands

Campbell Island

160°E

55°S

▲   *Figure 1.15   In many cases the area of a state's EEZ is far greater
than its land area: the example of New Zealand.*

The 46 articles of Part XII of the 1982 Convention deal with the
'protection and preservation of the marine environment'. They avoided
getting to grips with the problems of pollution from rivers and land-based
sources: these raise the difficult issue of national sovereignty, and were
opposed by many developing states as well as groups in the developed
world. Developing countries argued that they could not afford to spend
money on environmental protection. Indeed, a Brazilian delegate even
implied that pollution was a symbol of economic progress in the third
world. By the end of the negotiations, in 1980–82, these attitudes were
beginning to change, but negotiations on this part of the treaty had been
completed and few wanted to risk reopening the issue. So the Convention
limited itself to general exhortations on pollution from sources on land,
and focused on pollution from ships instead.

In this area, a substantial number of agreements already existed such
as the MARPOL Convention (1973) and the London Dumping Convention

(1972), as described in Section 3.7 and the Introduction of this book. At the insistence of a number of states, such as Canada, Australia, Kenya, Indonesia and Spain, UNCLOS III was conceived as an 'umbrella' convention which sought to bring these existing conventions, and the declarations of the 1972 Stockholm Conference on the Human Environment (as discussed in the Introduction to the book and in Section 5) within one legal framework. Thus, various articles restrict 'harmful' dumping of waste or the release of oily waste from ships on the high seas. Further, there is an obligation on states to 'cooperate, to the extent possible, in eliminating all the effects of pollution and preventing and minimising the damage', and to 'jointly develop and promote contingency plans for responding to pollution incidents' on the high seas as well as in coastal areas.

In the main, the further development of specific environmental protection regimes beyond the conventions of 1972 and 1973 mentioned above was left to existing 'competent organisations' such as the International Maritime Organisation and the International Atomic Energy Authority. However, the 1982 Convention did create a new category of state with rights and duties: the 'port state'. Such states can start proceedings against a ship in one of its ports that is suspected of making illegal discharges on the high seas or in another state's EEZ. For example, if a ship unloading at Rotterdam was suspected of discharging pollutants illegally in the North Sea, the Dutch government would be entitled to begin proceedings against its owners.

Much the most contentious aspect of the negotiations related to Part XI of the treaty, which dealt with arrangements to control and manage seabed resources under the high seas. This is not surprising, in view of the differences of interest between most developing and developed states on this issue, as discussed above.

The third world governments, organised in the 'Group of 77' (but consisting of 116 members by 1980), argued strongly for an **International Seabed Authority (ISA)** that would control and manage the exploitation of deep seabed resources and the distribution of the profits to the governments of the whole international community. The prospect of receiving vast amounts of capital to contribute to economic development meant that the Group of 77 was unwilling to compromise on the principle that the deep seabed resources were part of the 'common heritage of mankind'. For inland states, which would not benefit from the establishment of EEZs, Part XI of the Convention was the only part that promised direct benefits, and they were prepared to obstruct negotiations on other parts of the treaty in order to obtain them.

Not all third world states had an unambiguous interest in the mining of minerals on the seabed. Several countries, such as Zambia, Zaire, Papua New Guinea and Botswana, depend greatly on earning foreign currency by mining copper and other minerals in their territory (Figure 1.16). Seabed minerals threatened to reduce world prices and thus foreign currency earnings. These states therefore joined with developed states in a similar position, such as Canada, to restrict and regulate the rate at which seabed resources could be mined. Interestingly, however, the political solidarity of the Group of 77 was sufficient for them to present a united front against the United States, United Kingdom and West Germany and other developed states that were strongly opposed to the proposed ISA.

Most developed states were basically opposed to international control and management of these seabed resources. In opposing the Group of 77 proposal, they argued that the key to seabed mining was to provide

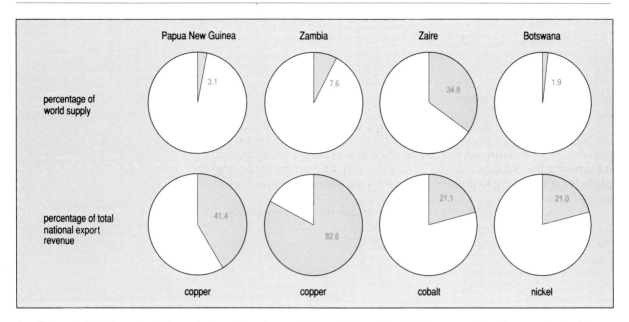

▲ *Figure 1.16   Some land-based mineral producers that would be vulnerable to competition from seabed mining.*

assured access, security of tenure, and assurance of a reasonable profits that would make it feasible to risk the billion dollar investments that would be necessary even to begin exploiting these resources.

In the end, a compromise was formulated. The ISA and mining consortia would mine 'in parallel'. Adjacent parcels of seabed would be exploited: one by a private company and the other managed by the ISA. Any company or state wishing to extract mineral nodules or mine the deep seabed would apply to the ISA for a licence, and would pay tax on its earnings. The ISA would have first choice of which parcel to manage, and its own mining operations would initially be underwritten by the West. It would have access to western technology 'at fair commercial rates'. To accommodate mineral producers such as Zambia, seabed mining would be limited to supply only a proportion of growth in world demand.

4.5   *The ratification process*

The UNCLOS III negotiations finished in 1982, when the new Convention was signed at Montego Bay, Jamaica, by 119 states. Another 38 states signed the agreement in the following two years. Since it was not possible to agree only to parts of the treaty, the governments of the USA, UK and West Germany refused to sign, declaring opposition to the international regime for deep seabed mining. Twelve other states also decided against signing, for a mixture of reasons.

Legally, the 1982 Convention only comes into force after it has been ratified by 60 states. By spring 1991 only 45 states had ratified the treaty, and further progress seemed to be slow. Even if it does ultimately come into force – there are enough third world states to ensure that it does – the reality is that the new regime would be gravely weakened if the USA, UK and Germany continued to oppose important sections of the treaty and if many other developed countries maintained their reservations.

Throughout the 1980s the United States, United Kingdom and West Germany tried to detach the unwelcome seabed regime from the rest of the Convention. They argued that the other parts of the treaty have entered into international common law – a disputed contention. Arguably, their continued opposition to Part XI of the convention threatens to undermine the international agreements to rights of passage that the USA and other maritime powers want so much to sustain.

In the late 1980s the USSR, France, Japan and India became the first 'Registered Pioneer Investors' in the seabed regime, and four multinational mining consortia were similarly registered. However, the decline in mineral prices, and the discovery of substantial mineral deposits on the continental shelf adjacent to the United States, meant that hopes in the Group of 77 for substantial profits from deep-sea mining came to little.

Thus the Third UN Convention on the Law of the Sea was not yet established by 1990, and may be subject to revisions in the future. Nevertheless, the Convention provides an important framework for ocean management and a major example of efforts to construct international regimes to manage global resources.

4.6   Summary

The Third UN Convention on the Law of the Sea (UNCLOS III), signed in 1982, provided for a new international regime for the management and exploitation of the oceans. This section has examined the development of this new regime, and discussed some of its main provisions.

Activity 5

Review this section and prepare notes on:

(a) the main reasons why a new law of the sea was needed;

(b) the main interest groups involved in UNCLOS III negotiations; and

(c) the extent to which these interest groups have achieved their objectives.

---

5   Ocean management

5.1   Introduction

This section examines the management of the ocean and its resources. UNCLOS III has, in some situations, helped to clarify rights and responsibilities, but does not solve all management problems. Only a few issues can be discussed here, so these have been selected as representative of the different aspects of ocean management.

Fisheries management and pollution control are large-scale ocean management topics in this section, involving all parts of the ocean. A study of the whaling industry is used as an example of fisheries management in the high seas area that involves international cooperation and agreement.

The management of the North Sea is used as a comparison. This is an area which is also under the control of more than one state, but is within the states' EEZs, with national legal rights and responsibilities.

5.2   Management of fisheries

It may seem initially that the UNCLOS III has solved one of the major problems of fisheries, that of international disagreement over fishing rights and quotas. It establishes the right of each coastal state (and places a responsibility on each coastal state) to implement policies which will achieve and maintain an optimum yield from the living resources within its 200-mile wide EEZ and to decide on allocations of fishing rights to fishing vessels of other countries. We have already seen that coastal regions have the most abundant and important food resources (Section 3.4) so the national control of fisheries in these regions clarifies the responsibility of management for most of the world's fisheries. However, fisheries management still has problems. These arise from the mobility of fish (they do not recognise national boundaries!), interaction between various fish and other species, and overfishing. To understand these problems, it is necessary to look at what controls the population in a fishery.

The total biomass (weight) of a fish species (the **stock**) is increased by the growth of adults in the population (G) and from young fish (recruits) joining the population (R): see Figure 1.17. ('Stock' is a term that may also be used to mean number of fish.) The stock is depleted by death from disease, old age and predation (natural mortality M) and capture by fishing (fishing mortality F). The stock, gains and losses are related by the equation:

end stock = beginning stock $+ (G + R) - (M + F)$

In an equilibrium fishery, the stock does not change, so that:

end stock = beginning stock

and:

$$(G + R) = (M + F)$$

The efficient management of a fishery should give the greatest catch year after year (the **maximum sustainable yield**) while maintaining an equilibrium stock. It is unfortunate that the maximum sustainable yield can often only be estimated once a fishery has been overfished. The following discussion illustrates this.

A stock of fish is generally greatest when it is not being exploited. In this state it includes a high proportion of larger and older fish. When

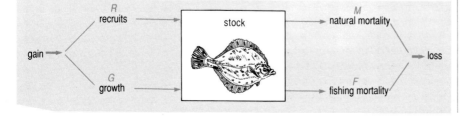

◀   *Figure 1.17*
The controls on stock size in a commercial fishery.

fishing begins, the large stock yields large catches to each fishing boat, but because there are few boats the total catch is small. Increased fishing reduces the stock, so the loss due to natural mortality decreases, and is less than the gains from growth and recruitment ($G + R$ greater than M). If the catch is less than the difference between natural gains and losses the stock will tend to increase ($G + R$ greater than $M + F$); if the catch is more, the stock will decrease ($G + R$ less than $M + F$): this is **overfishing**. When the stock neither increases nor decreases, it is in equilibrium, making a sustainable yield possible. This sustainable yield is a maximum when the stock is somewhere between two-thirds and one-third of the unfished stock. In this state the average size of the individuals will be smaller and the age will be younger than the unfished stock, and individual growth will be highest.

The maximum sustainable yield can also be related to fishing effort. Initially the total catch increases as the fishing effort increases (more or bigger boats or better fishing gear). This tends to encourage an even greater fishing effort, until the total catch begins to fall due to overfishing (shown in Figure 1.18). The maximum sustainable yield is possible when there is a moderate amount of fishing. This can either be obtained by fishing the older fish heavily and leaving the younger ones alone, or by catching moderate amounts of fish of all sizes.

There are two types of overfishing – growth and recruitment. **Growth overfishing** occurs when too many small fish are caught, so that their growth potential is not exploited. **Recruitment overfishing** occurs when too many adults are caught, leaving not enough fish to spawn to produce new recruits. This occurs rarely, as fish lay so many eggs that usually recruitment does not depend on the adult stock but on other factors, although if it does occur it is more serious than growth overfishing as it can threaten the survival of the whole stock.

The herring fishery in the North Sea is an example of overfishing. The fishing effort increased gradually between 1950 and 1962 but the catch remained fairly stable at 0.85 million tons. There was a big increase in effort from 1963 onwards, which combined with good natural recruitment in 1961 produced a peak catch of 1.4 million tons in 1965. The catch decreased to 0.7 million tons in 1970 and continued to decrease throughout the 1970s. This decline was due to first growth overfishing, then recruitment overfishing: by 1969 herring larvae numbers had declined to only about 20% of their numbers at the beginning of the 1960s, severely depleting the recruitment to the adult stock and endangering the population. The situation was so severe that in 1977 Britain imposed a ban on North Sea herring catches, and the stock has now begun slowly to increase. If this fishery can be managed effectively after it has recovered, the maximum sustainable yield is estimated at 0.75 million tons a year.

The North Sea herring fishery demonstrates another problem of multinational fisheries management that UNCLOS III does not solve, that of the migration of fish between waters controlled by different countries. There are three groups of North Sea herring, which lay eggs on the seabed in different spawning areas, in waters controlled by Britain and France (see Figure 1.19). The eggs hatch to produce larvae which then drift to the German and Danish coasts. The larvae develop into young fish (whitebait) and swim offshore to the nursery area in Dutch, German and Danish controlled waters. When they are two to three years old the young herring join the adult population (recruitment) in the adult feeding grounds in British and Norwegian controlled waters. The action of one country to control the herring fishery is therefore ineffective without controls by other

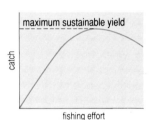

▲ *Figure 1.18*
The relationship between fishing effort and maximum sustainable yield.

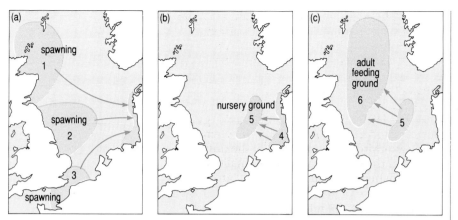

Figure 1.19
The movement of herring in the North Sea.

(a) Herring lay eggs mainly in three different sprawning areas (1, 2, and 3). The planktonic larvae drift to shallow water off Germany and Denmark (4).

(b) The young herring swim offshore to the nursery ground (5).

(c) Young herring join the adult population in their feeding grounds (6).

countries. For example, the British ban on herring catches in 1977 would need not only an equivalent ban by Norway, but agreement between the Netherlands, Germany and Denmark to stop or reduce fishing for whitebait in the nursery grounds (which threatens recruitment) and agreement between Britain and France to protect the spawning areas.

This discussion of the North Sea herring fishery has considered herring in isolation from any other species (**single species management**) but a more realistic approach is to also consider the effects and changes in other species on the herring (**multi-species management**). Adult herring, for example, feed mainly on planktonic animals and are in competition with other pelagic fish, and the herring are also a food source for cod and other benthic fish, so a change in the stock of another species by fishing may also affect the herring stock.

Unfortunately multi-species fisheries management is far from straightforward, as often the detailed effects of one species on another is not known, and the importance of each species may be difficult to balance. The reduction of pelagic fish species in the North Sea has coincided with an increase in some demersal species, but there is no direct link. The North Atlantic cod catch was 3–4 million tons a year throughout the 1960s, but has fallen since then: this may be due to overfishing in the late 1960s, and/or to the growth of the fishery for capelin, one of the important food items for cod. The North Pacific fur seal has declined in numbers since the growth of the Alaska pollack fishery, an important food for the seal: which is more important, the commercially more valuable pollack, or the seals, essential to small populations of Eskimo?

Fisheries can also affect each other when boats hunting for one species of fish catch – without intending to – many species, some of which may even be wasted. The US shrimp boats catch a wide variety of animals in their trawls, but usually only the shrimp are retained, and the rest of the animals, often three or four times the quantity of the shrimp, are discarded at sea, because a boat's limited hold space is more profitable to use for the higher-value shrimp. The tuna fishery that uses nets in the Pacific catches many dolphins, which – being air-breathing – drown when caught in the nets. The dolphins are not used: they are thrown overboard as they are commercially less valuable than tuna. This need not happen, as tuna can be caught by long-line methods which will kill far fewer dolphins, but this is often a commercially less efficient way of catching tuna. Do you prefer to have cheaper tuna even if it means killing dolphins that are not then used for food? Or would you be prepared to pay more to avoid this?

There are various controls that can be used to regulate a fishery, in an attempt to obtain a maximum sustainable yield.

1   *Net size/landing size*   A minimum size can be set for the mesh of a net, which lets the younger fish go free, and/or a minimum size of fish can be landed. This may be able to control growth overfishing. Regulations of this type were applied partially successfully to the North Sea herring in the 1950s and 1960s. It provided some protection for the adult herring, but recruitment still declined due to a whitebait fishery with much smaller net sizes in the herring nursery ground.

2   *Annual catch limit and fishing vessel limit*   The total catch can be limited (by quota: whereby fishing stops when this is reached) and/or the size and number of fishing vessels can be limited. This has also been applied to the North Sea herring, with quotas of 0.5 million tons in 1971 to 0.25 million tons in 1975 and none (a ban) in 1977. These usually very effective remedies for overfishing come at a cost: many of the fishers out of work and boats laid up. However, if not implemented the alternative can later prove to be a collapsed fishery, with *all* the fishers out of work.

3   *Restricted fishing seasons and areas*   This can be used to encourage recruitment, by protecting spawning areas and times and nursery grounds.

Implementation of these controls in the past has often been accompanied by international disagreements over restrictions and quotas. The Law of the Sea has clarified the position in some cases but will not prevent other disagreements. For example the Anglo–Icelandic mid-1970s 'Cod Wars', in which Iceland wished to limit fishing within 50 miles of its coast to protect stocks, would now be a clear case of Iceland having the right to do so. There have been many multi-national regional fisheries commissions, often supported by the United Nations Food and Agriculture Organisation (FAO), but states often disagree on what action to take. The North-East Atlantic Fishery Commission was unable to reach agreement on action after the 1955 collapse of part of the North Sea herring fishery: states acted individually and therefore ultimately ineffectively.

◀   *Whaling in 1835. Whaleboats (large rowing boats) were used to get close enough for a thrown harpoon to reach the whale. The whales were usually larger than the whale boats and could overturn them, making whaling a very dangerous occupation.*

5.3   *Whaling*

Whales are not fish, but air-breathing mammals. There are two kinds of whale, the toothed whales and the baleen whales. The toothed whales include the sperm whale, which is the largest toothed whale (up to 20 metres long), the killer whale and dolphins. They eat fish and squid, and the sperm whale can dive to depths of around 1000 metres in search of food. The baleen whales do not have teeth, but instead horny baleen plates ('whalebone') that hang from the roof of the mouth, forming sieves which filter their food, usually planktonic crustaceans, such as krill, from sea-water. Baleen whales include the blue whale, which can be up to 27 metres long and is the largest animal that has ever lived on the Earth, the sei at 18 metres long and the minke, up to 9 metres long.

Whales have very different birth rates from fish, which produce thousands of eggs. Whales produce a maximum of one calf (young whale) every two years. The baleen whales live mostly in polar waters, where there is high productivity of their food in spring and summer. They migrate to warmer tropical waters in winter where their calves are born. The toothed whales are not restricted to polar waters, because their food occurs throughout the oceans.

The history of whaling provides an extreme case of over-exploitation of a marine living resource. Whaling began around a thousand years ago in the North Atlantic, catching whales that swim close to shore. By the seventeenth century, whales were caught in deeper water, by the British and Dutch. These were bowhead whales, also called right whales as they did not sink when they died and could be retrieved by small boats, so they were the 'right' whales to hunt. The North Atlantic right whale stock declined, so whalers began to hunt sperm whales in other oceans as well as the North Atlantic. The development of larger and faster motor-boats and of the explosive harpoon about a century ago led to an expansion of the whaling industry and the ability to catch other whales, the fin and sei whales.

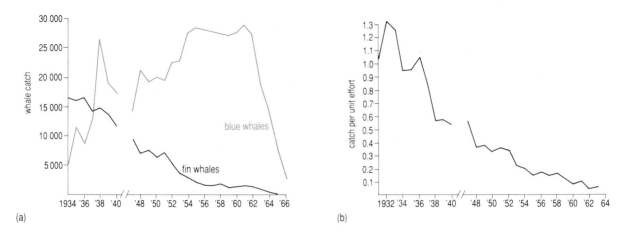

Figure 1.20   (a) The catch of blue and in fin whales in the Antarctic. (b) The catch per unit effort (catch per catcher–day's work) of blue whales in the Antarctic.

This led to a decline in whale stocks in the North Atlantic, so British and Norwegian whalers began hunting whales in the Antarctic at the beginning of this century, establishing land-based processing factories. The whaling industry expanded further when Japanese, German and Russian ships also began whaling in the Antarctic, and by 1925 factory ships began to be used to process the whales.

This expansion began to affect whale stocks in the Antarctic, with the catch of the largest and therefore most profitable whale, the blue whale, falling in the 1930s (Figure 1.20a). The catch per unit effort of blue whales also fell (Figure 1.20b) indicating that more whales were being caught than the maximum sustainable yield. As blue whale numbers declined, whalers began to catch more fin whales (Figure 1.20a) and then the smaller sei and humpback whales.

The falling whale catches caused the whaling states to set up the **International Whaling Commission (IWC)** in 1946, to set guidelines on protected species, restricted areas, catch quotas, size requirements and the import of whale products. The obviously over-exploited blue and humpback whales gained complete protection from the 1960s and catch quotas were set for many others, such as the fin and sei whales.

The IWC tried to steer a course between what was good for the whale stock, and what was good for the whalers. The whaling industry was based on a large labour force and capital investment in ships and did not want to stop catching whales, but neither did it want to over-exploit them to the extent of destroying their own livelihood. The IWC had to conserve whale stocks, with a sensible balance between the current catching of whales and maintaining the stock for future use. Unfortunately this has proved difficult to achieve, for a number of reasons.

One reason is that the IWC jurisdiction extends only to those states who are members, and in addition not only are there no means of legal enforcement to members, but also an IWC member can avoid being bound by decisions by filing an objection, although diplomatic and economic pressure has sometimes been used successfully to prevent this. Past violators have included the USSR in 1974 and 1975, Chile, Peru and South Korea in 1978 and Norway in 1986. An objection filed by Japan in 1987 was withdrawn after US threats to cut the Japanese fishing quota in the US

EEZ. UNCLOS III has been of little use to the IWC as a legal means to enforce its jurisdiction, as most whaling occurred in the high seas areas.

Another problem for the IWC occurred when many states who were not involved in whaling joined in the early 1970s. These states joined with the aim of stopping whaling altogether: whales, along with pandas and seals, had become a major symbol of the environmental movement. This polarised the IWC into the whalers, who wanted to conserve the stock but still exploit it as any other living resource, and the non-whalers who believe killing whales is wrong, either because the whales are in danger of extinction or regardless of how many whales there are. There is no doubt that catching whales by harpooning is far more cruel than the slaughter of domestic land animals, but how endangered are whales?

Some are endangered to the point of extinction. The population of such widely scattered marine animals cannot be estimated accurately, and blue whales have such a low population that even their numbers have proved especially difficult to estimate: as many as 14 000 or as low as 200. If the lower estimate is correct the blue whale has almost no hope of survival. The North Atlantic right whale is estimated at about 1000: the stock has not increased since the 1920s and there is little hope of recovery. There are about 2000 Pacific bowhead, but these are in real danger, as 20–30 of these are still caught each year in the Arctic by the Eskimo, a catch allowed by the IWC to support Eskimo culture (whales are the traditional prey of the Eskimo). Humpbacks number about 10 000 and grey whales 21 000 and both are considered as endangered species. On the other hand, sperm whales, at around 2 million and minke whales at $\frac{3}{4}$ million appear to be in no danger. The minkes may even have benefited from the depletion of the other baleen whale stocks by reducing competition for food.

Because of the protection of some whales, and catch quotas on others, the whalers began to catch mostly minkes in the 1970s. The maximum sustainable yield for whales is between 3–5% of the stock (this is a very different value from the maximum sustainable yield of a fish stock because of the difference in birth rates), so for a minke whale stock of $\frac{3}{4}$ million this would allow 22–38 000 minke a year to be caught whilst still conserving the stock. However, the IWC decreed a total ban on commercial whaling in 1985, a victory for the environmental non-whalers, even though some minkes and sperm whales could probably be exploited without endangering the species.

The ban is, in part, an understandable reaction – or over-reaction – to the endangering of so many of the whale species, but the lack of scientific grounds for banning whaling of all species caused some states to exploit a loophole in the ban, which permits the catching of some whales for scientific purposes. The only state that now continues to do this is Japan, which catches about 300 minke a year (1990), despite condemnation by many as commercial whaling in disguise, and harassment by the ships of environmental groups.

5.4   Pollution

Pollution of the ocean occurs on every scale, from the local collection of bottles, floats and other plastic objects on beaches, to the international effects of major oil spills and the worldwide presence of the pesticide DDT in the oceans. These examples are unquestionably pollution, but how about ocean dumping: is the disposal of sewage in the oceans, which can have beneficial as well as detrimental effects, pollution? Is the natural seepage of oil from the ocean floor into sea-water that occurs in some areas pollution? It depends on how pollution is defined. The definition used here is that stated at the UN 1972 Conference on the Human Environment:

> Pollution means the introduction by human beings, directly or indirectly, of substances or energy into the oceans resulting in harm to living resources, hazards to human health, hindrance to marine activities including fishing, impairment of quality for use of sea-water and reduction of amenities.

Q   Are (a) sewage disposal, and (b) natural oil seepages, pollution as defined above?

A   (a) Sewage may or may not be a pollutant, depending on whether it has harmful effects on living resources, human health, sea-water quality or amenities. (If dumped in limited quantities in appropriate places it will not usually be a pollutant.)

(b) Natural oil seepages, as they are not human-made, are not considered pollutants. (This still holds even in areas where natural seepages are much higher than the introduction of oil to the oceans through human causes, or where natural seepages have damaging effects.)

Marine pollution can be continuous (a cooling-water outfall) or episodic (sewage dumping). It can be deliberate (radioactive waste dumping) or accidental (oil spills). Pollutants vary in how long they remain in the ocean before being broken down into other substances or removed into sediments or to the atmosphere. Naturally occurring substances, such as domestic sewage, usually persist for a short time in the ocean, but human-made substances, such as pesticides, persist for a longer time (Figure 1.21). It is the very persistent and permanent pollutants, such as pesticides and toxic metals, that have continuous and long-term effects on the ocean and are of most concern.

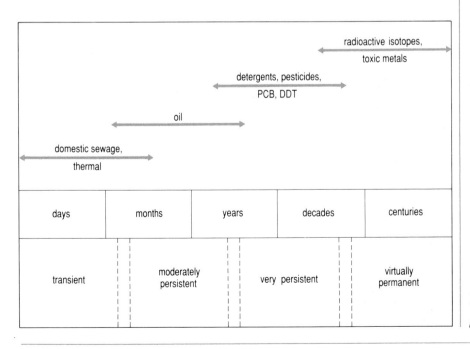

◀ *Figure 1.21*
The persistence of pollutants in the ocean.

Pollutants enter the ocean by diverse routes. The main source is
directly from land, through outfall pipes into the ocean or from rivers,
which can carry sewage, industrial waste, fertilisers and pesticides.
Pollution also comes from the ocean, both accidentally and deliberately
from ships and by mining of ocean resources. Some pollutants reach the
ocean by fall-out or wash-out from the atmosphere.

Oil is often thought of as the major pollutant in the ocean, prompted
largely by the visible results – tarred beaches and oil slicks – with the
attendant damage and death to marine life. Estimates of the amount of oil
reaching the ocean from human-made sources range from 1.9 million
tonnes to 4.8 million tonnes annually. The oil industry is responsible for
about one-third of this, from tanker transportation, offshore production
and refineries; shipping accounts for about another quarter, the rest
coming from land sources, in sewage and rivers. Much of the latter arises
from careless or thoughtless discharges: in Britain about 20 000 tonnes of
oil annually from do-it-yourself car oil changes is poured down the drain,
most of which reaches the sea. Only about 5% of the oil reaching the ocean
is accidental, due to oil rig blow-outs or tanker accidents, although these
are the most spectacular and often most damaging incidents.

Oil varies in its persistence in the oceans from days to years depending
on the type of oil: see Figure 1.21. Persistent oils are crude oil, heavy fuel oil
and lubricating oil. Non-persistent oils are gasoline and light fuel oil. In a
crude oil spill at sea, about 25% of it, the lighter volatile fraction, will

◄   *Clean-up of a beach
in France after an oil
spillage from a tanker.
Oil spills are most
damaging in coastal
areas.*

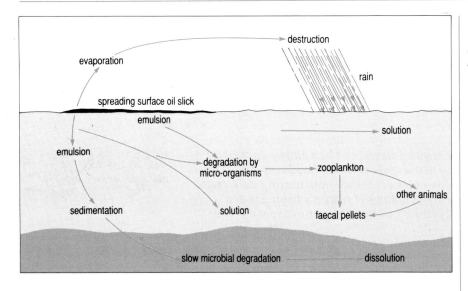

◀   Figure 1.22
The dispersal and
degradation of an oil
spill in the ocean.

evaporate in a few days (athough this takes longer under cold conditions)
(Figure 1.22). This fraction tends to be the most toxic. The oil vapour is
finally broken down by reactions with oxygen in the atmosphere. Part of
the remaining oil dissolves, and part is stirred by wind and waves into an
emulsion with sea-water, most of which floats on the surface. It looks like,
and is referred to as, 'chocolate mousse'. Micro-organisms can break down
the oil, both in the water and in the ocean-floor sediments. Around 60%
of the oil is degraded within a few months of the spill, but like evaporation
this process is much slower in the colder oceans. The remaining 15% or so
of oil forms dense, persistent clumps called tar balls, which may float, wash
ashore or sink to the bottom.

  Oil can have damaging and often lethal effects on marine life. These
effects are usually not severe in the open ocean, where most of the
organisms live below the surface, as most of the oil floats. The major
casualties are seabirds, whose buoyancy and thermal insulation depend on
feathers which repel water but attract oil. Fortunately, the population of
seabirds in the open ocean is usually low. Oil has the most damaging effect
in shallow water and coastal areas where the oil cannot disperse so easily
and can affect benthic habitats and beaches. Here oil penetrates the fur of
seals, otters and other marine mammals, which are affected in much the
same way as birds. Fish are relatively immune to coating with oil, and so
are some seaweeds, as they have a surface that repels oil, but most smaller
organisms can do nothing to prevent being smothered, and are killed by
lack of light, lack of food or asphyxiation. The lighter oil fractions are also
often poisonous to marine organisms, but the effect varies with type of
organism, the season and the stage in the life-cycle.

  The oil spill off Alaska from the VLCC *Exxon Valdez* was one of the most
studied, and environmentally disastrous, oil spills. The tanker collected
140 000 tonnes of crude oil from the oil terminal of Valdez, which is at the
southern end of the Trans-Alaska oil pipeline. 37 000 tonnes of this oil were
released into Prince William Sound on 24 March 1989 when the tanker
foundered on a rock outcrop off Bligh Island (see Plate 2). This is the largest
oil spill to date (August 1990) in US coastal waters. The response to the spill
was very slow, which allowed the slick to disperse into the Sound, and
high winds and rough seas made the dispersed slick difficult to recover or

contain. Plate 2 shows the progress of the slick two weeks after the spill. The oil had spread southward from Bligh Island, to the west of Montague Island, and further out of the Sound. It can also be seen on some of the shorelines in the area. In two weeks the slick had travelled up to 250 kilometres from the holed tanker, spreading over an area of 3–4000 square kilometres and washed up on 1100 kilometres of shoreline.

The Alaskan coast is an area with a rich diversity of wildlife and living resources (fishing is the main industry), but is also a very fragile environment, with many species living at the limit of their ecological ranges, so this oil spill had a catastrophic effect. Most of the sea otters in the area were killed, and many of the seals and vast numbers of seabirds, estimated at 30 000. The main fisheries are for salmon, herring, cod, crabs and other crustaceans; almost the whole 1989 season's fishing was prevented and the effects will extend over subsequent seasons, by the damage to spawning areas, killing of crustaceans and tainting of fish. The shoreline, despite an attempted clean-up operation that cost the Exxon oil company $1 million a day, remains vastly polluted. Assessments of the situation highlight the inadequacy of contingency plans for an oil spill of this size in such bad weather in a polar environment. The slick spread over too large an area, and was too broken up by bad weather for methods of recovery or containment – skimmer boats, booms, ignition and chemical dispersants – to be effective. Once the oil hit the shoreline there seemed to be no effective method of removing it.

Most of the environmental problems caused by the *Exxon Valdez* oil spill were caused by its occurrence in an area that was coastal, polar and fragile. This is illustrated by the very different impact of another spill the same year. The VLCC *Kharg 5* was in the Atlantic on passage from the Middle East around Africa to Europe with 284 000 tonnes of crude oil when it was holed by an explosion on 19 December 1989. 70 000 tonnes of oil leaked into the ocean, but this has had little environmental effect. The oil had a high proportion of the lighter oil fractions, and this more toxic part rapidly evaporated from the warm waters. The spill occurred steadily over a period of about two weeks, and most was emulsified and dispersed by wave action. There was concern that the slick might be washed up on the Moroccan coast and ruin beaches and hence the tourist industry, but although it came within 30 kilometres of the coast the slick never reached the shore. A few months later the slick seemed to have largely disappeared due to dispersal and micro-organism degradation. World War II was a time of many oil spills into the ocean from sunken shipping, but the ocean was able to recover from such temporarily devastating pollution.

Activity 6

Q1 What was the maximum speed of movement of the oil slick from the *Exxon Valdez* up to 7 April 1989, in km hr^{-1}?

Q2 What area could the slick cover at this speed one day after its release, if it spread out in all directions? (The area of a circle is πr^2 where π is approximately 3 and r is the radius.) What implications does this have for recovery of the oil?

Q3 In which direction or directions did the slick mainly move, based on Plate 2?

Another group of pollutants of great concern in the ocean are some synthetic compounds containing carbon, hydrogen and chlorine. These include dichlorodiphenyltrichloroethane (DDT), a pesticide, and polychlorinated biphenyls (PCBs) which are used in a number of products, such as plastics, paints and electrical equipment. DDT and PCBs enter the ocean mainly from the atmosphere, so they are most concentrated in surface waters, and they are ubiquitous throughout the world oceans. They are stable compounds that persist for a greater time in the ocean than does oil (Figure 1.21), and although they are present in low concentrations in the ocean, around 1 part per billion parts of sea-water, organisms tend to accumulate DDT and PCBs in their bodies at higher concentrations than those in the surrounding sea-water. Oysters, for example, living in sea-water with 0.1 p.p.b. DDT were found to have 7000 p.p.b. DDT. This process is called **biological magnification**, and continues up the food chain, so it can ultimately affect human beings. DDT and PCBs are toxic, and can have adverse effects even in low concentrations: they can reduce the productivity of phytoplankton, cause abortion and foetal abnormalities in marine mammals, thin and break the eggshells of birds and cause skin diseases.

An intrinsic problem in the management of marine pollution is that a pollutant that enters the sea in one part of the ocean can move into other parts, so that pollution-control measures, to be effective, often have to be international. For example, in an attempt to control pollution of the Mediterranean Sea, seventeen Mediterranean coastal states agreed on a Mediterranean Action Plan in 1976. The North Sea is an area where there are similar international agreements. The Law of the Sea has had some success in controlling pollution from dumping in the high seas, such as banning the discharge of oily water from tank washing. This has reduced the pollution, but not stopped it: the problem of detection and legal enforcement remains.

The ocean, because of its immensity, has been able to dilute, disperse and so mitigate the worst effects of many of the pollutants, but pollution occurs to some extent in all parts of the ocean. Some pollutants are a problem everywhere because of their toxicity and persistence, and some are only a problem in local areas. Some seas which are partially isolated or have a limited water exchange with the open ocean are very polluted, for example, by sewage at the mouth of the Ganges and off New York, by oil in the Persian Gulf, sewage and industrial waste off Buenos Aires and by mining waste off British Columbia. In contrast to these areas, the centres of the oceans are relatively much less polluted: however, the author of this chapter was very saddened to recover tar balls and plastic bottles when towing a net to collect plankton in the centre of the Atlantic – it seems that no part of the ocean, however remote, is completely immune to pollution.

5.5   *The North Sea*

The North Sea is a partially isolated part of the ocean that is relatively shallow and mostly less than 100 metres deep (Figure 1.23). The southern part is less than 50 metres deep, but it gets deeper to the north. The North Sea is bounded by eight coastal states – Belgium, Britain, Denmark, France, the Netherlands, Norway, Sweden and Germany. It is about 500 kilometres wide between Britain and Norway in the north, but in the south the distance between Britain and the other European states is much less, so that the EEZs of each state extend not to 200 miles, as they would overlap,

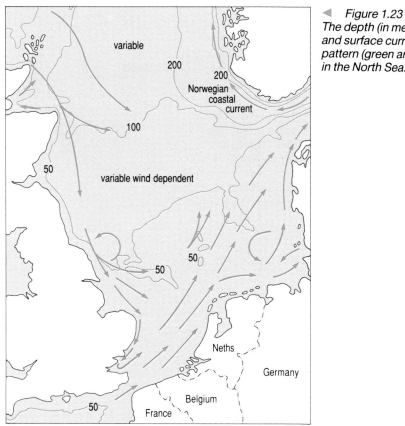

◀   *Figure 1.23*
The depth (in metres)
and surface current
pattern (green arrows)
in the North Sea.

but to a median line at lesser distances from the shoreline. The relatively small size of the North Sea, its natural resources and proximity to areas of high population and industrialisation have made the North Sea the most intensively exploited part of the ocean, with a management problem that has to involve eight states.

The North Sea, particularly the southern part, has always been one of the busiest shipping areas in the ocean, particularly into the ports of Europoort/Rotterdam, Zeebrugge/Ostend and Harwich. The ship traffic density on the approach to these ports is such that ships must keep to traffic lanes (i.e. drive on the right) in the major shipping channels, like on roads on land. There is also a considerable amount of ferry traffic between Britain and the rest of Europe which cuts across the main shipping lanes. The northern part of the North Sea has had an increase in tanker traffic in the last twenty years because of the development of oil and gas fields. The effects of this traffic density on the marine environment include the construction of docks and dredging of estuaries, deliberate discharge of waste, accidental loss of cargo overboard, collisions and sinking. However, no port-of-refuge has been designated around the North Sea for a damaged oil tanker: no state wants to accept a dirty and dangerous stricken tanker.

Fishing is of major importance in the North Sea. The fish catch doubled from 1948 (1.75 million tonnes) to 1974 (3.5 million tonnes) but reduced to around 2.4 million tonnes from 1978.

Q   What proportion of the world fish catch is provided by the North Sea?

A   The world fish catch is around 70 million tonnes (Section 3.1), so the
      North Sea provides $(2.4 \div 70) \times 100\%$, about $3\frac{1}{2}\%$ of this.

This is a very significant catch for such a small area of ocean. In addition to
fish, 0.17 million tonnes of molluscs (oysters, mussels and other shellfish)
and 0.04 million tonnes of crustaceans (crabs and lobsters) are caught.
    The major pelagic fisheries of the North Sea are for herring and
mackerel, which made up a large proportion of the catch in the 1950s and
1960s. The main demersal fisheries in the North Sea are for plaice, sole,
cod, haddock and whiting. The plaice catch has risen from 0.07 million
tonnes in 1957 to 0.15 million tonnes in 1984. Sole catches have been stable
at around 0.02 million tonnes for the last ten years. However, the cod and
haddock fisheries are in trouble. Cod catches rose to 0.34 million tonnes in
1972 and have since declined to 0.2 million tonnes. Haddock catches have
fluctuated between 0.05 million tonnes and 0.55 million tonnes in the last
twenty years.
    Another type of fishery has developed in the North Sea from the 1980s,
which takes smaller species – sand-eels, sprats, pout and blue whiting – for
conversion to fish-meal. The catch is large (around 0.35 million tonnes) and
has implications for other fisheries as these smaller species are often the
prey for other fish, as well as for other animals such as sea birds.
    We have seen that overfishing of herring led to a collapse of the stock
in the 1950s and a total ban on fishing in 1977. The stock had recovered
sufficiently for the ban to be lifted and limited fishing allowed by 1982. The
herring has not been the only example of overfishing: in a 1977 report on
North Sea fish stock, cod, haddock, whiting and plaice were identified as
subject to growth overfishing, mackerel to recruitment overfishing and
sole to both. The situation with cod and haddock developed into
recruitment overfishing, and by 1988 both were subject to strict control of
catch and net sizes.
    This overfishing of many of the stocks in the North Sea was partly
caused by the past absence of any fisheries agreements or legal
enforcements for stocks other than those close to the shore. In the late
1960s fishery resources of the North Sea were managed by the 1966
European Fisheries Convention, by which the coastal state has sole rights
to fish less than six miles from shore, and to share rights between six and
twelve miles with those states that had fished in those waters between 1953
and 1962. This left the rest of the North Sea (most of it) as an unmanaged
free-for-all fishery. After the UK, Denmark and Ireland joined the EC, the
Common Fisheries Policy (CFP) changed management rights and
responsibility from the states to the Community, with equal access to all
member-states. Norway, which has an economy that is more dependent on
fishing than the economies of other states, rejected membership of the EC
largely because of this CFP. Following Iceland's claim to a 200-mile
fisheries limit in 1976, in 1977 the EC states also claimed jurisdiction up to
200 miles, which put most of the North Sea under CFP control. The main
effect of this was to stop fishing by Eastern bloc countries, Iceland, the
Faeroes, Sweden and Spain and it did, at least in theory, provide the power
for the EC to manage fish stocks effectively. UNCLOS III confirmed these
200-mile fisheries limits. Britain, although a non-signatory, takes full
advantage of the limits.
    CFP management of the North Sea has, however, been subject to much
disagreement between members on individual quotas and multi-species
management objectives. The UK, for example, argues that as a large share

of the fish stocks lie within its water it is entitled to a large proportion of the total catch. There are also different consumer preferences in each country, leading to disagreements over which stocks have priority: the English want to eat and maintain the cod stocks, the Germans redfish and saithe, the Dutch plaice, the French whiting, the Scots haddock. The result is that CFP management of the North Sea fisheries is not as effective as it could be.

The other two main resources that are extracted from the North Sea are aggregates and petroleum. Aggregates (sand and gravel) are used in the construction industry and although they are available from land sources, from the 1960s onwards increasing amounts have been extracted from the North Sea, to about 6 million tonnes annually from the UK North Sea waters, about 15% of the total UK supply of aggregate. Extraction of marine deposits were considered as often more economic for coastal areas and less environmentally disruptive than extraction on land, leaving no large holes in the ground. The damage to the marine environment has often seemed less important (out of sight, out of mind). Marine aggregate extraction in UK waters is controlled by the Crown Estate Commission, which consults with the NCC, DoE, MAFF and the Hydraulics Research Station over environmental implications. There are at present (August 1990) six principal extraction areas, mainly between 7 and 20 miles offshore, as well as extraction from shoreline areas. Environmental problems arising from marine aggregate extraction include the destruction of benthic communities, including fish spawning and nursery grounds and mollusc fisheries, damage to bottom trawls by an uneven seafloor and an increase in turbidity of the sea-water.

Production of gas from the North Sea began in 1968 and about 90 million tonnes are now extracted each year. Oil production started in 1971, and is now producing about 160 million tonnes, with a value of £8000 million a year. This has resulted in the location of many exploration rigs and fixed production platforms in the North Sea. These can have beneficial effects – they become rapidly colonised by benthic organisms which attract fish – but also increase the risk of oil pollution from blow-outs or collisions between a ship and platform. The largest oil spill in the North Sea so far has been the blow-out on the Ekofisk Bravo platform in 1977. This was in the central North Sea and was less of an environmental disaster than it could have been, as the wind kept the slick away from the shorelines, allowing it to be broken down by wave action and by chemical dispersants.

◄   *A fireboat continues safety spraying of sea-water onto the Ekofisk Bravo platform after the blow-out.*

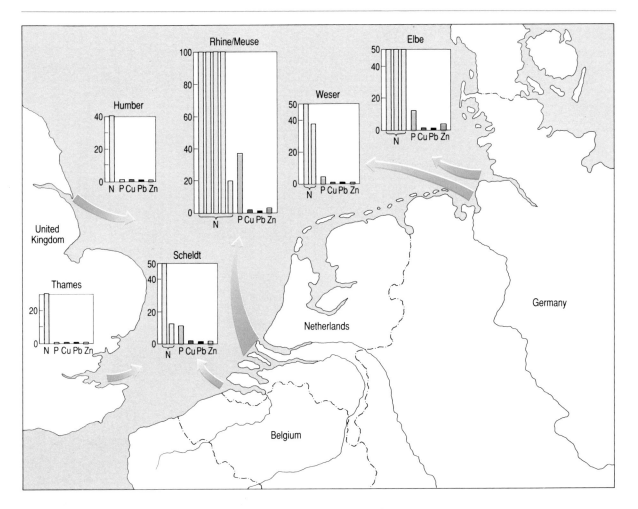

▲ Figure 1.24
*Main sources of river
pollution in the southern
North Sea (thousand
tonnes per year):
nitrogen (N), phosphorus
(P), copper (Cu), lead
(Pb), zinc (Zn).*

The use of the North Sea that has caused most international disagreement and most environmental concern is for waste disposal. The North Sea receives waste from rivers, coastal discharge, direct dumping and atmospheric incineration of waste at sea.

The southern part receives most of the river-borne waste, from major rivers that flow through highly populated and industrialised parts of Europe, such as the Rhine, Weser and Elbe. Much of this river water is highly polluted with sewage and industrial waste (Figure 1.24). What happens to these pollutants when reaching the North Sea depends on the circulation within the sea and water exchange with the Atlantic Ocean. Water generally circulates in an anticlockwise direction in the North Sea (Figure 1.23) which means that water discharged from UK crosses the North Sea towards German waters in the east. Pollutants from continental rivers also move east to Dutch and German waters, causing a build-up of pollution in the eastern coastal zone: Figure 1.25 shows the distribution of dissolved zinc as an example of this. This happens to be fortunate for Britain – its pollution becomes someone else's problem – but not much fun for the Netherlands, Germany and Denmark.

Whether pollutants will accumulate in the North Sea or be diluted by the large body of water in the ocean depends on the rate of exchange of water between the two. Table 1.4 gives the major inputs and outputs of water to the North Sea.

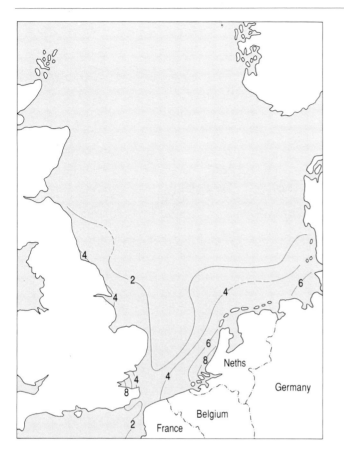

◀   *Figure 1.25*
The distribution of dissolved
zinc in the North Sea
(10^{-6} grams per litre).

Table 1.4   Annual water budget for the North Sea

	Volume/km^3
Input	
Between Scotland and Norway	50 450
Through Straits of Dover	4 900
From Baltic Sea	500
Precipitation	330
From rivers	370
Output	
Norwegian coastal current	56 300
Evaporation	250

The volume of water in the North Sea is about 47 000 cubic kilometres, so with a water input or output of 56 550 cubic kilometres a year this gives a residence time for water in the North Sea of 47 000 ÷ 56 550 years – a bit less than a year. This is often referred to as the *'flushing time'* for the North Sea, that is on average water (and any associated pollution) will move out of the North Sea within a year. This prevents an extreme build-up of pollutants, but many problems remain. The increased amounts of nutrients (nitrogen and phosphorus) particularly in the coastal waters of the Netherlands, Germany and Denmark is a major concern, and has caused algal blooms that have contained enough toxins to kill animals which consume them and also to deoxygenate the sea-water when they die and decompose. Another concern is the build-up of persistent pollutants (toxic metals, DDT and PCBs) in the water and sediments in the same areas. Some of the diseases in fish have been linked to the high levels of these contaminants and there are many local examples of their effect on organisms. The epidemic in 1988 that killed about half of the common seals in the North Sea by a distemper virus was suspected to have been (although not proven to be) exacerbated by the effect of pollution on the seals.

There have been many multinational agreements by the coastal states on specific environmental problems in the North Sea, such as the 1974 Convention for the Prevention of Marine Pollution by Dumping from Ships and Aircraft, but until 1984 no overall environmental management agreement. In 1984 West Germany, prompted by the pollution problems in West German waters and by the growing political influence of the Green

Party, organised a ministerial Conference of North Sea states for protection of the North Sea, to review the state of the North Sea and formulate proposals to improve its quality. A second conference was held in London in 1987 and agreed on declarations of intent for protective measures. These included a ban on dumping rubbish overboard from ships, the reduction of riverborne pollutants, and the phasing out of waste-dumping or incineration at sea. This sounds as if it should solve all pollution problems, but this has proved not to be so, because of a loophole in the declaration, which is 'No material should be dumped in the North Sea unless there are no practical alternatives on land and it can be shown to the competent international organization that the material poses no risk to the marine environment'. Some states, although signatories of this declaration, are using this loophole to continue dumping, claiming no practicable alternatives on land or no risk to the North Sea. The UK, for example, continued to dump 5 million tonnes of sewage sludge a year in the North Sea, claiming no risk, and saying that it has reduced the concentrations of toxic substances in the sludge. The other states disagree and have stopped dumping sewage sludge. The UK also continued to dump colliery spoil and

▲ *The North Sea is heavily used, for shipping, fishing and waste disposal. Sludge dumping from a UK barge in the North Sea, a practice which is to be phased out over the 1990s (top left). Protests over the continued pollution of the North Sea by the dumping (top right). Tanker and petrochemical storage tanks and refinery at Europort in the Netherlands (below). Europort is the largest petrochemical port in Europe.*

ash from power stations at sea off the north-east coast of England, claiming no practical alternatives on land. However, at the third conference at The Hague in March 1990 the UK agreed to end dumping of sewage sludge by 1999 and industrial waste by 1993, mainly because of condemnation and pressure from the other states and environmental groups.

Despite disputes, the 1987 and 1990 Conferences on the Protection of the North Sea were the first attempt to manage all types of pollution in the North Sea on a whole North Sea basis. Management of the North Sea has to balance environmental integrity and exploitation. The problems have not yet been solved, but they have at least been recognised and plans agreed for improvement.

5.6   Summary

Fisheries management is complicated by the mobility of fish, as they ignore national boundaries, so fisheries policies often involve multi-national agreements. Most fisheries occur within EEZs, which gives the coastal state the legal fishing rights, and also the responsibility for conservation of fish stocks. Ideally, fishery policies, including catch quotas and net sizes, should allow a maximum sustainable yield of a fish stock. To achieve a maximum sustainable yield the population dynamics of the fishery must be known. A falling catch despite a greater fishing effort is known as overfishing. Growth overfishing occurs when too many small fish are caught. Recruitment overfishing occurs when too many adults are caught and not enough fish are left to spawn and produce new recruits. Fisheries policies, to be effective, need to involve multi-species implications.

Whaling is a fishery that takes place mainly in the high seas area, so is not under the legal control of one or even a few nations. It has a history of over-exploitation and some species of whales are in danger of extinction. At present there is a ban on commercial whaling, although some whales could be exploited without endangering the species.

Pollution, like fishing, is a problem without national boundaries. Substances that may be harmless in some areas of the ocean or at low concentrations may become pollutants in other areas or at higher concentrations. The substances of greatest concern are the persistent pollutants that are ubiquitous and increasing in concentration in the world ocean. Sewage, although locally damaging, has a short-term effect. Oil spills are extremely damaging in coastal areas, but less so away from land. The ocean is able to dilute many pollutants and mitigate the worst effects, but pollution is present throughout the oceans and can be a major problem in coastal areas.

The North Sea is an area with unique management problems: it is bounded by eight coastal states with high population and industrialisation, and, although relatively small in size, is intensively exploited by shipping, fishing, aggregate extraction, petroleum extraction and waste disposal. It has a limited water exchange with the open ocean, so pollutants are not quickly diluted. Management of the North Sea has required multi-national agreement and is now within the control of the coastal states as it is within the EEZs.

Ocean management involves a balance between conservation and exploitation. Unfortunately in many instances exploitation has gone too far, resulting in problems such as overfishing or oil spills. In contrast, in the present management of whaling, the total ban may be taking conservation further than necessary.

6   Conclusion

This chapter on the marine environment is an investigation of an area that we know less about than the land, even though it is larger in size. We have looked at the main features of the ocean – the different regions, the salinity, chemical composition and movement of sea-water and oceanic life – as a basis for understanding the marine environment. The chapter examined our uses of the ocean in the past, and looked at how the uses have developed to the present. The ocean has important natural resources, both food and physical resources, which are exploitable, but have often been over-exploited, damaging the environmental integrity of the ocean.

Competition for these resources was a major factor leading to the establishment of a Law of the Sea, which divided the ocean into areas under the control of the coastal states, out to 200 miles from the shoreline, and the high seas area, to be managed for the benefit of all. UNCLOS III is upheld by most nations, although two major maritime states – the United Kingdom and the United States – have not signed and most have not yet ratified it.

Environmental problems in the ocean arise from inappropriate use or over-exploitation. It is, for example, an appropriate place to dump limited quantities of some substances, or to catch controlled amounts of fish, but it is not a universal waste disposal site or unlimited larder.

Management of the ocean environment is as critical as management of the land environment, and similarly has to balance conservation and exploitation. In the ocean these views can reach wider extremes than on land, from the ultra-conservationist view that any exploitation of marine environment is wrong, to the out of sight, out of mind view that we can do what we like to the ocean as it is far enough away not to bother us or big enough to look after itself. A more realistic view is between the two: the ocean is a very useful part of the Earth, but must be used sensibly.

References

GRIGG, D. (1991) 'World agriculture: productivity and sustainability', Ch. 2 in Sarre, P. (ed.) *Environment, Population and Development*, London, Hodder and Stoughton/The Open University (Book Two in this series).

SARRE, P. (1990) 'Environmental issues in Cumbria', Ch. 1 in Silvertown, J. and Sarre, P. (eds).

SILVERTOWN, J. (1990a) 'Earth as an environment for life', Ch. 2 in Silvertown, J. and Sarre, P. (eds).

SILVERTOWN, J. (1990b) 'Inhabitants of the biosphere', Ch. 3 in Silvertown, J. and Sarre, P. (eds).

SILVERTOWN, J. (1990c) 'Ecosystems and populations', Ch. 4 in Silvertown, J. and Sarre, P. (eds).

SILVERTOWN, J. and SARRE, P. (eds) (1990) *Environment and Society*, London, Hodder and Stoughton/The Open University (Book One in this series).

Further reading

First, two general books on oceanography, the former elementary, the latter more advanced:

SMITH, S. (1982) *Discovering the Sea*, Longman (UK), Time-Life (USA).

MEADOWS, P. S., and CAMPBELL, J. I. (1990) *An Introduction to Marine Science* (2nd edn), Glasgow, Blackie.

To follow up the issues in Section 4 see:

UNITED NATIONS (1983) *Official Text, UN Convention of the Law of the Sea*, (Sales No E.83.V.5).

The UN also published a useful set of background pamphlets on UNCLOS III, including *A Quiet Revolution* (E.83.V.7), and *Law of the Sea – the new UN Convention* (a set of nine papers).

SANGER, C. (1986) *Ordering the Oceans: the making of the law of the sea*, (London, Zed Books) is a useful historical discussion of UNCLOS III.

CHURCHILL, R. and LOWE, A. (1988) *The Law of the Sea* (2nd edn) (Manchester, Manchester University Press) is a detailed description and discussion of the terms of the treaty.

A comprehensive report and assessment of current marine pollution and future threats is:

GESAMP (1991) *The State of the Marine Environment*, Oxford, Blackwell Scientific.

For a detailed report on the North Sea see:

NORTH SEA FORUM, *Report*, March 1987 (ISBN 0 903158 30 2 and ISBN 0 903158 31 0).

Finally, two journals which cover marine environmental topics are *Marine Policy* (Butterworth Scientific) and *Marine Pollution Bulletin* (Pergamon).

Answers to Activities

Activity 1

We can see from Figure 1.3 that the North Sea is mainly part of the continental shelf so should be around 100 metres deep.

Figure 1.2 shows that the Mid-Atlantic Ridge lies at the middle of the Atlantic, and the top of this should be between 2 and 3 kilometres deep.

The ocean trenches are the deepest parts of the oceans, and these are not usually in the middle of the oceans.

Activity 2

Q1 1 km^3 of sea-water is $10^3 \times 10^3 \times 10^3$ m^3 = 10^9 m^3.
If the density is 10^3 kg m^{-3}, 1 km^3 has a mass of $10^3 \times 10^9$ kg = 10^{12} kg.
A gold concentration of 4×10^{-6} p.p.m. is:

   $4 \times 10^{-6} \times 10^{-6}$ kg in 1 kg sea-water.

that is 4×10^{-12} kg gold in 1 kg sea-water.
The amount of gold in 1 km^3 = $10^{12} \times 4 \times 10^{-12}$ kg = 4 kg.

Q2 Value = amount $\times$ price = $4 \times$ £10 000 = £40 000.

Activity 3

●   The main factor is the distribution of food for the marine animals, and this is dependent on the distribution of plants, the ultimate food source of all animals.

●   Plant growth needs (a) light, which means they live in the surface layers of the oceans (the photic zone), and (b) nutrients.

●   The nutrient supply is greatest where nutrients are supplied from land or by upwelling.

Activity 4

(a) Land disposal

Advantages:

●   Apart from building rubble, natural land material.
●   Useful for land-fill.

Disadvantages:

●   Transport costs to land-fill sites, at a distance from central London.
●   Environmental impact of road transport.

(b) North Sea disposal

Advantages:

●   Material not toxic.
●   Short transport distance by road to docks.

Disadvantages:

●   Unless dumping strictly controlled, can damage benthic communities.

Activity 5

(a) After 1945 the old regime governing the use of oceans, based on freedom of the high seas and 3-mile territorial waters, began to erode. As the use of ocean resources intensified, the oceans came to be regarded as an area of competition for the extraction of potentially scarce goods rather than as the inexhaustible resource of old. The USA and Latin American states began to declare jurisdiction over fisheries and minerals up to 200 miles from their coasts, followed by other states. An increasing number of states had little stake in the old regime, which was widely seen to work in the interests of the developed maritime powers and their allies. In this context, agreement on a new Law of the Sea regime became a priority. Otherwise, unregulated claims to ocean resources and unilateral actions and restrictions threatened to lead to chaos, conflict and over-exploitation.

The First and Second UN Conventions aimed to slow the erosion of the old regime. In this they were partially successful. But by the mid 1960s it became clear that a Third UN Convention on the Law of the Sea (UNCLOS III) was needed to update and further codify existing laws and create a new international regulatory framework for the use and exploitation of the oceans. Negotiations started in 1973, and continued for ten years. Not surprisingly, the task of agreeing to regulations governing most aspects of the use and exploitation of the oceans was extraordinarily complex and prone to delay and obstruction. However, to properly understand the difficulties experienced in the talks and the ultimate results, it is important to appreciate the major interest groups involved.

(b) There was a common interest in establishing an agreed regulatory framework to avoid conflict and mismanagement of ocean resources, though the details would obviously be controversial. But the major maritime powers were primarily interested in establishing rights of passage and 'freedom of the seas'. Coastal states were interested in establishing rights to an Exclusive Economic Zone stretching up to 200 miles from their coasts. Developing countries wanted to ensure that the resources of the deep seabed were shared amongst all states, and not just by the developed states and large companies with the technology to extract the resources.

(c) The final UNCLOS III document in 1982 provided for all of these interests, and dealt with many other issues besides. It provides the basis for the international management and exploitation of the oceans, and is among the most important pieces of international law ever agreed. Most of its provisions are now firmly established in common law and international practice. Yet by 1990 it was still well short of the number of ratifications needed for it to come into force. Although they supported most parts of the Convention, the USA, UK and other developed states were determined to block the establishment of an International Seabed Authority to manage and redistribute any benefits from the exploitation of the deep ocean floor.

Activity 6

Q1 The slick travelled up to 250 km in 14 days. 14 days is 14×24 hours = 236 hrs. This gives a maximum speed of about 1 km hr^{-1}.

Q2 Oil could have travelled up to 24 km from the tanker in 1 day, so could cover a circular area of radius 24 km. This is 3×24^2 km^2 = 1800 km^2. After just a day the oil has covered a considerable area of ocean, needing recovery methods capable of coping with a large area of oil.

Q3 The slick is visible to the north and west of Montague Island and in the south-west of the map. Oil is also visible on shorelines around the spill location, on the west coast of Montague Island and the islands to the west, and the shorelines in the Gulf of Alaska to the west. The slick therefore probably travelled south, mainly to the west of Montague Island into the Gulf of Alaska, and then south-west. (Because of this movement out of the Sound, some of the shorelines in the northern part of the Sound were unaffected.)

1 Introduction

Measures aimed at protecting the natural environment on a global, rather than just a local, scale figured increasingly prominently on international agendas in the 1980s. The preceding chapter described one of the first major steps in international cooperation on environmental issues: the framework that the 'Law of the Sea' agreement provides for the protection and management of the oceans. More recently, international concern focused on the atmosphere, as evidence accumulated that human activities are upsetting a natural balance and might result in climatic changes of a sort never before experienced within historic time. One consequence of the breakdown of natural balances, the 'ozone hole', prompted concerted international effort, finally resulting in the Montreal Protocol that controls the use of CFCs; this story is the subject of Chapter 3. Another manifestation of a change in atmospheric balance, the probability of global warming, gave rise in the late 1980s to an explosion of (often highly sensationalised) media reports, and to much scientific, lay and political debate. Some cuttings from (carefully reported) articles of this period are reproduced in Figure 2.1. Yet despite worldwide concern about potential climatic change the international community entered upon the 1990s without having developed any active response. Given the cooperative efforts that have been made to cope with other global environmental problems, why is it so difficult to reach a consensus as to the policies that should be adopted to confront the possibility of global warming? This chapter will explore some of the reasons, and the question will be taken up again in Chapter 4.

One of the articles of Figure 2.1 has a very British perspective. In fact, however, few scientists would claim to forecast with any degree of certainty or detail the likely effects of global warming on individual nations or societies. Herein lies the core of the problem. Proposals for any kind of action require immediate costly investment as insurance against possible future changes whose exact nature is still uncertain. Defining the point at which available information is deemed to be sufficient to trigger a societal response (as distinct from simply generating further research) is a matter of value judgement. In order to make such a judgement, we need to understand not only the political and economic factors involved in any particular course of action, but also the scientific evidence. A major theme of this chapter, therefore, is to present the underlying science, to distinguish areas of scientific consensus from areas of controversy, and to illustrate some of the scientific uncertainties. Our understanding of the processes of climatic change is still very sketchy. The overall aim of this chapter is to provide a background that will enable you to follow future developments in an informed way and to assess the relevance and reliability of new research data as these are reported in the media and in popular scientific articles.

Britain could be the new Sunshine State

WITHIN the lifetime of today's children, South-East England could enjoy a semi-Mediterranean climate as average temperatures increase by more than 6 degrees fahrenheit. The garden of England could become its sunporch, and farming could boom in the North.

These are the benefits which Britain could enjoy thanks to the greenhouse effect, according to evidence being collected by a United Nations panel.

Britain will warm more than the global average, because the greenhouse effect will heat up cooler regions faster than the tropics. South-East England could become like today's south-western France, with warmer, drier summers and warmer, but wetter winters. Huge golden fields of sunflowers could flourish across southern England.

And if the warming continues, Britain could grow its own baked beans: at present they all have to be imported.

But the South could also suffer much more frequent droughts and present forms of farming would suffer. There would probably be more thunderstorms.

Observer, 26 November 1989

I n February scientists at the British Meteorological Office and the University of East Anglia's Climatic Research Unit reported that 1988 was the world's hottest year since reliable records began to be kept almost a hundred years ago. The East Anglia group, like Goddard, monitors world climate year by year. They use surface data gathered from thousands of international stations on land and on ships at sea.

Moreover, the British scientists said the six hottest years of the century all fell in the decade of the 1980s. In descending order, they were 1988, 1987, 1983, 1981, 1980 and 1986. The average global temperature in 1988 was 0.612 degree F higher than the 1950 to 1979 average, which meteorologists use as a baseline for comparison.

Popular Science, August 1989

The report says that the weather is so complex that it will take another 30 years of observations to prove that the climate has changed permanently. But even conservative climatologists now say they are 90 to 95 per cent certain that unprecedented warming is now inevitable. So far the world has warmed by about half a degree centigrade. It is expected to get four degrees hotter by the year 2030, but increasingly scientists are expecting that this may be an underestimate because newly discovered processes appear to be accelerating the warming.

Another unpublished report, by scientists working for the UN Environment Programme, concludes that the destruction of the ozone layer will greatly speed up global warming. The ozone protects plankton, and other living things, from the . . .

Observer, 25 February 1990

T he world is warming. Climatic zones are shifting. Glaciers are melting. Sea level is rising. These are not hypothetical events from a science-fiction movie; these changes and others are already taking place, and we expect them to accelerate over the years as the amounts of carbon dioxide, methane and other trace gases accumulating in the atmosphere through human activities increase.

There may be controversy over whether the data are adequate and whether the warming is caused by changes in the atmosphere. Yet there is an unusually powerful consensus among climatologists that the dominant influence on global climate over the next centuries will be a warming driven by the accumulation of heat-trapping gases. The consequences are threatening enough so that many scientists, citizens and even political leaders are urging immediate action to halt the warming.

Scientific American, April 1989

▲ Figure 2.1 1989 and early 1990 reports of global warming.

Much of the content of this chapter is scientific, embracing a range of disciplines. However, an effort has been made to keep the number of technical terms used to a minimum. If you do not have a science background, the activities within the text should help you to focus on the most important points and it is essential that you attempt these as you come to them, before reading on. Activities at the ends of sections can be used for further self-assessment or revision.

2   Climate: past, present and future

In the late 1980s the phrase 'the greenhouse effect' came into common usage, often in the context of global warming that had occurred during the present century and was being linked to human activities. This is not an accurate use of the terminology. The 'natural' greenhouse effect has operated for over four billion years, maintaining temperatures suitable for life on Earth; it is perhaps the main key to understanding past and present climates, as outlined in Book One of the series. Thus it is appropriate to begin the story of climatic change with a review of the natural greenhouse effect and the evolution of planetary atmospheres.

2.1   The greenhouse effect

All hot objects emit electromagnetic radiation at a range of wavelengths, the exact range depending on the temperature of the object.

Activity 1

Figure 2.2 shows part of the electromagnetic spectrum. (This was introduced in *Reddish* (1991).) General experience tells us that a poker heated in a fire glows 'red-hot'; if heated to a higher temperature, in an oxy-acetylene flame say, it would glow 'white-hot'. Generalising from this example, and remembering that 'white light' is a combination of all the visible wavelengths, work out whether the average wavelength of emitted radiation increases or decreases as the temperature of the emitting object falls.

The Sun, with a surface temperature of over 6000°C, emits radiation with wavelengths between 2×10^{-7} m and 4×10^{-6} m (i.e. 200 nm to 4 μm), with its peak emission in the visible band. Objects, such as planets, illuminated by solar radiation *reflect* some of it (without change in wavelength) and absorb the rest, so warming up. They then *emit* radiation with a wavelength that will depend on their temperature but will certainly be *longer* than that of the incoming solar radiation, since the objects will be cooler than the Sun. Well-established laws of physics can be used to calculate what is called the *effective radiating temperature* of a spherical body

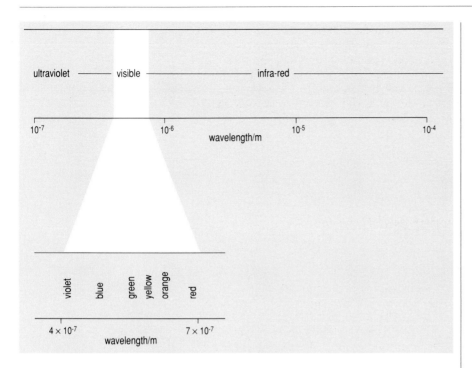

▲ *Figure 2.2 A portion of the electromagnetic spectrum.*

of known reflectivity heated by a known amount of solar radiation. In this context, both the Earth and the Moon can be treated as spherical bodies and the appropriate calculations show that their effective radiating temperatures should be approximately -18°C. This is indeed the average temperature of the Moon, which orbits the Sun at the same distance as the Earth, and if, like the Moon, the Earth had no atmosphere, it too would be at -18°C. A body at this temperature emits radiation with wavelengths in the range 4×10^{-6} to 10^{-4} m (4 to 100 μm), i.e. in the infra-red band. These spectra of emitted radiation from the Sun and the Earth are shown in Figure 2.3(a). (Ignore parts (b) and (c) of this figure for the moment.)

The total radiation budget must be balanced: there always has to be an equilibrium between the incoming solar radiation and the out-going radiation. If there were no atmosphere, this equilibrium could be represented schematically by a diagram such as Figure 2.4. However, the Earth *does* have an atmosphere, and this changes the picture substantially. Gases in the atmosphere absorb radiation, but they do so selectively: different gases absorb different wavelengths. This kind of process is familiar in domestic microwave ovens: water molecules in the food happen to absorb strongly in the microwave band (radiation with a wavelength of a few centimetres), whereas solid substances that contain no water, such as china and plastic containers, do not. The energy from the absorbed radiation is transferred to the water molecules, causing them to rotate and this heats the food from the inside, far more quickly than would the conduction from the food surface that occurs in a conventional oven. The energy that atmospheric gases acquire by absorption of infra-red radiation makes their molecules vibrate, rather than rotate, but the principle is similar. Figure 2.3(b) and (c) shows the percentage of absorption by

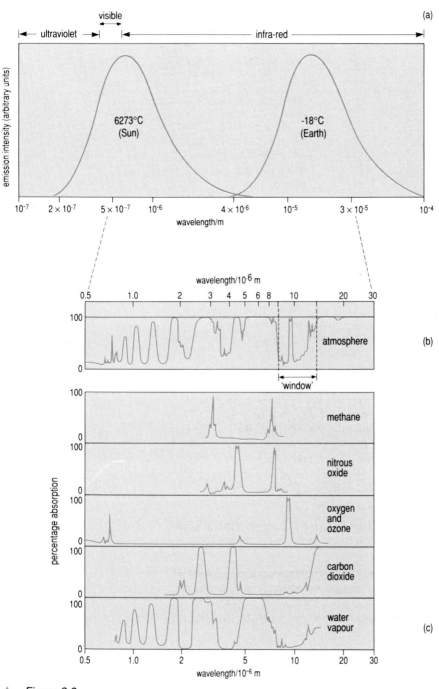

▲   Figure 2.3
(a) Specification of emitted radiation from bodies at 6273°C and -18°C,
corresponding to the effective radiating temperatures of respectively the Sun
and the Earth.
(b) Percentage of atmospheric absorption of radiation passing through the
atmosphere, as a function of wavelength.
(c) Percentage of absorption attributable to various atmospheric gases occurring in
their natural proportions.
(Note that nitrogen – the main constituent of the atmosphere – does not absorb in
the infra-red waveband: it is not a greenhouse gas.)

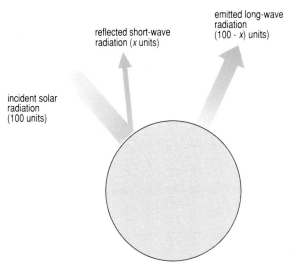

reflected short-wave
radiation (*x* units)

emitted long-wave
radiation
(100 - *x*) units)

incident solar
radiation
(100 units)

◁   *Figure 2.4*
Schematic illustration of radiative balance for a planet with no atmosphere.
100 units of radiation are incident on the planet, and [x + (100 − x)], i.e. 100, units escape back out to space from the planet's surface, by a combination of reflection and emission.

(Note that this is a diagrammatic representation; in practice the solar radiation would be incident on the complete hemisphere and the planet would radiate in all directions.)

atmospheric gases for radiation emitted from the Sun and the Earth. The diagram is complicated, and you are not expected to remember any of the details. For now the important points to note are:

1   Each peak represents absorption of a range of wavelengths by one or more gases. If a peak shows 100% absorption, the atmosphere will be completely opaque to radiation within that wavelength. Remember that the radiation is of different wavelengths and comes from opposite directions in the two cases. Solar radiation of a wavelength that is 100% absorbed will never reach the Earth's surface; infra-red radiation that is 100% absorbed will never reach the top of the atmosphere.

2   Most of the gases absorb in several different wavebands, but are more or less transparent to radiation of intermediate wavelengths. Those that absorb in the infra-red are known as **greenhouse gases**.

3   There is comparatively weak absorption in the visible spectrum: most of the solar radiation passes through the atmosphere and reaches the Earth's surface.

4   On the other hand, most of the long-wave spectrum emitted from the Earth is absorbed. There is just one region of weak absorption, between about 8×10^{-6} and 13×10^{-6} m (i.e. 8 and 13 μm); this is the 'window' that allows some infra-red radiation to escape into space and stops the Earth heating to temperatures inimical to life.

The simple picture of Figure 2.4 therefore has to be modified. A better representation is shown in Figure 2.5. Some of the infra-red radiation from the Earth's surface is absorbed in the atmosphere, so heating it. The warm atmosphere radiates in its turn, again at infra-red wavelengths since its temperature is roughly similar to that of the Earth. Some of this re-emitted radiation goes out into space (the radiative balance with incoming solar radiation still has to be maintained at the top of the atmosphere), but some goes back towards the Earth's surface and heats it up. This phenomenon, which keeps the Earth warmer than its effective radiating temperature is known as the **greenhouse effect**. The average air temperature at ground-level is in fact about 15°C. As we have seen, without the atmosphere the Earth, like the Moon, would be at about -18°C. The natural greenhouse

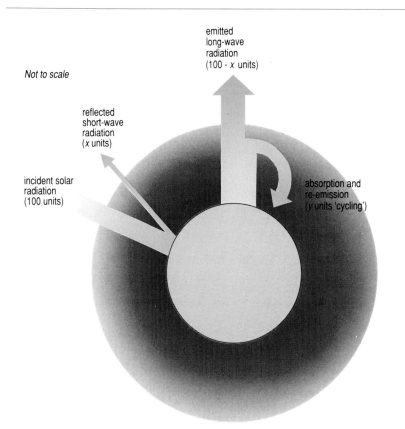

Not to scale

emitted
long-wave
radiation
(100 - x units)

reflected
short-wave
radiation
(x units)

incident solar
radiation
(100 units)

absorption and
re-emission
(y units 'cycling')

◀ Figure 2.5
*Schematic illustration of
radiative balance for a planet
with an absorbing
atmosphere. The 100 units
of incident solar radiation are
again balanced by a total of
100 units of radiation
escaping back into space.
However, y units of long-
wave radiation also cycle
within the atmosphere.*

*(The same diagrammatic
representation has been
used as in Figure 2.4.)*

effect keeps the Earth roughly 33°C warmer than it would be if there were
no atmosphere.

As an aside, it is worth noting that the greenhouse analogy is a very
misleading one. The main reason that a greenhouse heats up on a sunny
day is that the air is trapped inside it and the natural process of convection
is prevented. This is quite a different situation to the climatic 'greenhouse
warming' we are discussing here, which is a purely radiative effect.

Activity 2

Figure 2.6 is a more detailed version of Figure 2.5, and gives a
quantitative picture of the radiation budget. (You may see slightly
different values quoted in different texts, depending on how the
various contributions have been calculated, but these minor
variations are not important here.)

(a) How many units of the incoming (short-wave) solar radiation are
directly reflected? How is this figure related to the albedo?

(b) How many units of long-wave radiation ultimately escape into
space?

(c) What does the sum of your answers to (a) and (b) show about the
total radiation budget?

(d) Why does it appear that we 'accumulate more than we receive',
with 114% of the original input involved in the greenhouse cycle?

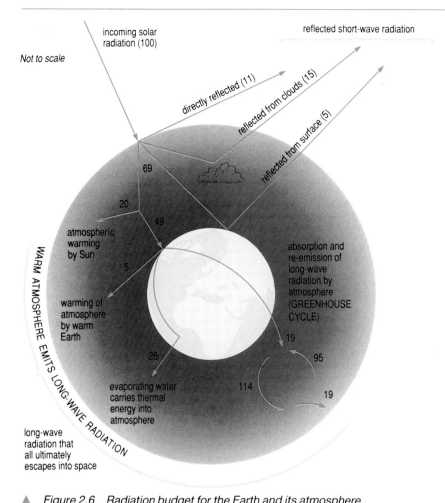

incoming solar
radiation (100)

reflected short-wave radiation

Not to scale

directly reflected (11)

reflected from clouds (15)

reflected from surface (5)

69

20

49

5

26

atmospheric
warming
by Sun

warming of
atmosphere
by warm
Earth

evaporating water
carries thermal
energy into
atmosphere

114

absorption and
re-emission of
long-wave
radiation by
atmosphere
(GREENHOUSE
CYCLE)

19

95

19

WARM ATMOSPHERE EMITS LONG-WAVE RADIATION

long-wave
radiation that
all ultimately
escapes into space

▲   *Figure 2.6   Radiation budget for the Earth and its atmosphere.*
Figures represent percentages of the amount of solar radiation incident on the upper
surface of the atmosphere. The amount of radiation escaping to space has been
measured directly by satellite instruments; other data may be derived from
measurements or from computer models. (Numbers may not total exactly, due to
independent rounding.)

The schematic representation of Figure 2.5 helps to explain the
temperature profile of the lower parts of the atmosphere, which is shown
in Figure 2.7. Infra-red (i.e. long-wave) radiation is absorbed and re-emitted
in a series of stages as it works up through the atmosphere, before finally
escaping into space. Therefore the troposphere is warmest at ground-level
and temperature then decreases with height. The bottom of the
stratosphere is warmed to a considerable extent by the radiation from the
top of the troposphere, but the main heating effect in the stratosphere
comes from absorption of ultraviolet (i.e. short-wave) solar radiation by
molecules of oxygen and ozone. The role of ozone in the stratosphere will
be examined in detail in the next chapter. For the moment, it is enough to
note that, because the absorption of ultraviolet radiation is obviously
greatest nearer the source of that radiation, the temperature of the
stratosphere increases with height above the Earth's surface. The upper
reaches of the atmosphere are also shown in Figure 2.7 for the sake of
completeness, but will not concern us much here.

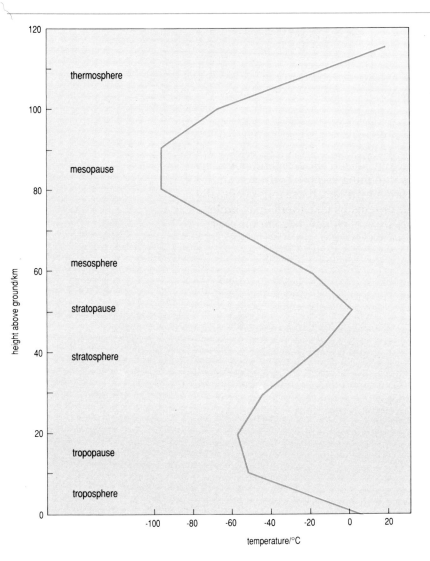

◀ Figure 2.7
The vertical structure of the atmosphere is defined by the way in which temperature varies with height. In each successive 'sphere' the temperature gradient is reversed.

2.2 Atmospheres, climates and thermostats

The natural greenhouse effect keeps our planet more than 30°C warmer than it would be otherwise, but over geological time-spans it has not kept it at a *constant* temperature. Ice-sheets have built up and retreated, steamy swamplands have come and gone. Yet, overall, there has been a climatic stability. At the coldest times of the last two glacial periods (roughly 20 000 and 160 000 years ago), average surface temperatures were about 3°C lower than they are now. During the warmest time between these two glacial periods (roughly 152 000 years ago), temperatures were only a degree or so higher than they are now. Such variations may have resulted in the extinction of individual species, but in the global scheme of things they posed no threat to the presence of life on Earth. It could even be said that there is a global thermostat operating that somehow keeps the Earth's temperature within certain limits. A great deal of research in the 1970s and 1980s was devoted to finding out exactly how this thermostat works.

The mechanism of the Earth's thermostat is complex, with both geochemical and biochemical components, and the debate as to the relative importance of these two components is an ongoing one, involving many of the principal workers in the field. For the purposes of this chapter, it will be enough just to gain an overall understanding of how the two parts of the system operate.

The geochemical component of the thermostat works broadly speaking as follows. Rainwater dissolves carbon dioxide from the atmosphere, forming an acid – carbonic acid. This reacts with rocks that contain calcium silicate minerals (compounds of calcium, silicon and oxygen), releasing calcium ions and bicarbonate ions (containing carbon, hydrogen and oxygen) into groundwater. Transported by rivers, these ions eventually end up in the oceans, where various organisms take them up to build chalky shells chiefly composed of calcium carbonate (a compound of calcium, carbon and oxygen). When the organisms die, their shells settle on the sea floor, forming layers of carbonate rich sediments. On a geological timescale – millions of years – sea-floor spreading carries these sediments to the edges of the continental crust, where they are partly subducted (i.e. pushed down under the continental crust). At the high temperatures and pressures that exist in the Earth's mantle, the calcium carbonate reacts with silica (quartz), so new silicate rocks are formed, along with carbon dioxide. This gas is released to the atmosphere through leakage from the Earth's surface or, more violently, through volcanic eruptions near subduction zones. Figure 2.8 summarises the process and shows that it is cyclical, which is of course the reason that it can function as a thermostat. Imagine that the temperature were to fall significantly, perhaps because the Sun was emitting less radiation than it does now.

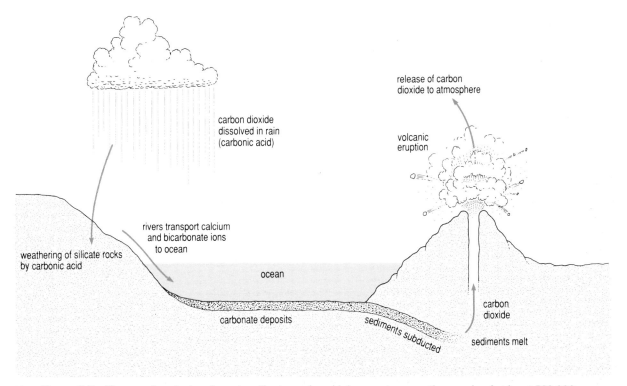

▲   Figure 2.8   The geochemical carbonate-silicate cycle, which operates on a time scale of at least 500 000 years.

(This is not implausible: 4.5 billion years ago, when the solar system formed, it has been estimated that the Sun's radiative temperature was only about 70% of what it is today.) On a cooler Earth, less water would evaporate from the oceans, so there would be less rain, and less carbon dioxide removed from the atmosphere. The output of the carbon dioxide from volcanoes would remain unchanged, however, so the concentration of the gas would build up in the atmosphere, enhancing greenhouse warming. As the Earth then became hotter, evaporation would increase and the increased rainfall would remove more carbon dioxide from the atmosphere so that the level of greenhouse warming would be reduced again. Figure 2.9(a) shows the process schematically. All thermostatic systems – indeed all types of regulatory systems – operate on this principle of **negative feedback**, whereby the system acts to counter changes in conditions. Figure 2.9(b) illustrates this.

However, rain is not the only form in which water vapour enters the story. Figure 2.3(c) illustrated that water vapour is an important greenhouse gas in its own right. Furthermore, the concentration of water vapour in the atmosphere is controlled by temperature – the higher the temperature, the more liquid water evaporates and the more water vapour there is in the atmosphere.

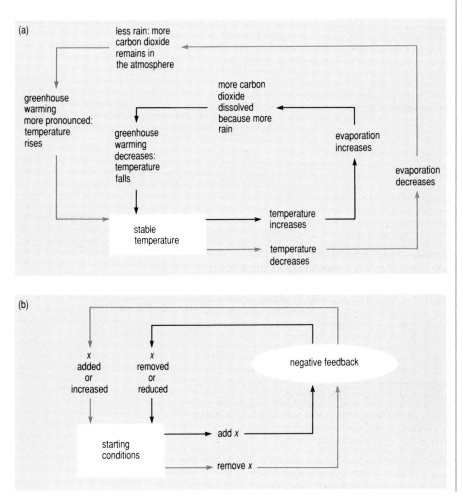

◀ *Figure 2.9*

(a) Negative feedback in the carbonate-silicate cycle.

(b) Generalised flow diagram of a negative feedback process.

Activity 3

This situation is one of **positive feedback**: as the temperature, and therefore the concentration of water vapour in the atmosphere increases, the greenhouse effect is reinforced, so the temperature rises and the evaporation rate increases. By analogy with the black cycle in Figure 2.9(a) and (b), draw a schematic diagram representing this cycle of events and a generalised diagram of a positive feedback loop.

A positive feedback loop just carries on increasing the effect of a change in conditions: indeed the phrase often used to describe what happened on our neighbouring planet Venus is a 'runaway' greenhouse. There was certainly water in the original material of Venus, just as there was on Earth, and plenty of carbon dioxide in its atmosphere. But Venus is closer to the Sun than the Earth, so its original atmosphere was warmer than that of the Earth. Water vapour in the Venusian atmosphere did not condense to form rain – it merely rose, enhancing the greenhouse effect, until, towards the top of the atmosphere, the water molecules dissociated into hydrogen and oxygen and were lost. A few hundred million years after its formation, Venus became completely dehydrated, and there was then no process by which carbon dioxide could be removed from its atmosphere. With no natural thermostat operating, the greenhouse effect caused temperatures on the planet to soar. Today, Venus is a dry hothouse, with an average surface temperature of 460°C.

It will not have escaped your notice that even in a cycle described as 'geochemical', shelled organisms featured. Clearly, since such organisms are known to have existed on the Earth, it would be perverse not to include them in the cycle, but some scientists consider that they are not *essential* to the operation of such a cycle. Some workers believe that the purely geochemical mechanism maintained the Earth's surface perhaps 10°C above its present temperature until the first shelled organisms appeared about six hundred million years ago, and could have continued to do so. Their thesis is that 'the Earth would still have remained [hotter but] habitable even if it had never been inhabited'. Many other scientists disagree, however, arguing that not only were photosynthesising organisms essential to the evolution of the Earth's oxygen-rich atmosphere, but also that biological feedback mechanisms have been crucial in determining the climate. The foremost proponent of such views is James Lovelock, founder of the Gaian theory, which in one form states that natural feedback loops involving living organisms always operate in such a way as to stabilise the conditions for the perpetuation of life. But the greenhouse effect is central to Gaian mechanisms too.

As an example, Lovelock points to the time, about 3.5 billion years ago, when the first photosynthetic bacteria appeared on Earth. The carbon required to build their cells came from atmospheric carbon dioxide, and as the concentrations of gas fell, so did the average temperature – from about 28°C to 15°C according to Lovelock. What then stabilised the temperature was a biological feedback mechanism: the bacteria's metabolism resulted in the release of methane. Figure 2.3(c) showed that methane too is a greenhouse gas (and, as we will see later, a more efficient one than carbon dioxide); therefore an increase in the concentration of atmospheric methane pushes up the temperature. Because the greenhouse properties of carbon dioxide and methane are slightly different, the amount of greenhouse warming is affected by their relative concentrations, and this in turn depends on the rate of growth of the bacteria, which is itself temperature-dependent. The crucial point is that the amount of greenhouse warming is linked to (Gaian enthusiasts would say 'controlled by') biological activity. Lovelock believes that the Earth's thermostat is still biologically regulated today, with living organisms actually controlling the carbonate-silicate cycle. Marine organisms are responsible for taking carbon dioxide from the atmosphere and dumping carbonates on the sea floor, a mechanism often referred to as the **'biological pump'**. Land plants too accumulate carbon as they grow; micro-organisms then break down dead plant tissue to release carbon dioxide within the soils where it contributes to (or, according to Lovelock, dominates) the weathering of silicate rocks.

While there continues to be controversy about the relative importance of the various components of the global thermostat, everybody agrees that, just as changes in the climate and in the physical environment as a whole have influenced the course of biological evolution, so some biological activity does influence the climate. Stephen Schneider, an American climatologist who is at the forefront of the current debates, has called this interplay 'the co-evolution of climate and life'. The workings of the global thermostat may still be imperfectly understood, but there is no doubt that it exists. The worry now is whether human activities are likely to 'reset' or even 'break' it. Before we can begin to answer that question, we need to look in a little more detail at the limits within which the thermostatically controlled climate can vary.

2.3   Rhythms in the climate

Changes in climate, and other environmental changes with which they are associated, take place over a considerable range of time-scales. Many of these changes occur in a regular rhythm. For example, in the last million or so years, there has been a pattern in which a glacial period, that lasts about 100 000 years, is followed by a warmer, interglacial, period of 10 000 to 20 000 years' duration.*

The interglacial period in which we now find ourselves has already lasted a little more than 10 000 years, as shown in Figure 2.10. This sets the perspective, both with respect to temperature changes and with respect to the speed at which the changes occur. As mentioned in the last subsection, the total range of average global surface temperatures over the past million years spans only a few degrees Centigrade. The temperature has risen fairly steadily since the time of the last glacial maximum, but an increase of less than 3°C has taken 20 000 years to achieve.

The rhythm of the glacial and interglacial periods is linked with slight, but regular, variations in the Earth's orbit round the Sun. Over a period of about 100 000 years, the shape of the orbit changes, from elliptical to almost circular, and back again. The more elliptical the orbit, the greater the differences between the seasons. Secondly, the tilt of the Earth's axis of rotation to the plane of the orbit varies, with a periodicity of 41 000 years, causing slight shifts in the positions of the tropics and greater or lesser differences between summer and winter in any given place. Thirdly, the axis wobbles, with a periodicity of 21 000 years. As a result, there is a slow drift in the time of year at which the Earth is closest to the Sun and the pattern of the seasons gradually changes over many such cycles. A Serbian

*You may come across popular books or articles in which the term 'ice age' is used to describe what is properly called a 'glacial period'. In scientific terminology an ice age is a very long span of time, during which there is an alternation of glacial and interglacial periods. The present (Pleistocene) ice age has already lasted for about 4 million years. The most recent previous ice age spanned the time between 270 and 310 million years ago. In the time intervening between these two ice ages (i.e. between 4 and 270 million years ago), the climate was more stable.

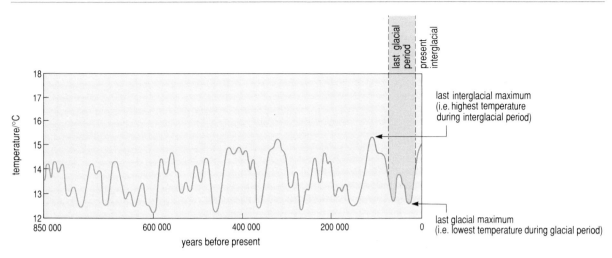

▲ Figure 2.10
Globally averaged surface temperatures on the Earth during a succession of ice ages and interglacials.

▲ In 1814 the Thames froze to such a depth that fairs were set up on the ice. There are considerable variations in
temperature within the longer-term climatic changes.

astronomer, Milankovic, first proposed in the 1920s that the pattern of
glacial periods might be linked to these fluctuations in the orbital geometry
of the Earth, but at that time his hypothesis could not be tested because the
periods of glaciation had not been accurately dated. When this was finally
done, in the mid 1970s, it became clear that the amount of ice cover over
the past 800 000 years does indeed fit with three cycles of 100 000, 41 000
and 21 000 years' duration. However, one very fundamental question

remained. If the Sun's output remains constant, the Earth will receive the same amount of radiation every year. The Milankovic cycles only result in slight seasonal or geographical temperature changes. How are these changes enough to trigger the onset or the end of glacial periods?

One suggestion is that there is an amplification system, the working substance for which is carbon dioxide. A complicated series of studies, involving the analysis and dating of sediments formed from the carbonate shells of marine organisms (called planktonic *Foraminifera*), has revealed that changes in temperature and ice cover are always *preceded* by changes in the concentration of atmospheric carbon dioxide. These changes in carbon dioxide levels, on the other hand, lag just slightly *behind* the Milankovic cycles. It appears that once the astronomical mechanism heralds the approach of a glacial period, the 'biological pump' increases its activity, removing carbon dioxide from the atmosphere and reducing greenhouse warming. A positive feedback loop then becomes established, whereby cooler summers result in less melting of the icecaps and the high albedo ice reflects an increasing amount of solar radiation back into space, further reducing the temperature. If this interpretation is correct, the question is, of course, what stimulates the activity of the biological pump and so results in the fall in carbon dioxide. This is still the subject of research and debate.

Even if we do not yet understand all the details, it is clear that the greenhouse effect has played an important role in the major climatic shifts of the last billion or so years. The additional question scientists have to address now is whether human activities are altering the climate on a much shorter timescale, so disrupting the natural patterns of climatic variation.

2.4   *Climatic futures*

Climatologists have no doubt that the Earth has got warmer in the last century. In this subsection we shall examine this warming trend in some detail and look at the evidence that links the rise in temperature to human activity.

Q   Looking back to Figure 2.1, what evidence was presented that global warming accelerated in the 1980s? Is such evidence necessarily indicative of a long-term trend?

A   As reported in 1989, the six hottest years of the twentieth century were all in the 1980s. However, this does not necessarily imply that temperatures would continue to rise thereafter: the 1980s might be anomalous years in a long-term trend of falling temperatures, or might fall on the rising curve in a cycle of variation with a periodicity of a decade or two.

A better idea of current temperature trends is given by Figure 2.11 which shows the variations that have occurred over the past 130 years. Once the annual fluctuations are averaged out, these cumulative data show an increase in global mean temperature of more than 0.5°C over the past century. Other types of measurement confirm this general trend. Records of the sea surface temperature follow a similar pattern to the land-based records of Figure 2.11, and also stretch back to about 1850. Temperature-sensing balloons were not launched routinely until about 1950, but we now have forty years of data from such instruments and they show quite

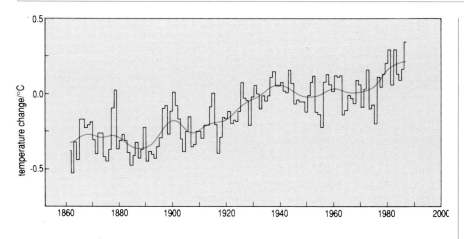

◀ Figure 2.11
Global average
temperatures for land-based
measurements, plotted as
deviations from the mean
for 1940 to 1960. The
smooth curve is the mean
over successive five-year
intervals.

dramatic warming of the troposphere: in the southern hemisphere
tropospheric temperature increases averaged over the period 1950 to 1985
were between 0.1 and 0.5°C *per decade*, and accelerating in the second half
of the period. (See Plate 3.) Measurements of sea-level changes over the
past century show that mean levels have risen in that time, in a way that
roughly parallels temperature trends and suggests thermal expansion of
sea-water as the principal cause. We will return to sea-level changes in
Section 4; for now it is sufficient simply to appreciate that measurements of
these changes provide some independent evidence for recent global
warming, in that they build up evidence not based on temperature
readings.

    Is this a case of cause and effect? Certainly the presence of carbon
dioxide in the atmosphere gives rise to greenhouse warming. But has this
particular trend of rising temperatures come about *because* of an increase in
the atmospheric concentration of carbon dioxide?

    The longest-running continuous monitoring of carbon dioxide levels is
that carried out at the Mauna Loa observatory in Hawaii. The results of this

◀ The Mauna Loa
observatory in Hawaii,
site of the longest-running
project to monitor levels
of atmospheric carbon
dioxide.

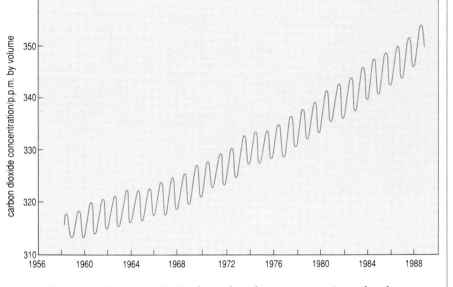

*Concentration, in parts
per million by volume, of
atmospheric carbon dioxide
measured at the Mauna Loa
station, geographically
remote from any sources of
industrial pollution. Annual
oscillations arise from
seasonal changes in
photosynthesis and other
biological processes.*

study, illustrated in Figure 2.12, show that the concentration of carbon
dioxide in the atmosphere has increased steadily over the past 30 years: the
1988 concentration (350 ppm) is over 10% greater than that recorded for
1958 (315 ppm). However, before we can attach any significance to this
result, we need to know what the natural variation in carbon dioxide levels
has been over various timescales: have there perhaps been 10%
fluctuations in the concentration in the past as a result of some natural
cyclical process? For some answers to these questions we can turn to
ice-core data.

As glacier ice is formed by compaction of successive layers of snow,
small bubbles of air become trapped. When a sample of ice is drilled out,
these air bubbles can be dated quite accurately and so form an 'archive' of
past atmospheres and climates. The deepest layer of ice extracted from the
Antarctic Vostok core (from 2.2 km below the surface) formed from snow
that fell over 160 000 years ago, in the last but one glacial maximum. The
record of the Vostok core shows that at the end of both the two most recent
ice ages the atmospheric concentrations of carbon dioxide increased
sharply, from around 190 ppm to about 280 ppm, with a probable
maximum of 300 ppm. It does indeed seem that the Mauna Loa data are
showing up something other than natural variation; even when the
observations began in 1958, the levels of carbon dioxide were higher than
they had been at any time in the current or preceding interglacial. Analysis
of another ice-core has given more detailed information about the build-up
of carbon dioxide over the past 250 years, as shown in Figure 2.13. The
increase in carbon dioxide levels at the start of this period was linked to
deforestation and agricultural activity. Since the beginning of the industrial
age, it is undoubtedly the burning of fossil fuels that has made the greatest
contribution to the change in atmospheric concentrations of carbon
dioxide. The 1988 level of 350 ppm represents an increase of 27% over the
pre-industrial level of 275 ppm. At the end of the '80s, annual emissions of
carbon dioxide worldwide amounted to over 5 Gt (i.e. 5×10^9 tonnes)
of carbon.

There is no doubt at all that human activities are profoundly affecting
the natural balance of gases in the atmosphere, and little doubt that the
build-up of carbon dioxide from anthropogenic sources will lead to some

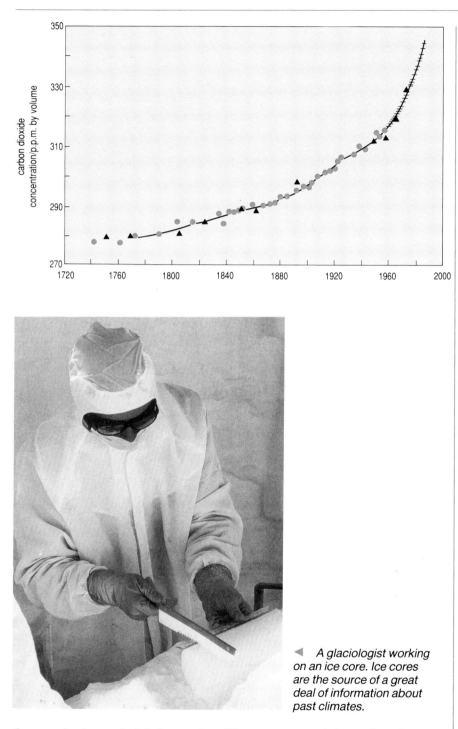

◀ Figure 2.13
Increase in the atmospheric
concentration of carbon
dioxide, determined from ice
core measurements of Siple
station, Antarctica
(triangles), isotope analysis
(circles) and direct
observation at Mauna Loa
(crosses).

◀ A glaciologist working
on an ice core. Ice cores
are the source of a great
deal of information about
past climates.

degree of enhanced global warming. However, a remaining point of
contention among climatologists is whether anthropogenic greenhouse
warming can truly be said to have been observed, and if not, how long it
will be before it is considered to have 'arrived'. The most cautious suggest
it may require another 20 or 30 years of accumulated data conclusively to
demonstrate that global warming is occurring primarily due to
anthropogenic emissions of carbon dioxide.

In fact this timescale may be shortened because carbon dioxide is not the only greenhouse gas whose concentration is increasing as a result of human activities.

Q   Looking back to Figure 2.3 what are the other naturally occurring greenhouse gases?

A   Water vapour, methane, nitrous oxide and ozone.

The relative importance of several of these gases in modifying the climate is increasing, for two reasons:

(a) their atmospheric concentrations are building up more quickly than that of carbon dioxide; and

(b) molecule-for-molecule they are more 'efficient' greenhouse gases than carbon dioxide.

Water vapour, as Figure 2.3(c) showed, plays a very important role in the greenhouse effect. It is, however, unique among greenhouse gases in that its atmosphere concentration is dependent on temperature (with which, as you saw in Activity 3, it is directly linked via a positive feedback loop), and on very little else. It is therefore normally considered as part of the climatic cycle, rather than as a separate greenhouse gas.

Methane, like carbon dioxide, is a gas that occurs naturally in the biosphere. It is produced by bacteria under anaerobic (i.e. oxygen-free) conditions, for example in the intestines of ruminant animals and in waterlogged soils, hence its common name of 'marsh gas'. Rice paddies, which in that respect are artificial marshes, are major sources of methane, and so are herds of cattle. While such sources are undoubtedly biogenic, they also clearly have an anthropogenic element, as Figure 2.14 demonstrates: the increase in atmospheric methane over the last 300 years shows good correlation with the growth of world population, suggesting that the rise in concentration of the gas is indeed related to human activities, in this case agricultural production. The rotting of any organic matter (e.g. on waste disposal sites) releases methane, and leakage from fuel-extracting operations (such as natural gas pipelines and coal mines) adds further to the atmospheric burden of this gas.

Nitrous oxide is another naturally occurring greenhouse gas, cycled by biological processes. However, substantial quantities of nitrous oxide are also being generated as a result of human activities, such as the cultivation of newly exposed soils and the ever-increasing usage of nitrogenous fertilisers. In addition, combustion of fossil fuels (or indeed the combustion of anything in air, 80% of which is nitrogen), produces nitrous oxide and other compounds of oxygen and nitrogen.

Ozone also occurs naturally in the upper atmosphere, where it plays a vital role in shielding the surface of the Earth from harmful ultraviolet solar radiation. Some of this ozone does descend to the lower levels of the atmosphere, but its natural concentration there is low, which is just as well, since ozone is toxic to both plant and animal life. Unfortunately, in industrial societies ozone is now being generated at ground-level by the action of sunlight on gaseous pollutants – such as the hydrocarbons, oxides of nitrogen and carbon monoxide emitted by vehicle exhausts. The so-called 'photochemical smog' that results is in itself a hazard to environmental health and the ozone produced in this process also acts as a greenhouse gas in the lower atmosphere.

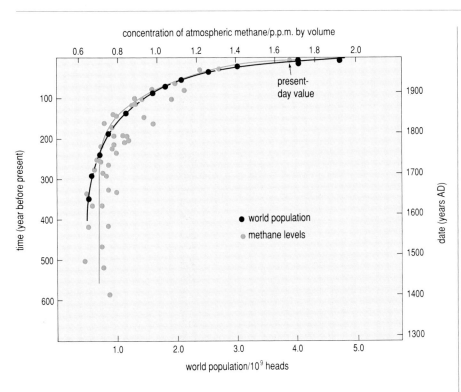

concentration of atmospheric methane/p.p.m. by volume

present-day value

● world population
● methane levels

time (year before present)

date (years AD)

world population/10⁹ heads

◀   Figure 2.14
Correlation of the increase in
the atmospheric
concentration of methane
with the growth of world
population.

◀   The vertical 'chimney'
at this landfill site will act as
a vent for methane once the
site is filled in.

◀ *Photochemical smog, in which ozone is produced by the action of sunlight on vehicle exhaust gases, in Oakland, California.*

Chlorofluorocarbons (CFCs) first became notorious in relation to their role in the destruction of the ozone layer, which story is the subject of the next chapter. However, they are also extremely efficient greenhouse gases. They do not occur naturally, so all the atmospheric burden of CFCs is anthropogenic in origin.

The life-span of molecules of some of these greenhouse gases in the atmosphere is long: nitrous oxide persists for about 160 years, CFCs for around 100 years (depending on type). This, coupled with their greenhouse efficiency and quickly rising emission rates, means that they now play a significant role in climate modification. Figure 2.15 shows that in the 1980s greenhouse gases other than carbon dioxide and water vapour were estimated to account for roughly half of the warming due to the anthropogenic greenhouse effect. In subsequent discussions focusing chiefly on carbon dioxide emissions (and implicitly incorporating water vapour), it is therefore important not to forget the additional contribution of the other greenhouse gases.

2.5   Summary of Section 2

Greenhouse warming, an effect arising from the successive absorption and emission of infra-red radiation by molecules of certain atmospheric gases, has occurred on Earth throughout the planet's history and is crucial in maintaining the surface at a temperature suitable for life. In the past two hundred years, anthropogenic sources of greenhouse gases, particularly carbon dioxide and methane, have begun to disturb the atmospheric balance. By 1990 carbon dioxide concentration had risen by nearly 30% above its pre-industrial level. There has also been an increase in the mean global surface temperature of more than 0.5°C over the past hundred years. There is growing evidence that this is a case of cause and effect, but it may take another few decades before that is established beyond doubt.

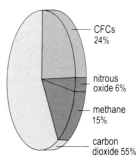

CFCs 24%

nitrous oxide 6%

methane 15%

carbon dioxide 55%

▲ *Figure 2.15 Relative contributions of various gases to the anthropogenic greenhouse warming of the 1980s. The contribution from tropospheric ozone may also be significant, but cannot be quantified at present.*

Activity 4

The following questions may be used to revise some of the key concepts of this section.

Q1 Radiation from the Sun is continually incident on the Earth, so why doesn't the Earth continually get hotter and hotter?

Q2 Describe briefly the heating mechanisms in the troposphere and stratosphere and explain why overall the temperature varies oppositely with height in the two regions.

Q3 The bottom-most layers of the stratosphere, near the troposphere, are warmed by convection from the upper levels of the troposphere. Measurements from balloons seem to indicate that the lower stratosphere has cooled over the last thirty years. Why is this taken as further evidence of anthropogenic greenhouse warming?

3   *Greenhouse warming: projections and scenarios*

3.1   *Introduction*

Little of the material presented in the previous section was controversial: certainly there is no dispute about the nature of the greenhouse effect and its importance as an element of natural atmospheric systems. However, there *is* still controversy surrounding assessments of the possible anthropogenic contributions to the greenhouse effect, in particular:

(a) the likely future levels of greenhouse gases in the atmosphere arising from human activities;

(b) the amount by which the Earth's surface temperature may rise as a consequence of the increased atmospheric burden of greenhouse gases; and

(c) the timescale and geographic distribution of any such temperature increase.

In this section we will examine these areas of ongoing research and debate, and explore some of the difficulties and uncertainties associated with them. Concern over global warming has prompted a tremendous concentration of scientific effort in this field over recent years, but scientists still have only a very sketchy understanding of the way in which the Earth's climate systems work. In the next decade we can expect many hypotheses and conclusions to be put forward. Quite a lot of this work will be reported in the popular media, with variable degrees of exactitude and objectivity. A major aim of this section and the next one is to enable you to follow future developments and to assess the importance and reliability of the research data on which they are based.

The problem of trying to predict the Earth's climatic future may be broken down into a series of steps:

1   'Projecting' (i.e. predicting) the emissions of carbon dioxide and other greenhouse gases into the atmosphere.

2   Projecting the build-up of the concentration of these gases in the atmosphere.

3   Forecasting the resulting climatic change.

Because each of these steps feeds into the next one, the process becomes increasingly more difficult and uncertain from step 1 to step 3.

We will tackle each of these stages in turn in Sections 3.3–3.6, and our conclusions will then inform the discussion in Section 4 about the impact of possible climatic change on natural processes and human societies. Before starting on this set of interwoven arguments, however, it is worth taking a brief look at the basic method underlying all the forecasts – the technique of 'modelling'.

3.2   Models and scenarios

In everyday language we use phrases such as 'architect's model' or 'model railway' to mean a scaled-down replica of the real thing. A scientist, however, uses the term 'model' somewhat differently. Scientific **modelling** may be described as an attempt firstly to break down the workings of a complex system into a series of well-defined processes, and then to find a way of simulating these processes so as to be able to predict how the system will react in a variety of circumstances. In constructing a model of the atmosphere, for example, one might start from the basic physical law that states that the temperature of an 'ideal gas' is directly proportional to the product of its pressure and its volume. The notion of an 'ideal gas' is a scientist's model if ever there was one, since no real gas ever conforms exactly to this notion of ideality (although at ordinary pressures and volumes most gases approximate to it), but the usefulness of the law lies in the fact that it is easily expressed in terms of a simple equation. There are well-established equations, too, to describe phenomena such as the change in atmospheric pressure with height, the rate at which a gas released at one point will diffuse through the atmosphere, and the radiative heating effect associated with particular gases as a function of their atmospheric concentration. It is the complete set of equations describing all the components of the system that finally constitutes 'the model'. The equations are the rules that a computer will follow so as to simulate the behaviour of the real system in response to various changes in conditions ('input') that are given to it as basic data.

The modelling process thus involves three major elements – the model itself, the capacity of the computer on which it is run and the input conditions. All three have their limitations and it is often necessary to read between the lines of various reports in order to appreciate these limitations and assess the reliability of claims made by the modellers.

Firstly, one has to consider the complexity of the model. Returning to the example of a model of the atmosphere, it is possible to construct simple models on the basis of equations expressing physical laws such as those described above. In the real world though, a great many other factors also operate. Some are quite well understood in an empirical way (i.e. their

effect is known by observation but there is no theoretical basis on which
prediction of their future effect can be made): an example of such a factor
in atmospheric modelling might be the influence of clouds. Still other
factors are known to be important to the system but are as yet very poorly
understood; the whole ocean–atmosphere–biosphere interaction falls into
this category at present. In such a complex system there are also almost
certainly factors that we have not even identified. Our models are therefore
incomplete, over-simplified and full of approximations and assumptions.
This is not to imply that simplification is necessarily a bad thing. Indeed it
is the essence of modelling: there is no point in constructing a model that is
just as complicated as the real world. On the other hand, a good model
should include all the important features of the real-world system. The art
of the modeller is to strike a balance between complexity, utility and
accuracy.

Secondly, there are computational limitations. Even in a very
simplified model of the atmosphere, a number of processes must be
included. Each process might be described by a fairly simple equation, but
because all the processes interlock with one another, a great deal of
computation is required to produce simultaneous solutions to all of the
equations. The computer's speed and the size of its memory become
important. In order to keep the task down to manageable proportions, it
may be necessary to instruct the computer to calculate values only at
individual points or only in an average way. In a model of the atmosphere,
for example, one might calculate temperature changes over just half a
dozen latitudinal bands with inputs appropriate to, say, July conditions
and December conditions.

The third limitation of the modelling process arises from the inputs
used – the numerical values or conditions the computer is told to apply to
the model. Some conditions are difficult to specify in a way that a computer
can use. For example, in the real atmosphere, cloud formation is an
important process, but on a model in which the atmosphere is represented
by large latitudinal bands a cloud is a phenomenon on too small a scale to
be simulated directly. Some quantity – perhaps a proportionality constant
in an equation – therefore has to be included to give an estimate of the
average cloudiness corresponding to other sets of conditions, such as
temperature and humidity, that can be specified or calculated more easily.
This technique, called **parametrisation**, by which small-scale phenomena
and feedback loops are incorporated into a model in an average way, is
widely used, but applied slightly differently in each individual case. As we
shall see, models can be very sensitive to small changes in parametrisation;
in evaluating models or in comparing the predictions of one against the
other, it is important to bear this in mind.

Other types of input would be relatively easy to specify to a computer
but are simply impossible to estimate. The future atmospheric
concentration of carbon dioxide is an example of such a quantity. Under
these circumstances, modellers fall back on constructing **scenarios** –
pictures of what to expect given certain basic premises. A scenario is not an
image of a definite future; it is an image of what *could* happen if particular
conditions are fulfilled. Some of the scenarios put forward by climate
modellers are frightening but may never come to pass: the fear engendered
by a scenario may be enough in itself to make us take steps to ensure that
the assumptions underlying that particular scenario are never fulfilled. The
rest of this chapter is all about constructing scenarios, examining the
models and assumptions on which they are based, and learning from them
about the consequences of future courses of action.

3.3   Projecting carbon dioxide emissions

Forecasting the rate at which carbon dioxide will be released to the atmosphere is a complex problem in social science. In outline it requires predictions of population trends, economic growth, policies of world trade, the relationship between economic development and energy consumption, and the proportion of those energy demands that will be met by burning fossil fuels. Fossil fuel usage will in turn depend on many factors, such as the price of oil, the availability and cost-effectiveness of alternative energy sources, energy conservation measures and even possible social pressures for countermeasures to anthropogenic greenhouse warming.

Even in the short term (of a decade, say), there are very large uncertainties associated with any projection of energy requirements and fossil fuel consumption. These uncertainties are different in nature from those that scientists attach to experimentally measured quantities or to the predictions of mathematical models. Demographic and economic factors are not amenable to modelling in quite the same way as quantities governed by natural laws, and economic factors are further complicated by political decisions. Predictions of fuel consumption for the 1970s based on the pattern set in the 1960s turned out to be badly wrong, because they obviously had not been able to take into account the major oil crises that in fact occurred in 1973 and 1979. In the same way, policy decisions regarding fossil fuel use could in the next decade substantially modify current patterns of carbon dioxide emissions. Faced with the impossibility of quantifying all these elements, we can only fall back on the construction of possible scenarios.

In the mid 1980s work of this kind was undertaken in a joint study by the UN Environmental Programme, the World Meteorological Organisation and the International Council of Scientific Unions. The resulting authoritative report, the 29th in a series published by the Scientific Committee on Problems of the Environment, and therefore known as SCOPE 29, came out in 1986 and provides the basis for much of the discussion in this chapter. It was supplemented in 1990 by a scientific report prepared for the Intergovernmental Panel on Climate Change (IPCC). The policy significance of the IPCC process is examined in Chapter 4. As we saw in Section 2, in the mid 1980s about 5 Gt of carbon, in the form of carbon dioxide, were emitted into the atmosphere each year from fossil fuel combustion. The conclusions of the SCOPE 29 workers,

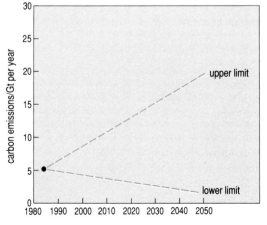

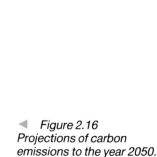

◁   *Figure 2.16*
Projections of carbon
emissions to the year 2050.

based on accumulated data from scenarios prepared by about ten separate teams of researchers and broadly confirmed in the IPCC report, are shown in Figure 2.16. Their assessment places an upper limit on probable emissions of about 20 Gt of carbon per year by 2050 – i.e. a fourfold increase in emissions by the middle of the next century. It is considered that logistic constraints, concern for the environment and social pressures will prevent emissions increasing beyond this level. The lower limit on probable emissions is put at 2 Gt of carbon per year in 2050. Such a reduction in emissions below the present level will only be approached if there is sustained international cooperation to curb energy demands and to develop alternative energy strategies that are not dependent on fossil fuels. The SCOPE 29 workers made the following statement about the 'envelope' of uncertainty contained within the dotted lines on Figure 2.16:

> narrowed by further research, because this envelope signifies a basic ignorance about future cultural evolution. Thus any particular trajectory implies some combination of political, technological and social developments that cannot be predicted.   (Keepin, Mintzer and Kristoferson, 1986, p. 55)

3.4   Projecting atmospheric concentrations of carbon dioxide

Given a particular scenario for the amount of carbon dioxide emitted into the atmosphere, the next step is to estimate how much of it will actually remain there. Unlike the issue of emission rates, this question is amenable to scientific modelling of the type described in Section 3.2. The basic features of the global carbon cycle, in which carbon circulates through the biosphere, the atmosphere, the hydrosphere (oceans and fresh water) and through soils and rocks, are well understood (see *Silvertown*, 1990). However, some links in the chain are still poorly understood and because of the complexity of the cycle, involving interactions between biological, chemical and geological processes, there are still many uncertainties inherent in the models.

The main problem is that scientists have not yet discovered how to balance the carbon budget completely. For one thing there is still considerable debate about exactly what proportion of carbon dioxide is taken up by the oceans. Another major complication is the existence of feedback loops. For example, it is thought that an increase in the concentration of atmospheric carbon dioxide might result in an increased take-up of carbon dioxide by plants through photosynthesis. On the other hand, it is not clear whether carbon dioxide uptake by the surface waters of the oceans will increase or decrease. Greenhouse warming of the climate could also speed up the decomposition of dead organic matter held in soils and result in further release of carbon dioxide. The major uncertainties in projections of carbon dioxide concentrations are due to inadequate knowledge of the details of such feedback processes. Nevertheless, the uncertainties inherent in estimating carbon dioxide concentrations for a particular emission scenario are not nearly so great as the uncertainties associated with the emission scenarios themselves. Thus the upper and lower limits on estimates of carbon dioxide concentration are effectively set by the upper- and lower-bound emission scenarios discussed in the previous subsection.

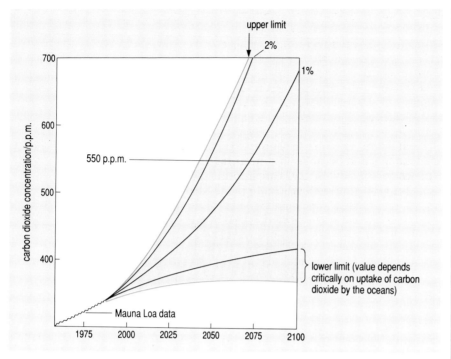

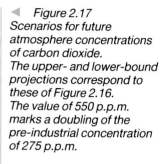

Figure 2.17
Scenarios for future
atmosphere concentrations
of carbon dioxide.
The upper- and lower-bound
projections correspond to
these of Figure 2.16.
The value of 550 p.p.m.
marks a doubling of the
pre-industrial concentration
of 275 p.p.m.

The SCOPE 29 workers translated the scenarios of Figure 2.16 into projections of carbon dioxide concentrations and their results are shown in Figure 2.17. The upper-bound scenario suggests that atmospheric concentrations of carbon dioxide could reach double their pre-industrial concentration before the middle of the next century. Such a doubling of carbon dioxide levels is often taken as a benchmark in the construction of future climatic scenarios. Note that, principally because of the slow response time of the oceans in removing carbon dioxide from the air, atmospheric concentrations of carbon dioxide could rise throughout the next century even under the lower-bound scenario that assumes a persistent *reduction* in emissions. Projections for annual growth rates in emission of 1% and 2% are also shown, and it is important to bear in mind that global consumption of fossil fuel is estimated at the time of writing (1990) to be increasing at 1.5% per year (with energy usage in the developing world increasing at 6% per year, as compared with 0.5% per year in the industrialised nations).

3.5   *Projecting the effects of other greenhouse gases*

If it is difficult to predict future levels of carbon dioxide emissions, it is even more difficult to forecast emissions of other greenhouse gases. In the case of the naturally occurring gases, especially methane, the sources and sinks are not well understood. In the case of the industrial gases, particularly CFCs, future emissions will be totally dependent on technological and political developments.

Methane is in some ways the most important greenhouse gas after carbon dioxide. At present, human activities have increased the concentration of carbon dioxide in the atmosphere by slightly less than

30% above its pre-industrial level, but analyses of air bubbles trapped in ice cores show that the amount of methane present in the atmosphere has more than doubled in industrial times. There are also several positive feedback loops linking natural methane emissions to climatic change: methane, like carbon dioxide, is released from decaying organic matter. Higher atmospheric concentrations of methane cause greenhouse warming; higher temperatures increase rates of decay. Large quantities of methane are also locked away in peat bogs below frozen Arctic tundra, so melting of areas of permafrost could lead to further release of methane.

Methane is important in global warming scenarios because its natural balance is disturbed by climatic change, and because its concentration has increased substantially from pre-industrial levels. CFCs are important for two quite different reasons – because they are such efficient greenhouse gases and because they have very long lifetimes. Even if CFC emissions were to be totally banned now, the current atmospheric burden of these gases would make a substantial contribution to greenhouse warming through most of the next century. By 1990, as Figure 2.15 showed, the relative contribution of CFCs to anthropogenic greenhouse warming was estimated to be 24% – a substantial effect for a class of chemical that was not released in any quantity until the 1950s.

It is a fairly straightforward scientific problem to calculate the radiative effects of each greenhouse gas for any given atmospheric concentration. The SCOPE 29 report concluded that the total temperature change *up to the mid 1980s* due to changing concentrations of greenhouse gases other than carbon dioxide (and water vapour) was about half the temperature rise calculated on the basis of anthropogenic carbon dioxide emissions. Figure 2.15 showed that the current levels of the other gases are *now* such that they account for just about half the present rate of warming. This means that scenarios based on a doubling of carbon dioxide concentration alone tell rather less than half the story. The upper band of Figure 2.17 suggested that a doubling of pre-industrial levels of atmospheric carbon dioxide could be reached by about 2040. Global warming equivalent to that expected for this carbon dioxide doubling could however be with us much more quickly – some researchers now suggest by 2020 – because of the effect of other greenhouse gases.

3.6   *Forecasting climatic change*

A great deal of research effort has been – and is still being – invested in the development of computer models for climate simulation. The most sophisticated are the **global circulation models (GCMs)**. Similar in principle to the types of models used for long-range weather forecasting, GCMs are, however, designed to simulate changes over much longer periods of time, ranging from years to decades.

The basic principles on which computer models are constructed were described in Section 3.2. In a GCM, the troposphere is divided into a three-dimensional grid, with horizontal spacing between grid lines of a few hundred kilometres and a typical vertical division of half a dozen layers through the troposphere. There are usually five basic variables whose behaviour is described by equations: north–south and east–west components of winds, atmospheric pressure, temperature and humidity. These simultaneous equations are solved for each box on the grid. The better the 'spatial resolution' of the model (i.e. the finer the grid), the greater the requirement for high computer capacity and speed. In addition, a variety of phenomena that occur on scales smaller than the grid, such as clouds, precipitation and radiative heating, are brought into the model using parameterisation techniques.

Once a model has been constructed, it has to be tested. This step is usually called 'validation'. In terms of short timescale predictions, validation may be done by checking whether the model correctly forecasts a seasonal cycle. At least in terms of temperature, most GCMs simulate seasonal changes quite well. This is a crucial test because, averaged over each hemisphere, these twice-yearly temperature changes are several times larger than the variation between glacial and interglacial, or between current temperatures and those projected on the basis of anthropogenic greenhouse warming. The validity of GCM predictions on a much longer timescale may be tested against their simulation of the hot climate of Venus, the cold one of Mars (both of which are usually well reproduced) or past climates on Earth. Finally, the most stringent tests of all involve checks on whether the model correctly reproduces the energy exchanges between space, the atmosphere and the Earth's surface. Few of the 1980s GCMs did so to very great accuracy, mainly because of the simplified way in which they treated feedback loops and the very important role of the oceans. The challenge for the forthcoming decades will be to develop models in which there is full coupling between atmosphere and oceans. It should not be forgotten, however, that even if all the main processes involved in the climate system were well understood and quantified in the models, there would remain a chaotic element to this system which would (and probably always will) preclude totally accurate predictions of its future behaviour.

Despite their limitations, the simulations produced by the current generation of GCMs are nevertheless quite sophisticated. Many have concentrated on determining climatic scenarios corresponding to a doubling of atmospheric carbon dioxide concentrations from their pre-industrial levels. One example of such a scenario is shown in Figure 2.18. The details vary from model to model but the following features stand out from all of them and are evident in Figure 2.18:

● A doubling of the atmospheric concentration of carbon dioxide would result in considerable global warming: typical estimates for the average temperature rise vary from 3.0 to 5.5°C, according to the more sophisticated models.

● The temperature changes will not occur uniformly across the globe: all the models agree that temperature increases will be greatest at the poles and least at the equator, and that the warming will be more marked in the winter than in the summer. In addition these same models also predict an increase in average global precipitation of around 10%.

At this point, it is worth remembering yet again that the models all produce *averaged* scenarios, and that there are other influences on the climate apart from the anthropogenic greenhouse effect. Taking the example of the northern hemisphere, in the 20 years from 1967 to 1986 the average air temperature just above land surfaces increased by about 0.3°C. But local variations were considerable: over north-west Canada and western Siberia average temperatures rose by 2.0°C and 1.6°C respectively, over Scandinavia and Britain they *fell* by 0.6°C and 0.25°C respectively. In assessing the evidence for climate change, it is important to take a global, not a parochial, view (look again at Figure 2.1).

Unlike the more general types of forecast, these models for anthropogenic greenhouse warming can be tested directly. Starting with the known atmospheric composition of a century ago, the model can be

(a) December–January–February averages

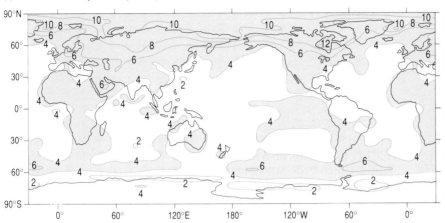

(b) June–July–August averages

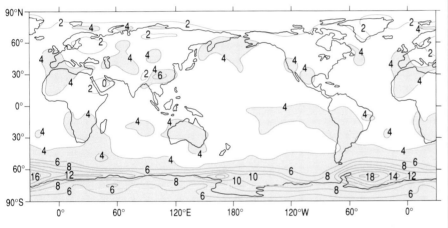

◄ Figure 2.18
(a) Winter and
(b) summer
scenarios for changes in
surface air temperature
resulting from a doubling of
the atmospheric
concentration of carbon
dioxide. Figures represent
increases in temperature
in °C. Increases greater than
4°C are shown in green
tone.

used to simulate the present climate given the known 25% increase in carbon dioxide and 100% increase in methane over the hundred-year interval. With these inputs, most models produce a scenario in which the average global warming over the period is of the order of one degree, rather than the half a degree that has actually been observed. It is this discrepancy, together with the difficulty of sorting out all the local effects, that have so far restrained climatologists from claiming that the observed temperature increases in the last 100 years are definitely the result of anthropogenic emissions of greenhouse gases. Most do, however, believe that the temperature increases predicted by the current generation of GCMs are broadly correct within a factor of 2. If that is the case, the Earth is already committed to a temperature rise greater than those that have marked the difference between glacial and interglacial periods, and one moreover that could take place on a timescale of decades or centuries rather than of thousands or tens of thousands of years. It is the speed at which temperature changes might take place that is the most worrying feature of anthropogenic global warming, as we shall see in the next section.

3.7   *Summary of Section 3*

Current assessments put an upper bound on carbon dioxide emissions of about 20 Gt of carbon per year in 2050, and a lower bound of about 2 Gt. The implications of these figures are that in the worst case the pre-industrial atmospheric concentration of carbon dioxide could double before 2050, although it is more likely that this doubling will not occur until the end of the next century. The concentrations of other greenhouse gases are, however, building up rapidly and their relative importance in anthropogenic global warming may soon exceed that of carbon dioxide. Scenarios produced by global circulation models (GCMs) suggest that increases in concentration of all greenhouse gases equivalent to a doubling of carbon dioxide levels will lead to a mean global temperature rise of between 3.0 and 5.5°C; this is of the same order as the temperature increase between the last glacial maximum and the current interglacial, but could take place 100 times more quickly. GCMs have rather coarse spatial resolution, but do indicate that warming will be greatest in the winter and at high latitudes.

Activity 5

The following question may be used to revise some of the key concepts of this section.

Q4 Briefly outline the types of uncertainties associated with:
   (a) projecting carbon dioxide emissions;
   (b) projecting the atmospheric burden of greenhouse gases;
   (c) developing scenarios for climatic futures;
   and explain how they are different in nature.
   Do you expect these uncertainties to be reduced by more research?

4   *Living in a warmer world*

4.1   *Introduction*

There is virtually no aspect of the environment that would be unaffected by a change of a few degrees (either way) in the global average temperature. Scenarios involving significant greenhouse warming are usually associated with a rise in the mean sea-level and in the late 1980s a number of media reports focused on potential sea-level changes in a highly alarmist manner. In one sense it is easy to see why: the dangers of coastal flooding are obvious and could affect many people. Most of the world's largest cities – London, New York, Los Angeles, Rio de Janeiro, Bangkok, Bombay, Shanghai and Sydney for example – are built virtually at sea-level.

Low-lying coastal areas, such as the East Anglian fens or the rice-producing deltas of Asia, constitute a major proportion of the world's croplands. However, since models and forecasts of global warming are subject to many uncertainties, predictions of the resulting rise in sea-level, made on the basis of yet another layer of modelling, must necessarily be even more uncertain. The threat of sea-level changes is a real one, but the detailed scenarios presented in some popular reports should be viewed with considerable scepticism.

A rise in sea-level will of course not be the only, nor indeed the most potentially damaging, consequence of global warming. Changes in both temperature and rainfall are likely to result in spatial shifts in patterns of agriculture and in crop yields; any such large-scale changes in food production systems are bound to have considerable social and economic impacts. Supply of, and demand for, fresh water may also be significantly affected. There is not enough space here to explore all the possible problems in detail, and anyway that would not be appropriate since projections and concerns are constantly changing as the models are refined. Instead, the aim of this section will be to look at just a few of the possible consequences of global warming scenarios, highlighting controversial issues and areas of current research.

4.2   Changes in sea-level

Sea-levels are normally measured relative to bench-marks on the shore and recorded by tide gauges which are operated over long timescales. When changes in sea-level are discussed in these contexts, the changes referred to are those of *mean* (i.e. average) sea-level. To obtain a global picture, the averaging must be done using data from many recording stations around the world. It must also be carried out over a reasonably lengthy period of time so as to eliminate short-term changes due to tides or to adverse weather conditions such as on-shore winds or storm surges. The total

◀ After storm surges in 1953, the Dutch started to strengthen their sea defences to withstand a 5-metre surge and to allow for a sea-level rise of 25 cm over the next century. The necessary construction work was a massive undertaking, planned on a 30-year programme. It is technically possible to keep the sea at bay, but the work requires long-term planning and is very expensive – probably prohibitively so for the less developed countries.

volume of sea-water is one of several important factors determining sea-level. Clearly, to obtain reliable data on overall global changes in the total volume of sea-water, it is important to establish a regular array of recording stations over all the world's oceans. Unfortunately, the network is still far from complete and the distribution of stations is patchy; many more records are available from the northern than from the southern hemisphere. Furthermore, a substantial number of existing stations are not ideally sited, being on continental margins that are not geologically stable (for example, in earthquake zones). In the discussion that follows, it should not be forgotten that a great deal more basic data are still needed. Also, because of difficulties arising from regional variations and the many ways in which bias may be inadvertently introduced into the analysis, the uncertainties in estimates of global sea-level are high. Finally, it is worth remembering that the total volume of sea-water is not the only factor that determines the change in sea-level observed at a given coastal site, although it is the most important one in the short term. Over longer timescales, deposition of sediments, local subsidence, and rearrangements of the Earth's crust either along boundaries between lithospheric plates ('tectonic' movement) or as a result of adjustments to changes in ice loading (so-called 'isostatic' movement) will also play a part, by changing the shape of the sea-water container.

Figure 2.19 summarises data collected between 1900 and 1980. Figure 2.19 is scaled, but presents no actual value for the sea-level at any particular date, since what is of most interest is not the absolute sea-level relative to some fixed standard but the *change* in that level with time.

Activity 6

(Note: it is important that you should attempt this activity, and read the comments on it at the end of the chapter, before continuing with the text.)

As well as changes in the global mean sea-level over the first 80 years of this century, Figure 2.19 also shows changes in the average global surface temperature over the same period.

(a) Given that at the time these results were first presented (the mid 1980s), the global temperature rise this century was usually quoted as $(0.5 \pm 0.2)°C$, estimate the mean increase in sea-level over the same time-span.

(b) Can you see a correlation between the two curves, and if so is it simple or complex?

(c) If on the basis on your answers to (a) and (b) you were asked to predict the sea-level change that might result from a future global warming of 3°C, what value would you give and on what assumption(s) would it be based?

This activity demonstrates that the construction of scenarios for future sea-level changes is fraught with difficulty. At the heart of the problem is the fact that the relationship between sea-level and global surface temperature is not a simple one. As the global temperature changes, different components of the hydrological cycle respond differently. Many processes in that cycle are still poorly understood, at least in quantitative

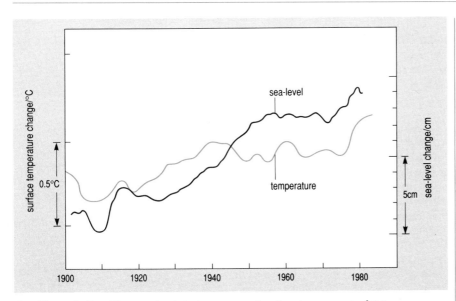

▲ *Figure 2.19 Changes in global mean sea-level and average surface temperature between 1900 and 1980.*

terms. In some cases, it is not even clear whether a particular process will result in a rise or fall in sea-level with increasing temperature! Another difficulty is that each process has a different response time to a given change in temperature. If the response time for a process is long compared to the period for which data are available (i.e. if the time lag between cause and effect is too great), then the resulting change in sea-level won't show up. To illustrate the complexity of the problem, let us look at just a few of the processes involved.

Broadly, changes in the total volume of sea-water resulting from increasing temperature can occur as a result of four different processes:

- thermal expansion of sea-water
- ice melt and run-off from mountain glaciers
- changes in the extent of the ice caps (for example, in Greenland)
- disintegration of the West Antarctic ice-sheet.

Most substances expand on heating and sea-water is no exception. For salt-water, the expansion process does respond quickly and approximately linearly to temperature change. It is thought that thermal expansion has probably been the major contributing factor so far in sea-level changes associated with anthropogenic greenhouse warming, and this helps to justify the linear correlation we used in the activity above. There are complications, however. For example, the amount of expansion for a given temperature change depends on salinity. The process is also difficult to model on a global scale, because it requires knowledge that we don't yet have on temperature changes and mixing processes in the oceans. At present, most estimates are based on very simplified models that involve only the surface layers (where admittedly the warming effect and consequent expansion are greatest).

The melting of small glaciers as a result of temperature increase is a process with a fairly short response time, but for larger glaciers and ice-sheets response times may be in excess of 100 years. It does seem probable that the Greenland ice-sheet would significantly decrease in extent if the global temperature were to rise by several degrees. However, it is also thought likely that there would then be an increase in the amount of snow falling in Antarctica. The effect of the melting of ice in the northern polar regions would thus be counterbalanced by an accumulation of snow and ice in the southern ones. It is not clear yet which of the two processes would involve the greater volume of water; it is even possible that the net effect might be a *fall* in sea-level. Interestingly, it was this same prediction of increased precipitation at the poles that a few years ago led to the most alarming forecasts of all – the possibility that under the extra weight of snow some ice caps might become unstable. The West Antarctic ice-sheet is thought to be the most vulnerable in this respect. Its total collapse would push enormous numbers of icebergs into the oceans; this could raise sea-levels by as much as 5 metres. Scientists now regard imminent disintegration of the West Antarctic ice-sheet as extremely unlikely; even if such a collapse were eventually to occur, it is estimated that the process would take place over a period of several hundred years. A great deal more research into both geological phenomena and climatic modelling, particularly with reference to polar latitudes, is required before more detailed predictions can be made.

Compared to the sea-level rises of many metres that would accompany the collapse of the West Antarctic ice-sheet, the rises of tens of centimetres, predicted on the basis of calculations along the lines of those in Activity 6 with an added component for mountain glacier melt, do not sound too threatening. The danger is very real, though, for the people of many nations. As described in Section 4.1, many coastal cities and low-lying croplands would become subject to permanent or periodic inundation. Small, flat islands might disappear almost completely or become too vulnerable to storm surges for their populations to remain; the Maldives, where the highest land is just 2.5 metres above current sea-levels, is an often quoted example. Continental countries do at least have the option of building sea-defence systems. As the Dutch have shown, it is technically feasible to keep the sea at bay, but such projects are hugely expensive – almost certainly prohibitively so for countries such as Bangladesh. The speed at which anthropogenic greenhouse warming occurs is a crucial factor in planning for the consequent sea-level rise, as indeed it is with other effects of increasing global temperature. If the oceans rose too quickly, we would simply have to abandon the inundated land and cities. It has been estimated that a sea-level rise of 1 metre would threaten about 5×10^6 km^2 of land – a relatively small proportion (about 3%) of the world's total land area, but – under current climatic conditions anyway – a very substantial proportion (about 30%) of its productive cropland.

4.3   *Effects on ecosystems, agriculture and forests*

In considering sea-level changes, we were concerned with two effects of the anthropogenic greenhouse effect, namely global temperature change and alterations to climatic patterns. In thinking about ecosystems, we also have to take into account a third factor – the direct response of plants to increased concentrations of atmospheric carbon dioxide.

The effect of enhanced carbon dioxide levels on plant growth and development (in the absence of any climatic change) has been quite extensively studied in controlled experiments, especially on crop species. In general, increased carbon dioxide concentrations stimulate photosynthesis and decrease transpiration, so that plants grow more quickly and use water more efficiently. Typical experiments in glasshouses suggest that a doubling of carbon dioxide concentration in the atmosphere can lead to increases in yield of between 10 and 50% for crops such as wheat and rice, with the exact figure depending on the crop strain and growing conditions. However, there are no data on the effects of increased carbon dioxide concentrations for plants in field situations (e.g. in large plots covered by glasshouses with artificially controlled atmospheres). Scenarios of the 'carbon dioxide fertilisation effect' are therefore based on a scaling-up from data for individual and isolated plants to whole ecosystems. The dangers of such a procedure are obvious: not every organism will respond in the same way to the change in conditions. Some plants may indeed grow faster, but the competition between plant species and the whole complex web of interactions within the ecosystem will change too. The uncertainties in the scaling process are just too great for meaningful analysis.

When it comes to the effect of climatic change on ecosystems or agriculture, predictions are scarcely less uncertain. A sensible analysis of the impact of temperature changes on agricultural practice would require a model that could accurately simulate those changes over distances of just a few hundred kilometres. As discussed in Section 3, the GCMs have nowhere near this degree of spatial resolution. Scenarios have been constructed on the 'broad brush' canvases of GCMs, but what they tell us is fairly obvious. If it gets warmer in the temperate latitudes, the growing seasons will be longer and the climatic zone suitable for a particular crop or ecosystem will shift polewards. On this basis it has been suggested that the cereal-growing belts of North America might shift northwards by several hundred kilometres for every Centigrade degree rise in temperature.

However, temperature is far from being the only climatic variable to determine the distribution of vegetation. The total quantity and seasonal variation of precipitation (see Plate 4), air humidity and soil moisture are all vitally important too. Uncertainties in GCM predictions of precipitation patterns are even greater than in their predictions of temperature variation. Simulation of changes in soil moisture, then, requires yet another layer of modelling. Figure 2.20 illustrates the problem.

Activity 7

Look at the northern mid-latitudes in Figure 2.20 (the world's major grain-growing areas). How do the predicted changes in soil moisture compare in the three different models?

As we saw in Section 3, the 'warmer world' scenarios developed in the late 1980s on the basis of various GCMs all tend to exhibit the same large-scale features but there is considerable variation in the detail. The differences between the models become even more marked when they are used to simulate changes in precipitation. They are most consistent at high latitudes, where all show increased rainfall, especially in the winter. In the tropics though, some models produce enhanced monsoon precipitation over south-east Asia, others suggest a decrease in the monsoon activity. In looking at the northern continental mid-latitudes of Figure 2.20, we are thus concentrating on areas in which the models are in reasonable agreement as to precipitation, yet the discrepancies again appear to be enormous. The main difference between the models is in the way they have been set up to deal with evaporation and run-off of surface water (for example, the degree to which snowmelt will be absorbed by the soil or will run off if the ground is frozen, which in turn depends crucially on the temperature simulations used). This example shows the great sensitivity of GCM results to the details of the particular model. It also illustrates why

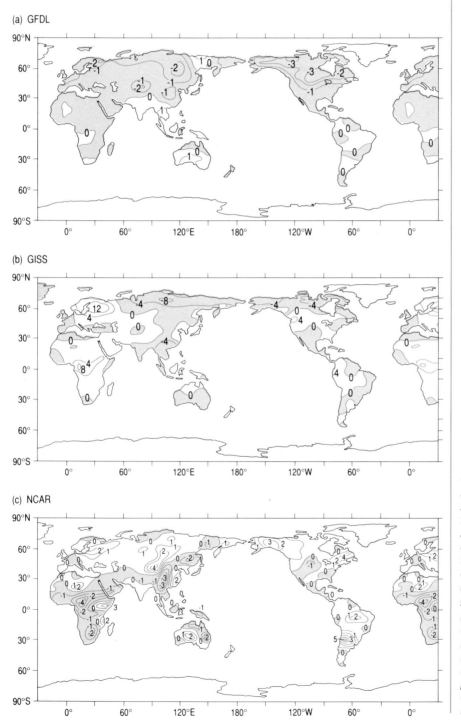

◀ *Figure 2.20*
Scenarios for changes in summer soil moisture following a doubling of atmospheric concentration of carbon dioxide. Negative figures correspond to a decrease in soil moisture (i.e. a drier surface) shown in green tone.

(Models developed at the Geophysical Fluid Dynamics Laboratory [GFDL], Princeton; the Goddard Institute for Space Studies [GISS]; and the National Centre for Atmospheric Research [NCAR].)

we cannot necessarily assume that in a warmer Britain we would be able to grow the crops that currently flourish in the south of France (compare Figure 2.1).

As far as diversity of ecosystems and global agricultural productivity are concerned, it is not yet clear whether the overall effect of anthropogenic greenhouse warming is likely to be adverse or beneficial (although for obvious reasons most reports concentrate on the more negative aspects). What *is* clear, however, is that the distribution of growing patterns will shift, with incalculable social and political consequences. A wide-ranging study for the UN Environment Programme, published in 1988, suggests for example, that although the total world production of grain might increase, the output of the traditional North American prairie belt could decline sharply, with any future surplus coming next from European Russia. We will return to these kinds of scenarios in Section 4.5.

Once again, it is not only the extent of climatic change, but the pace of it, that matters. On the basis of current models for temperate latitudes, we can expect a shift polewards of vegetation zones amounting to several hundred kilometres for each degree rise in global temperature. 'Migration' of the forests at the end of the last glacial period has been calculated as having taken place at a rate of 20–100 km per century. Maybe the tree-line could have moved a little more quickly had the temperature risen more quickly, but a global temperature increase of 3°C in the next fifty years would correspond to a rate of warming 50 times faster than that at the end of the last ice age. It seems highly probable that many tree species will be unable to respond quickly enough to the current rate of climatic change to be saved from extinction, even though a suitable environment may continue to exist in which they would actually be able to grow. And of course the 'migration' of a whole natural community is governed by the pace of its most slowly moving component. If a key species in a food chain gets 'left behind' then all the animals higher up the chain will be affected. In times of change, adaptability pays; this is a principle we need to apply to agricultural research. As was discussed in *Grigg* (1991), many modern strains of crop plants have been chosen to give maximum yields under ideal conditions. It might be wiser now to develop strains that are more adaptable to a wide range of climatic futures and less susceptible to occasional extremes of weather, even if their maximum yields are lower. Far more frequent extreme weather events will be part of the scene in a warmer world; it is to this part of the scenario that we will turn our attention in the next subsection.

4.4   Extreme events

In June 1988 a conference attended by over 300 government representatives, scientists and policy-makers from 48 countries was held in Toronto to discuss 'The Changing Atmosphere: Implications for Global Security'. The debates were all the more pointed because they took place in the middle of a period of particularly unusual weather conditions in North America, with record high temperatures and a widespread drought. Although Britain had a wet summer that year, continental Europe fared differently and in Moscow it turned out to be the hottest summer of the century thus far. The remainder of 1988 proved dramatic in many other parts of the world too. In August Bangladesh was devastated by a flood which inundated almost 80% of its land and rendered 25 million people homeless. In September Hurricane Gilbert brought a trail of destruction to the Caribbean in what the Jamaican Prime Minister described as 'the worst natural disaster in our modern history'. Just a month later, Hurricane Joan hit Nicaragua and flattened three-quarters of the trees in an area of 15 000 square kilometres of forest. In Africa, after years of continuing drought, there were unexpected torrential rains, which brought floods and plagues of locusts. At the end of 1988 scientists reported it to have been the hottest year within the previous hundred, on a global average.

Of course, freak weather conditions can occur at any time, in any part of the world. There have always been storms and floods and droughts, but by 1988 some scientists were pointing to the increasing frequency and severity of such events as evidence that anthropogenic global warming had truly begun. Other experts, however, mindful that the occurrence of severe weather conditions is naturally random, were not convinced at that stage that the apparently increasing number of such events could unequivocally be ascribed to greenhouse warming. The more cautious were worried that the detailed scientific case might be undermined if they were to cry wolf too early.

Still, whether or not the events of the 1980s marked the true onset of anthropogenic global warming, the climatologists were in agreement even then that overall warming would be accompanied not only by heat waves and droughts, but also by more frequent cyclones and storm surges. Higher sea surface temperatures would lead to increased evaporation from the oceans and might change the position of convective currents in the atmosphere. Cyclones (also variously called hurricanes and typhoons, but properly referred to as 'tropical revolving storms'), which are fuelled by a convective cycle of evaporation and condensation above warm tropical seas, would become both more common and more violent in a warmer world.

We often tend to think of extreme events in terms of their immediate aftermath – loss of human life, damage to property in the path of a hurricane, famine following a drought. But there are also many other less obvious economic costs associated with a climatic regime in which extreme events are more unpredictable and more severe. In almost every aspect of human activity that involves long-term planning – civil engineering, industry, agriculture, investment and insurance – there are built-in assumptions related to the weather. If past weather records cease to be a reliable guide to the future, on what basis should the planners operate, what safety margins should be allowed, and how should insurers assess the risks? Every answer carries a price tag.

Finally, however, we come back to the biosphere, since it is there that extreme events have their longest-lasting effect. After all, it is not so much the *mean* temperature or rainfall that determine whether a particular plant or animal can survive in a particular place as the *range* of temperature and the *pattern* of rainfall. As every gardener knows, some species cannot tolerate frost; some will die in just a short period of drought, others if the soil becomes waterlogged. Nothing is more disruptive to agriculture than an unpredictable series of severe weather conditions. Ultimately, it is not the average but the extremes of climate that matter most.

4.5   *Social, economic and political impacts*

With the recognition that human activities are increasingly upsetting the natural balances of our planet, a new concern has been thrust upon the decision-makers. It has been dubbed *environmental security*. Threats to

national and international peace and stability no longer come only from
weapons of war; environmental changes and decline are poised to become
a major source of tension both within and between nations.

The future of the US corn belt gives one example of the kind of
problems that can arise. Some models predict that the most suitable areas
for arable crops in North America might be shifted several hundred
kilometres northwards and eastwards as a result of changes in climate and
soil moisture. The farmers of Minnesota could rejoice while those in Iowa
were deprived of their livelihood. The social and economic consequences
within the United States would be enormous. Still more important would
be an overall decline in agricultural output and a reduction in the American
grain surplus. This would affect both domestic and world markets, have
major impacts on economic and food aid to developing countries and carry
undoubted security implications.

As is so often the case, the less developed countries might suffer even
more. Crop failure, whether due to flooding, drought or extreme events, in
a region where hunger is already an endemic problem could cause
large-scale migrations. Subsistence-level production offers little scope for
adaptation and is therefore particularly vulnerable to external events. In
the worst scenario, many millions of people become 'environmental
refugees'.

Projections of global warming into the next century suggest that the
implications of climatic change will be far-reaching indeed for national
economies and international relations. Patterns of agriculture, industrial
constraints and production, water resource and usage, fuel and electricity
demands will all be affected. However, there will be winners as well as
losers. The truly difficult questions are those of equity: not only who wins
and who loses, but how and by whom those who suffer the most severe
losses might be compensated. The issue is, of course, greatly complicated
by the fact that atmospheric pollution spans national borders. The activities
of one country in contributing to the build-up of greenhouse gases can be
seen to cause significant damage in another, quite remote, country that
may have added far less to the atmospheric burden. The detrimental effect
on international relations of 'exported pollution' was first highlighted by
the problem of acid rain. Beside the global nature of the anthropogenic
greenhouse effect, we may yet come to view the consequences of acid rain
as a little local difficulty.

4.6   Summary of Section 4

At current rates of global warming, the mean sea-level rise has been
estimated at (12 ± 5) cm per century. Empirical estimates suggest a rise of
between 30 and 120 cm for an average global temperature increase of 3°C,
the major contribution to this rise coming from thermal expansion of
sea-water. A doubling of the atmospheric concentration of carbon dioxide
would certainly have major impacts on ecosystems and agricultural
practice. Further research into the response of plants to enhanced levels of
carbon dioxide, and GCMs capable of producing climate scenarios on a
regional, rather than global, scale are required before these impacts can be
predicted in any detail. In a globally warmer climate it is anticipated that
extreme events (droughts, hurricanes, storm surges etc.) would occur more
frequently than at present and be more severe. Such events, as well as
changes in patterns of agriculture, may increasingly lead to problems of
environmental security, both within and between nations.

Activity 8

The following questions may be used to revise some of the key concepts of this section.

Q5 A policy often suggested as a countermeasure to anthropogenic greenhouse warming is afforestation. Explain very briefly why afforestation helps to control the build-up carbon dioxide, but cannot provide a long-term solution.

Q6 Discuss briefly the validity of attributing individual extreme events (such as the 1987 'hurricane' over southern England or the 1989 drought in the mid-western US) to the effects of anthropogenic global warming.

5   Choices and strategies

As realisation grew through the 1980s of the tremendous consequences of atmospheric pollution, it also became apparent that completely new types of global cooperation and policies would have to be developed to cope with the problem. Initially, the debate focused on the uncertainties in the projections and scientific models. It was possible simply to point to the need for more research and to postpone any other responses while the research was underway. Politicians were naturally cautious about committing themselves to costly legislation or capital investments as insurance against potential future changes the nature of which still seemed very uncertain. As the scientists moved towards a greater degree of consensus, however, the 'wait-and-see' response became less tenable. After all, the whole point about insurance is that you have to have paid the premiums before disaster strikes; no-one issues insurance retrospectively. The political debate is now becoming more heated than the scientific one.

Many different responses have been suggested to counter the threat of global warming, but broadly they fall into three categories:

● counter-measures – the so-called '**technical fixes**'

● adaptation – adjustment to environmental changes as they occur, without too much investment being made to anticipate or prevent such changes

● preventative action – legislation or incentives to reduce the emission of greenhouse gases from human activity.

Technical fixes have been suggested seriously by only a very small minority of the scientists researching in this area. Proponents of such schemes argue that since we have radically altered the balance of certain natural processes, perhaps we should now use technological means to redress that balance by deliberately engineering climate modifications. To take just one example, it is known that the surface temperature of the Earth can cool significantly following volcanic eruptions, because the dust blasted into the upper atmosphere reflects solar radiation back into space. It has therefore been suggested that we might mitigate global warming by releasing large amounts of dust into the atmosphere from high-flying aircraft. Few people, however, would advocate such experimentation with the climatic control systems of the planet. Given the degree of uncertainty already surrounding the inadvertent changes in climate that may result from the anthropogenic greenhouse effect, it would surely be foolhardy in the extreme to attempt other types of climate modification that cannot be modelled with any greater certainty. We might well end up worse off than before. Added to which, once a climate modification programme had been carried out, it would always be blamed for subsequent severe weather, storm or flood or drought, even though this might in fact be coincidental. We do not have the legislative or political systems to deal with such claims. Fortunately, there are other ways to combat the effects of global warming.

Adaptation is the strategy favoured by many economists. Their position is that it is unnecessarily expensive to anticipate climatic changes that may not in the end occur. Passive adaptation – adjusting to environmental change as it takes place – is cheaper, at least for the developed countries. Infrastructures such as coastal defences, or water reservoirs and distribution systems, are constantly being maintained or replaced anyway. It is not a major additional expense to modify existing refurbishment plans so as to cope with climatic change on an ongoing basis. More active types of adaptive strategies are built on the recognition of the likelihood of future environmental change, without commitment to particular predictions or scenarios. One example of such a strategy would be the development and more widespread planting of new crop strains that would be less susceptible than current ones to extremes of weather. Another, more controversial example, is the suggestion that water management and supply systems should be updated to make them more flexible, so permitting easier transfer of water across regional and national boundaries. However, the barriers to developments of that type are not so much technical or economic as legal and political.

Prevention measures, aimed at slowing down the build-up of greenhouse gases, are also subject to political value judgements. Any such measures – a reduction of carbon dioxide emissions, a ban on CFC production and use, a halt to the destruction of the rainforest or a vigorous afforestation programme – require enormous capital investment, together with major social and economic reforms, sometimes from the countries that can least afford them. The developed world is the main source of the current atmospheric burden of anthropogenic greenhouse gases, but might now be able to afford the installation of alternative technologies. Progress in the less developed nations is still heavily dependent on increasing fossil fuel consumption, especially where populations are expanding. The industrialised world cannot expect to demand controls on greenhouse gas emissions that would prevent improvements in living standards for the developing countries. Clearly, equity is a major issue, and this will be explored in detail in Chapter 4.

International agreements to limit atmospheric pollution on the required global scale will plainly be very difficult to negotiate, implement and enforce. Most experts would say that there is therefore all the more reason to begin the processes as quickly as possible. The Law of the Sea Convention has demonstrated that legal frameworks *can* address environmental issues on an international basis. More recently, the Montreal Protocol has committed many countries to reducing production and usage of CFCs in an effort to halt damage to the ozone layer. The background to this agreement will be covered in the next chapter; it is mentioned in the present context to show that one category of greenhouse gases is already subject to a measure of international control. The problem that must be overcome if such controls are to be extended to emissions of carbon dioxide, methane and nitrous oxide will be examined in detail in Chapter 4, but are obviously many and complex.

The danger in waiting for protracted negotiation of an international consensus is the same as in waiting for greater scientific certainty as to the details of potential climatic changes: the longer we delay before taking action, the greater the risk that we will be faced with major environmental change over a short timescale. To get us out of this spiral, many experts advocate what are called *tie-in strategies*, that is damage-limitation actions that are likely to confer long-term benefits even if some of the current prophesies about global warming are not in fact fulfilled. The pursuit of greater energy efficiency is the most obvious example of a tie-in strategy. A reduction in demand for energy from fossil fuels would cut not only carbon dioxide emissions, but also emissions of other atmospheric pollutants, so reducing the problems of acid rain and industrial smogs. Here, too, though, there are complex competing forces: oil-importing countries versus oil-exporting ones, free-market versus subsidised economies. Again these issues will be explored more fully in Chapter 4.

The developed world may in the end have to make enormous investments, not just in its own industries, power generation systems and infrastructure, but also in technical and financial assistance to developing countries, simply in order to stabilise atmospheric composition. Many scientists, Stephen Schneider among them, consider that by the time the possibility of anthropogenic greenhouse warming was recognised, it was already too late to halt it. Schneider believes that we have irretrievably committed the planet to warming by one or two degrees. However, in that very inevitability, he sees a positive aspect:

> the possibility that a slight but manifest global warming, coupled with the larger threat forecast in computer models, may catalyse international cooperation to achieve environmentally sustainable development, marked by a stabilised population and the proliferation of energy-efficient and environmentally safe technologies. A much larger greenhouse warming (together with many other environmental disruptions) might thereby be averted.   (Schneider, 1989, p. 47)

Let us hope that he is right.

Activity 9

Some experts have said that we cannot hope to control the anthropogenic emissions of greenhouse gases until we stop the growth in world population. Outline some of the pros and cons in this argument.

Further reading

The major work in the field at the time of writing (1990) was:

BOLIN, B., DÖÖS, B., JÄGER, J. and WARWICK, R. (eds) (1986) *The Greenhouse Effect, Climatic Change and Ecosystems*, Chichester, John Wiley (SCOPE Report 29).

Some scientific background is necessary in order to follow this, but it is fairly accessible to non-specialists, though very detailed. A further update has been provided by:

HOUGHTON, J. T., JENKINS, J. and EPHRAUMS, J. (1990) *Climate Change: the IPCC scientific assessment*, Cambridge, Cambridge University Press.

The most readable book on the subject is:

GRIBBIN, J. (1990) *Hothouse Earth: greenhouse effect and Gaia*, Bantam Press (new edn, pbk: Black Swan (Transworld)).

This goes in considerable detail into the science underlying our current understanding of past climates and possible futures. It is written at about the same level as this chapter.

Regular, and authoritative updates on the global warming story will appear in popular periodicals like *New Scientist* and *Scientific American*.

References

GRIGG, D. (1991) 'World agriculture: productivity and sustainability', Ch. 2 in Sarre, P. (ed.) *Environment, Population and Development*, London, Hodder and Stoughton/The Open University. (Book Two of this series.)

KEEPIN, W., MINTZER, J. and KRISTOFERSON, L. (1986) 'Emission of CO_2 into the atmosphere: the rate of release of CO_2 as a function of future energy developments', Ch. 2 in Bolin, B. *et al.* (eds) *The Greenhouse Effect, Climatic Change and Ecosystems*, Chichester, John Wiley.

REDDISH, A. (1991) 'Energy resources', Ch. 1 in Blunden, J. and Reddish, A. (eds) *Energy, Resources and Environment*, London, Hodder and Stoughton/The Open University. (Book Three of this series.)

SCHNEIDER, S. (1989) 'The changing climate', *Scientific American*, September, pp. 38–47.

SILVERTOWN, J. (1990) 'Earth as an environment for life', Ch. 2 in Silvertown, J. and Sarre, P. (eds) *Environment and Society*, London, Hodder and Stoughton/The Open University. (Book One of this series.)

Answers to Activities

Activity 1

Red light is at the long wavelength (low frequency) end of the visible spectrum. White light contains all the visible wavelengths. 'White-hot' objects therefore emit light of shorter average wavelength than cooler 'red-hot' ones. Generalising from this, as the temperature of an object decreases, the average wavelength of the radiation it emits will increase.

Activity 2

(a) (11 + 15 + 5) units = 31 units (i.e. 31%) of the incoming short-wave radiation are reflected. Since the albedo of a surface is defined (*Silvertown*, 1990) as its reflectiveness expressed as the ratio of reflected to incident radiation, the average albedo of the Earth's atmosphere system is 31%.

(b) (20 + 5 + 26 + 19) units = 70 units of long-wave radiation escape into space.

(c) The total amount of radiation escaping into space (31 units + 70 units) is equal to the amount of incoming radiation, within rounding errors. The radiation budget is balanced – as it should be.

(d) We do not 'accumulate more than we receive' because the radiation budget is balanced (as it should be) at the *top* of the atmosphere. The 'apparent' increase in radiation involved in the greenhouse cycle occurs because radiation is successively absorbed, emitted and reabsorbed in the atmosphere. The 95 units of 'additional' radiation correspond to the *y* units shown in Figure 2.5. It is precisely because this radiation cycles *within* the atmosphere that an absorbing atmosphere leads to greenhouse warming.

Activity 3

Compare your diagrams with Figure 2.21(a) and (b). The important thing to appreciate about a positive feedback loop is that it *amplifies* changes to the system. In every day terms, it might be called a vicious circle.

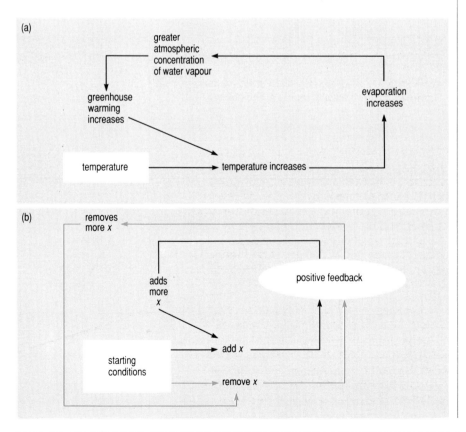

◀   *Figure 2.21*
(a) The effect of greenhouse warming on evaporation rates.

(b) Generalised flow diagram of a positive feedback loop.

Activity 4

Q1 The amount of radiation incident on the upper surface of the atmosphere is exactly the same amount reflected and re-emitted into space from the Earth–atmosphere system as a whole. The radiation budget is balanced.

Q2 The troposphere is warmed by long-wave radiation emitted from the Earth's surface and successively absorbed and re-radiated as it works upwards. The warmest part of the troposphere is therefore that nearest the ground and temperature decreases with increasing height. In the stratosphere, the warming mechanism involves absorption of incoming solar radiation and temperature therefore increases with increasing height. In effect the two regions are mainly warmed by radiation coming from opposite directions.

Q3 Emissions of greenhouse gases from the Earth's surface result in more radiation being absorbed near the ground. The lower layers of the troposphere warm up, but because the radiative balance must be maintained this means that less heat energy works up to the upper troposphere and less is therefore transferred across the tropopause. Simultaneous warming of the lower part of the troposphere and cooling of the lower part of the stratosphere are thus indicative of an increase in emissions of greenhouse gases, and most, if not all, of this increase is due to anthropogenic sources.

Activity 5

Q4

(a) The projection of carbon dioxide emissions is essentially a problem that needs to be tackled by social scientists. The uncertainties are mainly associated with difficulties in forecasting demographic, economic, political and social factors and such uncertainties are probably not significantly reducible.

(b) The projection of atmospheric concentrations of carbon dioxide – one of the greenhouse gases – is essentially a problem for scientists. However, they start with input data for emission rates that are themselves uncertain, as discussed in (a) above. Then there are further uncertainties resulting from deficiencies in the models of the global carbon cycle. These arise partly from a lack of understanding about some of the features of the cycle and partly from the difficulty of constructing models that incorporate all the known biological, chemical and geological elements of the cycle with its many feedback loops. Projections of concentrations of other greenhouse gases are subject to similar constraints. The modelling uncertainties will be reducible by further research, but only in the long term.

(c) The development of scenarios for climatic futures is also subject to modelling uncertainties associated with an incomplete understanding of the natural processes being modelled, difficulties in parametrisation of some elements and inadequate spatial resolution of the models. Further research and an increase in the storage capacity and speed of computers will reduce these uncertainties, but again only slowly. The complexity of the processes involved make it unlikely that totally accurate models will be built.

Activity 6

In carrying out this exercise, you will probably have begun to appreciate for yourself some of the problems that plague scientists working in this field!

(a) The temperature plot is a smoothed curve, representing accumulated data over many climatic zones as well as over short-term variations and seasonal cycles in the temperature (compare Figure 2.11). The quoted global temperature rise of 0.5°C seems to correspond to the difference between the lowest and highest points on the graph (A and B respectively in Figure 2.22), with a fairly large uncertainty (±0.2°C) to allow for the scattered nature of the individual temperature readings that have been used to construct the graph. On a similar basis, the change in sea-level between the minimum and maximum points on that curve (points C and D respectively) corresponds to an overall rise of about 9 cm. This change took place between roughly 1910 and 1980, i.e. over a period of about 70 years. On this basis, one could estimate the sea-level rise as

$$9 \text{ cm } \times \frac{100}{70} \approx 13 \text{ cm per century.}$$

During the 1980s, scientists were indeed quoting values of the order of (12 ± 5) cm for the rise in sea-level per century at the then current rate of global warming. As you see, the uncertainties are high ($\pm 40\%$), so if you read other accounts you may find that individual workers quote rather different values.

(b) There is clearly some correlation between changes in global temperature and changes in sea-level. In particular, both curves have a similar 'dip followed by hump' shape between 1900 and 1920. However, the fine structure of the two curves does not match, and there was a period in the 1940s when the sea-level rose despite a fall in the mean temperature.

(c) The difficulties of prediction become apparent here: you will have been trying to combine two uncertain quantities. Let us take a typical figure, based on Figure 2.19, of a sea-level rise of (10 ± 3) cm for a temperature

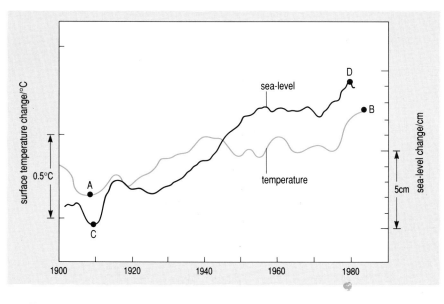

▲ *Figure 2.22   Temperature changes and sea-level rise.*

increase of $(0.5 \pm 0.2)°C$. (Your own figures may differ a little from this, but the principle of the calculation still applies.) One could reason as follows:

Minimum response

$$= \frac{\text{minimum value for sea-level rise}}{\text{maximum corresponding value for temperature change}}$$

$$= \frac{(10-3) \text{ cm}}{(0.5+0.2) °C} = \frac{7}{0.7} \text{ cm/}°C$$

$$= 10 \text{ cm/}°C$$

Maximum response

$$= \frac{\text{maximum value for sea-level rise}}{\text{minimum corresponding value for temperature change}}$$

$$= \frac{(10+3) \text{ cm}}{(0.5-0.2) °C} = \frac{13}{0.3} \text{ cm/}°C$$

$$\approx 40 \text{ cm/}°C$$

This could be expressed as a rise of (25 ± 15) cm/$°C$, suggesting a sea-level change of between 30 cm and 120 cm for a temperature increase of 3 °C. (There are more rigorous statistical methods for combining uncertain quantities, but, with the kind of data we are considering here, the 'commonsense' method outlined above is quite adequate to make the point.)

In performing this calculation, we have made the main assumption that the correlation, such as it is, between sea-level rise and a temperature increase of about half a degree would continue to apply for much larger changes in temperature. We have further assumed that if a temperature increase of x °C causes a sea-level rise of y cm, then an increase of $2x$ °C will result in a rise of $2y$ cm (i.e. what mathematicians call a linear relationship).

Activity 7

There are obvious discrepancies between the models in the northern mid-latitudes. The GFDL scenario shows a drier soil surface, while the GISS model indicates little change and the NCAR scenario is one of increased soil moisture.

Activity 8

Q5 Growing trees need carbon to make new wood; they obtain this from carbon dioxide in the air through the process of photosynthesis. An afforestation programme would therefore make some contribution to slowing the build-up of carbon dioxide in the atmosphere. Afforestation cannot provide a permanent solution, because of the problems associated with harvesting the 'crop' once the trees are mature: the wood could not be burnt or otherwise allowed to decay. (There are also snags in relation to the scale of the project: it has been estimated that an area as big as the USA would need to be planted in order to absorb the current anthropogenic emission of carbon dioxide.)

Q6 It is impossible to attribute a single extreme event to the anthropogenic greenhouse effect, since such events are anyway part of the natural variability of the weather and their occurrence and distribution has always been random. In climatic terms, such effects only assume significance when their frequency and/or severity over a considerable period of time clearly exceeds previous averages.

Activity 9

The anthropogenic emission of some greenhouse gases is clearly linked to population (see Figure 2.14). In the absence of alternative technologies an increasing population burns more fossil fuels, so adding to the carbon dioxide emissions. It also requires more land for agriculture and may cut down (and ultimately burn) forests to obtain this. Increased agricultural activity leads to increased emissions of methane and nitrous oxide. A stabilisation of the human population would probably also stabilise (if not actually reduce) the emission rates for greenhouse gases. However, this scenario is unlikely to be attained in less than about 100 years. Measures to control the emissions of CFCs and to reduce the consumption of fossil fuels could be taken on a shorter timescale, independently of population changes, though the implementation of such a proposition is greatly complicated by differences between industrialised and developing countries in the management of energy resources.

1 Introduction

The Montreal Protocol was signed on 16 September 1987. It was the first international agreement to restrict release to the atmosphere of substances deemed damaging to the global environment – specifically, the **ozone layer**. You will probably know that the substances controlled by the Protocol include a group of chemicals called **chlorofluorocarbons** – or **CFCs**, for short. These compounds first came on stream in the 1930s, as the 'ideal' – stable, non-flammable, non-toxic – substitutes for the decidedly noxious chemicals then used as refrigerants. They are also cheap to produce, and their uses soon expanded into the now familiar sectors – as propellants in aerosol spray-cans, as blowing agents (to put the bubbles into all manner of 'foamed' plastics), and as solvents and cleaning fluids in many speciality areas (notably, the electronics industry). Unless steps are taken to prevent it, all of these uses can lead ultimately to the CFCs being released into the atmosphere.

The signatories to the original Protocol pledged effectively to halve their use of CFCs by the end of the century. Just 18 months later, international opinion was hardening behind the need for a complete phase-out: this aim was finally adopted in June 1990. A powerful driving-force here was undoubtedly the real – and growing – concern about the massive loss of stratospheric ozone over Antarctica that occurs with the return of sunlight each southern spring – the so-called **ozone hole** – first detected in 1984. By 1988, there was irrefutable evidence linking this seasonal loss with the presence in the stratosphere of chlorine atoms, largely derived from CFCs. It would appear that the international community acted with commendable speed in tackling this problem.

But did it? This action was actually the culmination of a long-running saga about CFCs, initiated in 1974 by F. Sherwood Rowland and Mario Molina, two scientists at the University of California, Irvine, in the United States (see Figure 3.1). In fact, fears of a human threat to the ozone layer were first voiced even earlier (in 1970/71) through concern about the effects of supersonic aircraft (dubbed supersonic transports, SSTs – like Concorde and the American rival then on the drawing-board at Boeing) that fly within the stratosphere. That the projected fleet of 'super' SSTs never materialised owed more to simple economics than to their possible impact on the ozone layer, so we shall not dwell on the debate here, other than to note that the link between ozone loss and skin cancer was first raised in this context. The cancer scare made headlines, generating a degree of public concern and media attention that was to spill over into the new debate about CFCs (evident in Figure 3.1).

One aim of this chapter is to trace this debate through from its early focus on spray-cans in the United States, thence on to the international agenda, and finally culminating in the decision to phase out all CFC usage worldwide. In doing so, particular emphasis is given to the way that an evolving scientific understanding of the problem – in terms of both model studies and direct observations of the atmosphere (for example the ozone hole itself) has helped to shape the scientific, public and political debate. To follow that analysis in a critical way requires some acquaintance with the science itself – the myriad of processes that control the amount and distribution of ozone in the stratosphere. So a further theme of the chapter

◄ *Figure 3.1
Montage of 1974 newspaper
headlines.*

is to present the underlying science – and it necessarily includes some chemistry. An effort has been made to keep the chemistry, and other technical terms used, to a minimum. If you do not have a science background, however, you may wish to avoid the 'more technical' questions – flagged as such within the Activities; the remaining questions should help you to focus on the most important points.

With this scientific background in place, the chapter then looks briefly at the stepwise process that has led to the phase-out of the CFCs. The aim here is to highlight important interactions between scientific evidence, and the uncertainties associated with it, on the one hand, and the many other factors (political, economic and so on) that are involved in achieving truly international agreement to tackle a global environmental problem.

2   Ozone in the atmosphere

Ozone gas is perceptibly blue in colour and has a characteristic and pungent smell (*ozein* is Greek for 'to smell'). It occurs throughout the atmosphere, but only ever in small amounts, never exceeding around one molecule in every 100 000 present. Indeed, if all the ozone contained in the first 60 km or so of the atmosphere could be brought down and assembled at the Earth's surface, it would form a layer only some 3 mm thick. And yet all life depends on this minor by-product of its own existence (*Silvertown*, 1990) – most obviously through ozone's role as a filter of the Sun's ultraviolet radiation, but also in more subtle ways, as we shall see. Nearly all of the ozone in the atmosphere is contained in the lower two layers, with about 90% in the stratosphere. The profile sketched in Figure 3.2(b) is typical of the way in which the concentration of ozone varies with altitude.

Q Under average conditions at ground level, each cm^3 of air contains around 10^{19} molecules of all the gases present. Use Figure 3.2(b) to estimate the concentration of ozone at ground-level in both parts per million (p.p.m.) and parts per billion (p.p.b.).

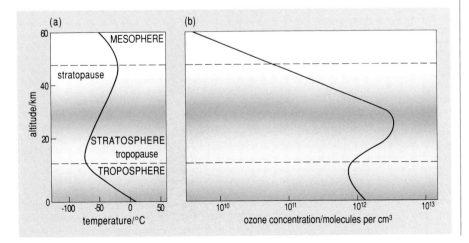

◀   *Figure 3.2*

(a) A reminder of the variation of temperature with altitude through the atmosphere.

(b) The altitude profile of the concentration of ozone.

A   From the figure, the ozone concentration at ground-level is typically about 10^{12} molecules per cm^3, amounting to one molecule in every $10^{19}/10^{12} = 10^7$ (ten million) present. 1 part in 10^7 is equivalent to 0.1 in 10^6 (dividing both numbers by 10) or 100 in 10^9 (multiplying both numbers by 100), so the concentration of ozone is 0.1 p.p.m. or 100 p.p.b.

Ground-level concentrations much higher than this are a serious problem, because ozone is highly toxic: even in very low concentrations, it irritates the respiratory system and can cause severe damage to human health. Plant growth may also be impaired. Indeed, ozone is now believed to be responsible for some of the damage to forests in Europe and Canada originally ascribed to acid rain.

Altogether, then, ozone is one of the more noxious pollutants of the troposphere. It is also a potent greenhouse gas. The beneficial effects of ozone depend on the fact that most of it *is* in the stratosphere, well away from direct contact with life. The region of highest ozone concentrations occurs between altitudes of around 20–35 km (Figure 3.2b) – the so-called **ozone layer**. The debate about 'damage to the ozone layer' essentially revolves around concern that human activities are changing this characteristic profile, leading, in particular, to a net loss of ozone from the stratosphere. To understand this concern requires a closer acquaintance with the processes that determine the ozone budget in the stratosphere.

2.1   The ozone balance: a first look

Ozone is a form of oxygen, but whereas molecules of ordinary oxygen each contain two atoms, the ozone molecule has three (Figure 3.3). In industrial societies ozone is now being generated at ground-level by the action of sunlight on gaseous pollutants, but the Earth's *natural* ozone factory is the stratosphere. Here the raw materials are ordinary oxygen seeping up from the troposphere, and sunlight, but the processes involved depend on how *both* oxygen and ozone respond to that radiation. The curve in Figure 3.4 is a reminder that the incoming radiation from the Sun peaks – is strongest, or most intense – in the visible region of the spectrum. Nevertheless, there are significant amounts of radiation to either side of this region – both at longer wavelengths (in the infra-red) and at shorter wavelengths (in the ultraviolet).

In the previous chapter, you saw that different atmospheric gases absorb different wavelengths of radiation in the infra-red band – the origin of the greenhouse effect. But molecules also absorb radiation of shorter wavelengths – notably in the ultraviolet (uv) region of the spectrum. Recall now the link drawn in Chapter 2 between the temperature of an object and the average wavelength of the radiation it emits. This link implies a connection between the wavelength of radiation and the energy associated with it: stated explicitly, the shorter the wavelength, the higher the energy. So absorbing uv radiation imparts more energy to a molecule than does the absorption of infra-red wavelengths – sufficient to break chemical bonds in fact, thus splitting the molecule into fragments.

Ordinary oxygen absorbs uv with wavelengths below about 2.4×10^{-7} m (240 nm): this provides the energy needed to split up – or **photodissociate** – the molecule into a pair of highly reactive oxygen atoms. Once released, an oxygen atom can combine with an intact oxygen

oxygen atom

oxygen molecule

ozone molecule

▲   *Figure 3.3 Experiments reveal just how the atoms in a molecule are 'stuck' together. A 'picture' of the molecule can then be built up by representing each atom as a tiny sphere. In this chapter, different colours or tones are used to represent atoms of different elements.*

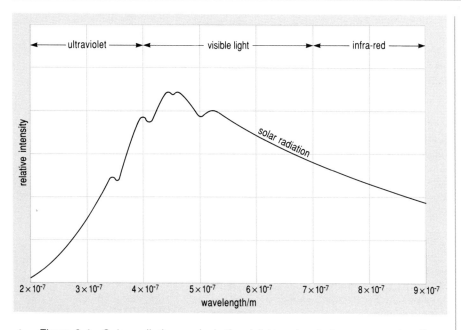

ultraviolet   visible light   infra-red

solar radiation

relative intensity

2×10^{-7} 3×10^{-7} 4×10^{-7} 5×10^{-7} 6×10^{-7} 7×10^{-7} 8×10^{-7} 9×10^{-7}

wavelength/m

▲   Figure 3.4   *Solar radiation peaks in the visible region, but spans wavelengths from the ultraviolet through to the infra-red.*

molecule, forming ozone (Figure 3.5a). This process not only produces ozone: it also thereby filters out most of the incoming solar uv with wavelengths less than 2.0×10^{-7} m, and some of that in the 2.0×10^{-7} to 2.4×10^{-7} m region as well.

But up in the stratosphere, the odds are stacked against ozone. The bonds holding the molecule together are significantly weaker than the one in oxygen, so rather less energy is required to dismantle the molecule – implying that radiation of longer wavelengths should do the trick. In fact, ozone mainly absorbs in a region from 2.15×10^{-7} to 2.95×10^{-7} m, although wavelengths up to 3.20×10^{-7} m are also absorbed to some extent. Further study of the curve in Figure 3.4 reveals that the Sun's radiation is richer in these longer wavelengths, so you might expect ozone to have a somewhat fleeting existence in the atmosphere. Concentrations build up because there is so much oxygen around, providing numerous opportunities for the interaction that makes ozone to take place. In effect, ozone is 'pushed' through a cycle of reactions: it absorbs uv, breaking into its constituent parts, only to be formed again (Figure 3.5b). After many trips around this cycle, the end comes when an ozone molecule encounters a free oxygen atom, and is converted back into ordinary oxygen (Figure 3.5c).

The reactions collected in Figure 3.5 comprise what is called a **chemical mechanism**, essentially a description of the individual steps believed to contribute to a particular chemical process – the chemistry that shapes the ozone layer in this case. It was first proposed as such in 1930. The enormous burst of research in recent years has revealed that matters are actually a good deal more complicated than this. Nevertheless, this simple scheme does capture the essence of the ozone budget, so it is worth dwelling on for a moment.

The crucial point is that ozone is constantly being created and destroyed in the stratosphere. But *given constant conditions* (and the force of this proviso will become apparent later), it settles into a **dynamic steady**

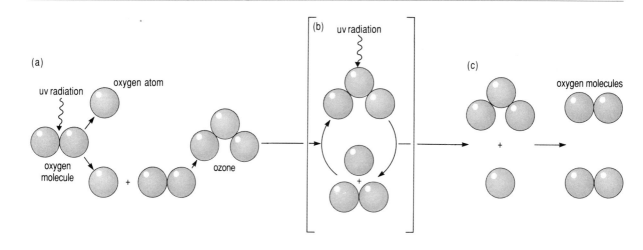

state: its concentration stays the same because the *rate* at which it is formed is balanced by the rate of its removal. A useful analogy here is with a bucket of water: think of it being filled from a tap at a steady rate, but also drained through a hole in the bottom of the bucket at the *same* rate. The level of water in the bucket (equivalent to the concentration of ozone) does not change.

Q   Can you see how the scheme in Figure 3.5 could also account for the characteristic bulge in the ozone profile (Figure 3.2b)?

A   Making ozone involves interactions between oxygen molecules and uv radiation, so you might expect the rate at which it is made to depend both on the amount of oxygen around and the 'amount' or intensity of the radiation. But these change with altitude in exactly opposite ways. Oxygen is released by plants close to the ground, and there is less of it the higher you get (whence the dangers of altitude sickness). By contrast, the uv radiation is most intense at the top of the atmosphere, before any of it has been absorbed. So there is a trade-off, such that the concentration of ozone (the result of a balance, remember, between its creation and destruction) peaks somewhere in between.

▲   *Figure 3.5*
(a) Ozone is created when uv radiation breaks up an oxygen molecule, freeing its atoms to combine with other oxygen molecules.

(b) The ozone so formed is repeatedly broken up and reformed, until (c) it is destroyed by collision with an oxygen atom.

2.2   *The influence of trace gases: catalytic cycles*

If the scheme in Figure 3.5 is subjected to a detailed *quantitative* test (and we shall look at what this involves in Section 4), a major discrepancy is revealed: the computed ozone profile mimics the shape of the observed profile surprisingly well – but it predicts steady-state concentrations of ozone that are too large. This is because the scheme seriously underestimates the rate of ozone loss. Think of the bucket again. Suppose you have a steady state set up, and then the hole in the bucket is made larger. Now the water can get away faster than before, so the level in the bucket starts to fall. But as it falls, the rate at which water runs out of the hole slows down again – until it once more matches the filling rate. A new steady state is established, but now the water-level is somewhat lower than before.

Returning to the ozone budget, the element missing from the picture so far is the presence in the stratosphere of a number of other gases in truly trace amounts – a few parts per billion (10^9) or even parts per trillion, p.p.t. (10^{12}) will do. They exert their influence by engaging in a kind of 'atomic quadrille' of changing partners that effectively speeds up the destruction of ozone, while allowing them to re-emerge constantly for a further round. To see how this works, it helps to move away from the pictures of atoms and molecules in Figure 3.5 to a more symbolic representation – using the universal language of chemistry. Thus we now write the ozone-loss step (Figure 3.5c) as a chemical equation as follows.*

$$O_3 + O \longrightarrow O_2 + O_2 \qquad\qquad\qquad\qquad\qquad \textbf{1}$$

Among the first of the trace gases to be recognised as an ozone destroyer was nitric oxide (NO). Here the 'dance' or cycle can be written as follows:

$$O_3 + NO \longrightarrow O_2 + NO_2 \qquad\qquad\qquad\qquad \textbf{2}$$
$$O + NO_2 \longrightarrow O_2 + NO \qquad\qquad\qquad\qquad \textbf{3}$$

In the first step (equation 2), nitric oxide (NO) 'steals' an oxygen atom from ozone, itself being converted to nitrogen dioxide (NO_2). It can then 'hand' this on, as it were, to a free oxygen atom, which turns NO_2 back into NO (equation 3). Notice that the *overall* effect of this cycle is just the same as equation 1: ozone and atomic oxygen are converted into molecular oxygen – a net loss of ozone. The crucial point is that nitric oxide emerges unscathed at the end of the cycle – free to destroy many more molecules of ozone. A substance that acts in this way is called a **catalyst**, and the cycle it passes through (here equations 2 and 3), a **catalytic cycle**.

Analogous cycles exist for oxides of hydrogen (see Activity 1 at the end of this section) and, of course, for chlorine – the focus of concern about CFCs.

Q   Try to write a cycle (a pair of reactions) that shows how a chlorine *atom* can destroy ozone catalytically – just like NO in equations 2 and 3.

A   The desired effect is achieved if a chlorine atom (Cl) first attacks an ozone molecule, forming a molecule of **chlorine monoxide** (ClO), and then this collides with another oxygen atom – freeing the chlorine atom for further destruction. In symbols:

$$O_3 + Cl \longrightarrow O_2 + ClO \qquad\qquad\qquad\qquad \textbf{4}$$
$$O + ClO \longrightarrow O_2 + Cl \qquad\qquad\qquad\qquad\quad \textbf{5}$$

The collection of atoms and molecules involved in each of these cycles have become known as *'families'* – the *nitrogen family*, the *hydrogen family* and the *chlorine family*. You may find many of these substances referred to elsewhere as *free radicals* or *radicals*, for short. Examples include atoms like O and Cl and molecules like ClO. Just what is meant by the term radical is beyond the scope of this series. Suffice it to say that they are highly reactive – eager, that is, to join up with other atoms or molecules. The ones involved here are avid 'scavengers' of ozone – thus ensuring that the indirect routes to ozone destruction via the catalytic cycles are faster than the direct one (equation 1). More telling is the fact that the cycles *are* catalytic: this is why trace constituents can have such a marked effect on the ozone budget. In particular, the chlorine cycle is especially efficient: current estimates suggest that every free atom of chlorine in the stratosphere can destroy *as many as 100 000* molecules of ozone before it is 'inactivated' or removed in some way.

*The crucial thing to check when you write an equation is that you haven't lost (or gained) any atoms. *Atoms are neither created nor destroyed during chemical reactions, although they can – and usually do – change partners.*

This possibility of inactivation reveals another level of complexity in the chemistry of the stratosphere. The nitrogen, hydrogen and chlorine families are *not independent* of one another: rather, they are coupled together by reactions between the atoms and molecules of different families. Because of this, the rate of ozone destruction for one cycle of reactions may well depend on the concentration of a catalytic species that strictly 'belongs' to another family.

Particularly important here are couplings that produce so-called holding cycles, whereby active radicals become 'locked up' as more stable **reservoir molecules** – and hence unavailable (on a more or less permanent basis) for participation in ozone-destroying cycles. As far as the chlorine family is concerned, the important long-term reservoir is hydrogen chloride (HCl): indeed, at any given moment some 70% of stratospheric chlorine is thought to be present as HCl. A second, but more temporary reservoir, is a molecule known as chlorine nitrate – formed by coupling into the nitrogen family (Figure 3.6), and hence tying up both active chlorine and active nitrogen. Do bear in mind, however, that the chlorine (and nitrogen) in these reservoir molecules is not actually *removed* from the atmosphere: if a process can occur which releases it into its active form again, then it can set about destroying ozone. You will see later that this is believed to be the key to the special chemistry of the 'ozone hole' over Antarctica.

If you are reeling somewhat from this sudden onslaught of molecules and chemical formulae, take heart! The main aim here is to give you a feel for the true complexity of ozone chemistry, but don't worry too much about the details. The crucial point to grasp is the notion of a catalytic cycle and the way that this allows minute traces of certain gases to speed up the rate of ozone destruction. In fact, we have only scratched the surface. The most recent models include some 100–200 interactions among the atoms and molecules of the families that control the ozone budget – far removed from the original mechanism in Figure 3.5.

It is important to be clear that most of these processes appear to be at work in the 'natural' atmosphere, unpolluted by human activities. The radicals active in destroying ozone are all derived from other gases that percolate up from the troposphere – the so-called **source gases** – and there have always been natural sources of these. This is what keeps the natural rate of ozone production in check and the ozone budget balanced at the 'normal' level. The problem is that in the contemporary atmosphere, the background concentrations of catalytic species – especially of chlorine – have already been supplemented by different and *growing*, anthropogenic sources. There is evidence that this rise *has* started to chisel away at the hole in the bucket and not only over Antarctica.

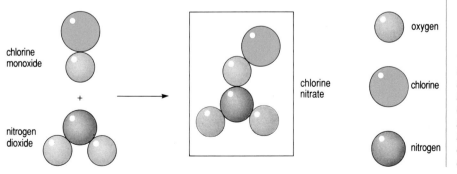

◄ *Figure 3.6*
Formation of the reservoir molecule chlorine nitrate – by reaction between chlorine monoxide (ClO) and nitrogen dioxide (NO$_2$) – interferes with the catalytic cycles for ozone destruction.

Activity 1

Write a cycle for the hydrogen family, showing how an atom of
hydrogen can catalyse the destruction of ozone. Assume that the first
step produces a hydroxyl radical, usually written OH.

3   *Source gases*

The source gases are again trace constituents of the atmosphere, produced
– or emitted – at ground-level. They carry the elements of the catalytic
families (nitrogen, hydrogen and chlorine), but in the form of stable
molecules, that are usually rather insoluble in water, the latter ensuring
that they are not rapidly 'rained out'. These trace gases can thus linger in
the troposphere for long enough to be moved around by the sort of
large-scale atmospheric motions that GCMs attempt to model. As a result,
molecules of these gases are not only distributed *around* the globe, they are
also transported *upwards* – and some, at least, are eventually carried across
the tropopause into the stratosphere. Mostly this happens over the tropics
– a region of rapidly rising air currents, often driven by violent storms.
Once in the stratosphere, the compounds eventually encounter a more
hostile environment. Molecules that were inert in the lower atmosphere
can now be broken down – often by sunlight (as are oxygen and ozone),
but sometimes chemically – to produce the active radicals that speed up the
destruction of ozone. Information on the main *natural* source gas for each
family is collected in Table 3.1.

You met the first two gases in Chapter 2, and there is little to add here.
The most important point to bear in mind is that the sources and sinks of
both gases are not well understood. And neither are they in balance –
which is why the atmospheric burden of each gas is increasing. Nitrous
oxide is effectively inert in the troposphere, hence the long lifetime
recorded in Table 3.1. In the stratosphere, however, uv radiation promotes
reactions which transform it into nitric oxide, NO – and so feed it into the

Table 3.1   *Tropospheric concentrations and lifetimes of natural source gases
(1986), and global trends*

Source gas	Concentration (p.p.b.)	Rate of increase (p.p.b./yr)	Rate of increase (%/yr)	Lifetime (yr)
nitrous oxide, N_2O	306–309	0.65–0.8	0.2–0.3	150
methane, CH_4	1 638	13–16	0.8–1.0	10
chloromethane, CH_3Cl	0.6	–	–	1.5

Source: R. T. Watson, M. Prather and M. J. Kurylo (1988) *Present State of Knowledge of the
Upper Atmosphere 1988: An Assessment Report*, NASA Reference Publications, NASA,
Washington DC. (Executive Summary: 15 March 1988.)

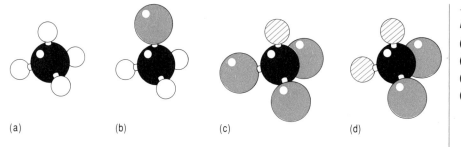

(a)   (b)   (c)   (d)

Figure 3.7
Representations of
(a) methane (CH₄)
(b) chloromethane (CH₃Cl)
(c) CFC-11
(d) CFC-12.

hydrogen

chlorine

fluorine

carbon

nitrogen family. Methane (Figure 3.7a) actually affects the ozone budget in a number of ways (of which more later), but the most direct of these is its role as the main stratospheric source of radicals for the hydrogen family.

Turning to the chlorine family, here the main *natural* source gas is chloromethane (Figure 3.7b; think of it as methane, but with one hydrogen atom replaced by a chlorine atom). Mostly this is of biological origin – being generated during wood-rotting and natural forest fires – but some arises from slash-and-burn tropical agriculture. Notice the short lifetime recorded in Table 3.1. Because of this, rather little of the gas that enters the atmosphere (only some 10%) actually reaches the stratosphere, where the chlorine atom is stripped off and enters its cycle of ozone destruction (equations 4 and 5 in Section 2.2). This input is now dwarfed by that from the many other organic (that is, carbon-based) compounds containing chlorine that are accumulating in the troposphere from strictly anthropogenic sources: this is where the now infamous **CFCs** enter the scene.

Q The report from which Table 3.1 was taken estimates that the total **'chlorine loading'** of the atmosphere – that is, the concentration of chlorine atoms effectively 'carried' in organic molecules – was around 3 p.p.b. in 1986. What proportion of this was due to anthropogenic emissions?

A Taking CH_3Cl to be entirely natural, at least $(3 − 0.6)$ p.p.b. $= 2.4$ p.p.b., or $(2.4 ÷ 3.0) \times 100 = 80\%$ was anthropogenic. Emissions of CFCs are the major contribution to this growing source.

3.1   Chlorofluorocarbons (CFCs)

As a class of compounds, CFCs *all* contain atoms of carbon, fluorine and chlorine, and only these elements – but combined together in varying proportions. To the cognoscenti, the precise composition is reflected in the code name used to identify each compound. The details need not concern us. Suffice it to say that the two most widely-used compounds – labelled **CFC-11** and **CFC-12** (Figure 3.7c and d) – can each be thought of as derived from methane.

Q Write formulae for these two CFCs.

A Methane is CH_4. From Figure 3.7(c), in CFC-11 one hydrogen is replaced by fluorine and three by chlorine, to give $CFCl_3$. From Figure 3.7(d), CFC-12 has two chlorines and two fluorines – giving CF_2Cl_2.

Table 3.2   Tropospheric concentrations (1986) and atmospheric lifetimes of artificial chlorine-containing source gases

Compound	Cl atoms per molecule	Concentration* (p.p.t.)	Lifetime† (yr)	Ozone depletion potential†
CFC-11 (CFCl$_3$)	3	226	60	1.0
CFC-12 (CF$_2$Cl$_2$)	2	392	120	0.9–1.0
CFC-113 (C$_2$F$_3$Cl$_3$)	3	32	90	0.8–0.9
CFC-114 (C$_2$F$_4$Cl$_2$)	2	5	200	0.6–0.8
CFC-115 (C$_2$F$_5$Cl)	1	4	400	0.3–0.5
carbon tetrachloride (CCl$_4$)	4	129	50	1.0–1.2
methyl chloroform (C$_2$H$_3$Cl$_3$)	3	139	6.3	0.1–0.2
HCFC-22 (CHF$_2$Cl)	1	92	15.3	0.05

Sources: *As Table 3.1. †Taken from *Scientific Assessment of Stratospheric Ozone: 1989* (input to Draft UNEP Integrated Report).

Information on the group of five CFCs included in the original Montreal Protocol is collected in Table 3.2. (For now, ignore the last three rows, and the final column. And ignore all the formulae that are unfamiliar to you.) The immediately striking feature is the very long lifetimes of these compounds. Ironically, this stems from the very characteristics that made CFCs seem so ideal: they are non-toxic, non-flammable – in short, effectively completely inert in the lower atmosphere. Despite prodigious research efforts, no evidence has emerged for *any* tropospheric sink for CFCs. On the contrary, the experimental programmes set up to monitor these (and other) trace gases at stations around the globe have only confirmed an inexorable build-up in the atmospheric burden of CFCs: some typical data are included in Figure 3.8.

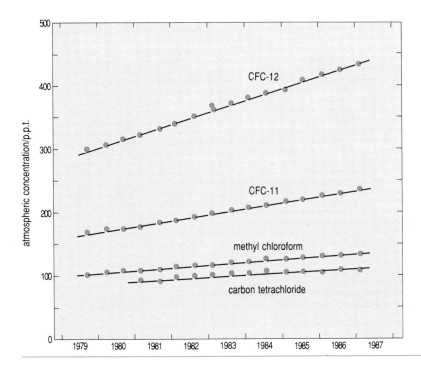

◀ Figure 3.8
Trends in the atmospheric concentrations of four chlorine-containing compounds, observed at mid-latitudes in the Northern hemisphere.

Tropospheric inertness of the CFCs was the central thesis in the seminal work published by Rowland and Molina in 1974: given this, they argued that the only plausible fate for these compounds is transport upwards until they reach altitudes in the stratosphere where the incoming uv radiation is sufficiently energetic to break them up – some 25–40 km for CFCs 11 and 12. Here, photodissociation strips off their chlorine atoms – the net effect being to add to the natural burden of stratospheric chlorine. The threat thereby posed to the ozone layer is no longer in any doubt. But a more detailed examination of the size and consequences of that threat – and the effectiveness of measures being taken to mitigate it – is in order. There is one final point to be made before we embark on that.

So far, the CFCs have been lumped together. However, the differences between them are important – and not only because this influences their uses, and hence emission rates. It also determines the 'efficiency' with which a given compound can destroy ozone. In general, this is enhanced by a long lifetime (mainly because this ensures optimal transfer into the stratosphere) and a high number of chlorine atoms per molecule. This idea is given quantitative expression by calculating an **ozone depletion potential**, or **ODP**, for each compound – the behaviour of CFC-11 being taken as a kind of bench-mark against which others are compared. Some recent estimates – and there are still considerable uncertainties here – are given in the final column of Table 3.2: numbers *less* than one mean the compound is *less* destructive than CFC-11, and vice versa.

The precise numbers need not concern us, but the ODP concept does raise an important general point. The extent to which the *potential* threat posed by a given compound is likely to be realised depends, of course, on the atmospheric burden of that gas – and this, in turn, depends on the amount of it being released into the environment. Thus the ODP effectively allows global emissions of different chlorine compounds to be 'translated' into 'contributions to ozone depletion'. An example is shown in Figure 3.9, based on worldwide emissions of the compounds given in Table 3.2 during 1985.

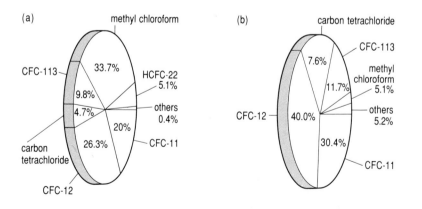

▲ Figure 3.9
(a) Estimates of global emissions of anthropogenic chlorine compounds during 1985. The tonnage of each compound is expressed as a percentage of the total tonnage. 'Others' includes CFCs 114 and 115 and certain halons (Activity 2).

(b) These figures 'translated' into percentage contributions to ozone depletion – using the ODP of each compound.

As expected, major contributions come from the CFCs that then dominated the market. But notice the not insignificant contributions from carbon tetrachloride and methyl chloroform. Neither of these compounds is a CFC (they contain no fluorine), and neither was included in the original Protocol, although both are controlled by the strengthened version agreed in 1990. Carbon tetrachloride is the archetypal dry-cleaning fluid, and an important chemical feedstock: it is also an efficient ozone destroyer (see Table 3.2). Compounds like methyl chloroform (widely used as a solvent and cleaning fluid) present a more subtle problem. Methyl chloroform itself is far less inert than a CFC: the hydrogens in the molecule make it liable to chemical attack in the troposphere – hence the short lifetime and low ODP recorded in Table 3.2. In this case, however, these desirable qualities are partly offset by the enormous amounts released into the environment (some 470 thousand tonnes in 1985). The take-home message is clear: put enough of an apparently 'safe' chlorine-containing compound into the environment, and at least some of the chlorine it carries will get through to the stratosphere and contribute to ozone depletion. The message is important because several of the compounds being contemplated as substitutes for CFCs have low ODPs, *but do still contain chlorine*. One example, already in use – labelled HCFC-22 – is included in Table 3.2.

3.2   Summary of Sections 2 and 3

Ozone (O_3) concentrations in the atmosphere vary, peaking in the stratosphere, at around 20–35 km.

Ozone concentrations result from a dynamic balance between creation and destruction. Creation is initiated by the photodissociation of oxygen (O_2); ozone is destroyed by reaction with atomic oxygen (O):

$$O_3 + O \longrightarrow O_2 + O_2 \qquad\qquad\qquad 1$$

Loss of ozone (by reaction 1) can be catalysed by a number of reactive atoms or molecules (radicals), that are constantly regenerated. To generalise the cycles you have met:

$$O_3 + X \longrightarrow O_2 + XO$$

$$O + XO \longrightarrow O_2 + X$$

where **X** can be nitric oxide (NO), or hydrogen (H), or chlorine (Cl) (or bromine, Br – see Activity 2, below). The catalytic families interact forming reservoir molecules (such as hydrogen chloride and chlorine nitrate) that act as holding tanks for active radicals.

The active radicals for these cycles are provided by relatively stable and insoluble source gases that are transported up from the troposphere.

The principal source gases for the nitrogen family (nitrous oxide, N_2O) and hydrogen family (methane, CH_4) have both natural and anthropogenic orgins. The sources and sinks of N_2O and CH_4 are still not fully understood.

The principal source gases for the chlorine family are now non-natural – including the long-lived CFCs and carbon tetrachloride, together with other less inert compounds like methyl chloroform and some CFC substitutes. The ODP assigned to each compound reflects its efficiency at destroying ozone.

Activity 2

The following questions may be used to revise some of the key concepts of Sections 2 and 3.

Q1 The concern about large fleets of SSTs referred to in Section 1 centred on the fact that their engines produce nitric oxide, NO: *any* engine that draws in air and uses the oxygen in it to burn fuel at high temperatures inevitably produces some NO.

(a) Why should this raise concerns about the ozone layer?

(b) Can you suggest why the vast amounts of NO produced by ground-based vehicles *do not* raise such concerns?

Q2 One of the compounds being developed (by ICI in the UK) as an alternative refrigerant is a hydrofluorocarbon labelled HFC-134a. It has an estimated atmospheric lifetime of around 15 years, but is assigned an ODP of zero. Can you suggest what this means?

The following questions are a bit more technical. Do not spend too long on them if you don't have a scientific background, *but do read the comments at the end of the chapter.*

Q3 The Montreal Protocol also seeks to control emissions of compounds known as **halons**, widely used in fire extinguishers. These are organic compounds that carry atoms of bromine, Br (and sometimes Cl as well) into the stratosphere. Write a catalytic cycle showing ozone destruction by bromine.

Q4 One of the compounds mentioned in Q3 is labelled halon-1301: each molecule contains one atom of bromine and no chlorine. The estimated atmospheric lifetime is 100 years, and the compound is assigned an ODP of 12.3. What do these figures suggest about the relative efficiencies with which Cl atoms and Br atoms destroy ozone?

(Hint: Refer to Table 3.2, and compare the figures for halon-1301 with those for CFCs of comparable lifetimes.)

4 Model predictions of global ozone change

Predicting the effect on ozone of changing concentrations of the source gases is like predicting the impact of enhanced levels of greenhouse gases on the climate. It shares many of the same difficulties – and the results that come out of the model studies are subject to the same kinds of uncertainties. As outlined in the previous chapter, these fall into two broad categories: on the one hand, those linked to the scientific description 'built in' to the computer model; and on the other, those that stem from the difficulty of projecting future emissions of different source gases – especially when these are subject to changing patterns of human activity.

In this section, we outline some of the assumptions and approximations that are usually incorporated into models, in order to keep the task of simulating the distribution of ozone within bounds. We do this in the context of a brief look at the evolution of model forecasts of ozone depletion – an essential backdrop for the material to come in Sections 5 and 7. First, it is important to delineate the problem.

4.1   Modelling the distribution of ozone: the problem

Central to any model of the ozone layer is a description of the chemistry outlined in Section 2 – a complex network of coupled, interacting and often competing chemical and photochemical reactions. The basic information comes from laboratory studies of the individual reactions – the rate of each process, and how this depends on the concentrations of the different species involved, and on other conditions, such as temperature*, or where appropriate, solar radiation. The results of such studies are incorporated into the model as a set of equations that constitute a description of 'ozone chemistry'. But this captures only part of the problem. In the real atmosphere, the observed distribution of ozone is shaped by subtle, all-pervasive interactions between ozone chemistry and atmospheric dynamics.

To see what this entails, take the characteristic *vertical distribution* of ozone – or ozone profile (Figure 3.2b) – as a first example. Here, the chemical balance that determines the concentration of ozone at any particular altitude depends not only on the local conditions (temperature,

*The rate of a reaction invariably depends on the temperature – usually speeding up as the temperature is raised. You may have noticed this yourself. For example, bicarbonate of soda (sodium bicarbonate) reacts with the acid in fruit to produce carbon dioxide – almost imperceptibly when cold, but with a vigorous fizzing when heated.

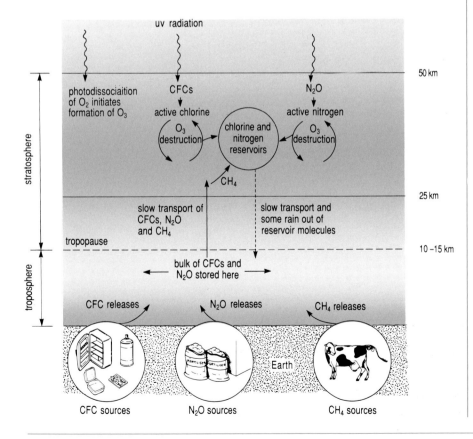

◀   *Figure 3.10*
Some of the key processes, both chemistry and transport, that determine the concentration of ozone in the stratosphere (as represented in a 1-D model, Section 4.2).

intensity of solar radiation, and so on) – but also on the supply of key catalytic species and other trace gases. This supply is itself driven by atmospheric motions. Source gases have to be transported into the stratosphere, and then move up through it. And there is evidence that long-lived reservoir molecules (like HCl, for example) can move down – and be washed out in rain in the troposphere. In short, the stratosphere is host to a constant traffic of ozone and the many gases that interact with it – as suggested in Figure 3.10. To simulate the ozone profile a model must capture this interplay between chemistry and dynamics.

On top of this, large-scale atmospheric motions also play a critical role in moving stratospheric ozone around the globe – and so determining its *global distribution.* There is evidence to this effect in Figure 3.11. Here, the 'contours' record measured values of the **total ozone column** (also known simply as **'column ozone'**) – that is, the total amount of ozone above a unit area (usually 1 cm²) of the Earth's surface. Notice that values of column ozone contain no information about the vertical distribution of ozone: just the total number of molecules in a column stretching up from the surface to the top of the atmosphere. The data in Figure 3.11 are typical of years before the ozone hole started to appear – recorded as a function of both *latitude* (from the north pole at the top to the south at the bottom) and *season* (from January to December across the figure).

Q   Where and when do the highest amounts of ozone occur? Is this what you would have expected?

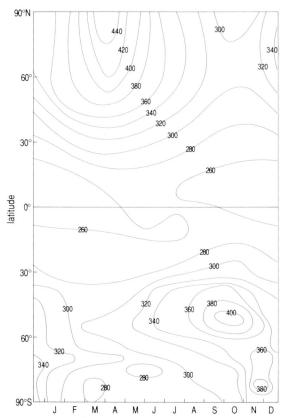

◀   *Figure 3.11 The global distribution of ozone, as a function of latitude and time of the year. The numbers are average values of the total ozone column in Dobson Units* (DU, where 1 DU = 2.7 × 10¹⁶ molecules per square centimetre), based on data from a network of ground-based measuring stations around the world – for years prior to 1974.*

* *An odd unit, named after Gordon Dobson – the Oxford Reader in meteorology who developed the technique used to measure ozone.*

A   According to Figure 3.11, the column ozone is greatest at high latitudes in late winter and early spring – around the end of March in north polar regions (top left), and in mid-October at around 60° south (bottom right). This is surprising. Since the production of ozone is driven by sunlight, one might expect maximum amounts at low latitudes, where there is the greatest amount of solar radiation: in practice, minimum amounts are found in equatorial latitudes.

In fact the main ozone factory *is* at tropical latitudes (at altitudes of some 30–40 km), but it is transported from here downward and toward the poles in a circulation that is biased in favour of the 'summer' hemisphere at the equinoxes – that is, toward the north pole in March/April and the south in September/October – as suggested by the highly simplified picture in Figure 3.12.

To capture what is known about atmospheric circulation strictly requires the sort of three-dimensional GCM described in the previous chapter. If detailed ozone chemistry could be incorporated into a GCM, then the resulting model would be ideal for simulating all the subtleties of ozone distribution – with altitude and latitude (and with longitude too, although this is less marked), and with the changing seasons. At the time of writing (mid 1990), this remains a largely unrealised goal, mainly because such models are so demanding of computer time and memory. The problem is particularly pressing when a model is used to forecast the effects on the distribution of ozone of changing concentrations of trace gases because then demanding calculations must be repeated many times over. To keep the task down to manageable proportions, most such forecasts have in practice used models that incorporate a much simplified treatment of atmospheric dynamics.

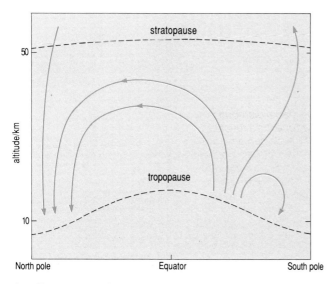

▲   *Figure 3.12   Stratospheric circulation, shown highly schematically for spring in the northern hemisphere. The flow is reversed during spring in the summer hemisphere – but does not travel further south than about 60°S, because the circulation encounters 'resistance' at that latitude (see Section 5.1). As a result, global ozone levels do not speak in the tropics – where most ozone is produced – but near the north pole and at 60°S. (Notice that the height of the tropopause varies with latitude.)*

4.2   Models and scenarios: changing perceptions

One-dimensional (1-D) models are the simplest: they effectively treat the atmosphere as a single vertical column. Averaging techniques are used to reduce *all* transport processes to simple vertical movement (up and down, along the lines portrayed in Figure 3.10). Such models can simulate the vertical distribution of ozone, but not any 'horizontal' (i.e. north–south or east–west) or seasonal variations. So the ozone profiles (and hence values of column ozone) they produce are necessarily *average* pictures – averaged around the globe, and usually over one or more simulated years as well.

The great strength of 1-D models is that they are computationally fast, even when they include very detailed ozone chemistry. As a result, they have been widely used to predict changes to the total (average) ozone column. A typical study involves introducing the perturbation of interest (effectively a change in 'input' conditions such as a specified increase in CFC emissions), and then running the model for many simulated years until the modelled atmosphere settles into a new steady state. The ozone column (and/or altitude profile) is then compared with a similar model calculation that did not contain the perturbing influence.

Since 1974, 1-D model forecasts of ozone depletion by CFCs have fluctuated widely: Figure 3.13 presents a fairly typical record through to the early 1980s. These fluctuations reflect the many uncertainties associated with the modelling process, but the marked shifts recorded here can all be largely attributed to changes in the scientific description, specifically the chemistry, incorporated into the model – to revised reaction rates and to the inclusion of reactions which had been overlooked earlier. As it happens, this ongoing programme of research produced a reassuring trend toward forecasts of lower levels of *total* ozone depletion – a trend that broadly continued throughout the 1980s. Hidden within this trend, however, is a far from reassuring recognition that the processes at work at different altitudes can produce significant *local* changes in the vertical distribution of ozone.

A compelling example is shown in Figure 3.14. As indicated in the caption, these forecasts come from the same model study, with the same unperturbed atmosphere: the precise details need not concern us. The crucial point here is the *pattern* of change they reveal – and this is typical of

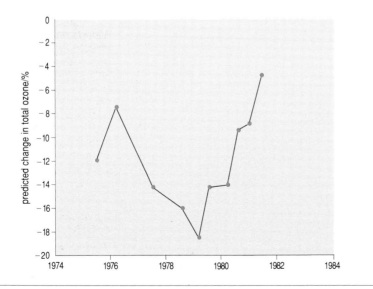

◀ Figure 3.13
Record of calculations of the expected change in total ozone (at steady state) from CFC release, as predicted by the 1-D model at the Lawrence Livermore National Laboratory (LLNL), United States.

more recent studies. Thus, as expected, a scenario that increases the total chlorine loading to a not unrealistic level (see Section 7.4) leads to ozone depletion (Figure 3.14a) – as does a 20% increase in nitrous oxide (though to a far smaller extent: see Figure 3.14b).

But notice the effect of doubling methane (Figure 3.14c). Since methane is a source of radicals for the hydrogen family, you might have again expected an overall loss of ozone. The striking feature is that this loss is restricted to the uppermost reaches of the stratosphere – and more than compensated by *increases* lower down. This reflects the complexity of methane's role in the atmosphere. In the low stratosphere, it actually interferes with the chlorine cycle (this is one route to the reservoir molecule, HCl). Lower still, it gets involved in just the same sort of processes that *produce* ozone in photochemical smog.

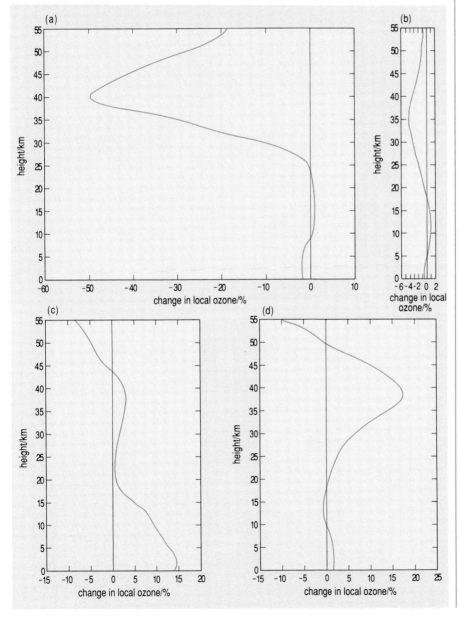

◀   *Figure 3.14*
Altitude profiles of the percentage change in ozone (at steady state) predicted by the LLNL 1-D model, due to certain perturbations. In each case, the change is relative to the model run with an 'unperturbed' atmosphere containing about 1.3 p.p.b. of total chlorine.

(a) Total chlorine increased to 8 p.p.b.

(b) Nitrous oxide increased by 20%.

(c) Methane doubled.

(d) Carbon dioxide doubled.

Concentrate now on Figure 3.14(d). Carbon dioxide is not involved in *any* of the chemical cycles that control the ozone budget, so why should doubling its concentration have any effect on ozone?

Q   Think about it. What effect *does* enhanced carbon dioxide have in the atmosphere?

A   Carbon dioxide is the archetypal greenhouse gas, trapping infra-red radiation in the troposphere and causing the lower atmosphere to warm up.

As you saw in Chapter 2, the same process *cools* the stratosphere. Chemical reaction rates depend critically on temperature – and some more so than others: in this case, it turns out that the net effect of more carbon dioxide is to slow the rate of ozone destruction and so *increase* ozone levels.

This example highlights two important points about all model studies. First, in the real world, the concentrations of *all* the source gases are changing simultaneously. To deal with this, recent calculations involve a 'multiple perturbation', in which the concentrations of the entire suite of important gases are varied at the same time. Secondly, *all* of the source gases considered here (including carbon tetrachloride and methyl chloroform) are also greenhouse gases, so increases in their concentrations – as in that of carbon dioxide – will tend to alter the temperatures of the troposphere and stratosphere. This introduces a temperature **feedback** into the chemistry: models which take this into account tend to produce very different results from those that do not. Notice how the twin problems of global warming and ozone depletion are becoming woven together.

Increased understanding of this set of interactions and feedbacks was a major factor in reducing forecasts of total ozone depletion to more modest levels. (Activity 3 in Section 4.3 should help to convince you here.) As you might expect, however, the exact results now turn out to be very sensitive to the assumed emission rates – not just of the CFCs (and other chlorine 'carriers'), but also of all the other gases. This is important. Chapter 2 stressed the difficulty of projecting future carbon dioxide emissions with any confidence – as well as the uncertainties associated with its consequent build-up in the atmosphere. Similar large uncertainties attend predictions of future trends in emission rates of methane and nitrous oxide. In the main, ozone modellers handle these uncertainties by adopting the same strategy as climate modellers: they construct scenarios – and generally speaking, they tend to be much the same ones. For example, forecasts of ozone change commonly assume a doubling of CO_2 levels by the middle of the next century (as in Figure 3.14d). By contrast, the task of predicting future chlorine loadings is usually subject to a more detailed analysis – especially when the forecasts based on these projections are intended to provide the scientific input to the, essentially political, process of agreeing controls on the release of CFCs (*and* possible substitutes). We will look at this again – in that context – in Section 7.4.

For all the valuable insights provided by 1-D models, they contain only a very crude description of atmospheric dynamics. Because of this, it is now recognised that they should not be used in isolation to predict actual atmospheric behaviour. Better in this respect are *two-dimensional (2-D) models*, which incorporate elements of transport north–south as well as in the vertical direction – but at the expense of somewhat less detailed chemistry. Such models can simulate atmospheric transport with considerable realism, and they can capture major feedbacks between ozone

chemistry, temperature and transport. They reproduce the general pattern of global ozone distribution shown in Figure 3.11 remarkably well.

   By the mid 1980s this 'validation' of 2-D models had produced a measure of confidence in forecasts based on them. There was an emerging consensus that continued release of CFCs at the then current levels (along with other source gases and CO_2, of course) *would* erode the ozone layer – but the agreed figures at the time suggested a relatively slow attrition of something less than 1% of global ozone per decade. Within these global figures there was some indication that ozone loss would probably be greatest at high latitudes in winter. But nowhere was there any hint of a sudden and dramatic decline on anything like the scale that has actually occurred. In short, none of the models predicted the ozone hole over Antarctica. We look at the reasons for this conspicuous failure in the next section.

4.3   Summary of Section 4

To simulate all aspects of the variation of stratospheric ozone – spatially and with the seasons – strictly requires a sophisticated 3-D GCM that incorporates detailed ozone chemistry. Because of computational limitations, most assessments of the threat to ozone posed by human activities have used models (1-D or 2-D) that contain a much simplified treatment of atmospheric dynamics. Such model forecasts have shown a trend to lower estimates of ozone depletion – largely because of a growing understanding that emissions of other trace gases (notably methane and carbon dioxide) mitigate the effects of CFCs on the total ozone column. All models failed to predict the ozone hole.

Activity 3

(Note: it is important that you should attempt part (b) of this activity, and read the comments on it at the end of the chapter. Do not spend too long on part (a) if you don't have a scientific background.)

The results shown in Figure 3.14 are part of a series of single and multiple perturbation studies using a particular 1-D model. A fuller set of results is collected in Table 3.3.

▲ *'There's a hole this big, I tell you . . .'*

Activity 3

(a) How do these results support the thesis:
   (i) that the different catalytic families interact;
   (ii) that temperature feedback is important?

(b) Suppose the figures in Table 3.3 and Figure 3.14 were used to support an argument that, since enhanced emissions of CH_4 and CO_2 will mitigate the effects of continued CFC release, there is no need to control the latter. What arguments would you marshal against such a claim?

Table 3.3   *Results from the same study as Figure 3.14*

Percentage column ozone change predicted			
single perturbation		multiple perturbation	
increase total Cl to 8 p.p.b.	−5.7%	increase total Cl to 8 p.p.b., and N_2O by 20%, and double CH_4	−2.8%
increase N_2O by 20%	−1.7%		
double CH_4	+2.9%		
double CO_2	+3.5%	increase total Cl to 8 p.p.b., and N_2O by 20%, and double both CH_4 and CO_2	+0.2%

5   *What is happening to the ozone layer?*

Large losses of total ozone in Antarctica reveal seasonal ClO_x/NO_x interaction.*   (J. C. Farman, B. G. Gardiner and J. D. Shanklin, *Nature*, 16 May 1985)

The measurements from the British Antarctic Survey (BAS) station at Halley Bay reported by Joe Farman and his colleagues are included in Figure 3.15. There is no doubt that this report marked a crucial turning-point in the long-running saga about CFCs. On one level, it provided an image – of a 'hole in the sky' (through which 'pour' deadly cancer-causing 'rays', in the more lurid press accounts), later given dramatic force by the publication of NASA's satellite 'pictures' (see Plate 5) – that has exerted a powerful hold on the public and political imagination. But the impact on the scientific community was, if anything, more profound.

Up to this point, the debate about CFCs had turned, almost exclusively, on the results from model calculations – *not* actual observations. True, monitoring programmes had revealed a steady build-up in CFCs and other important trace gases. But there remained a key area of uncertainty: was

▲   *Joe Farman, whose team first detected the ozone hole over Antarctica.*

*These symbols are often used to represent the chlorine and nitrogen families, respectively.

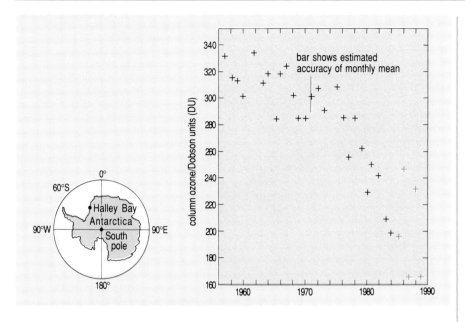

Figure 3.15
The October average ozone column measured from the BAS station at Halley Bay. Before the mid 1970s, values were around 300 DU, but since then a rapid decline has occurred.

A balloon launch at Halley. The instruments carried aloft signal back information about the meteorological state (temperature, pressure, humidity etc.) of the lower stratosphere. Other balloons carry instruments to measure the ozone concentration at different altitudes.

◄   Halley 4, part of the British Antarctic Survey station in Antarctica, where ongoing measurements of column ozone first detected the ozone hole. Like its predecessors, this station has now nearly disappeared under the snow!

anything actually happening to the ozone layer? Here, the underlying problem is that column ozone – like atmospheric temperature – is naturally highly variable, and over a wide range of spatial and time scales. Within the tropics, the average figures we looked at in Figure 3.11 present a typical picture – with small, but well-defined, variations with either latitude or season. Beyond the tropics, however, the detailed picture is much more complex. Here, there can be such large fluctuations in column ozone from day-to-day and year-to-year, and from place-to-place, that it becomes very difficult to detect any underlying 'signal' of a small consistent long-term downward trend that could be attributed to human activities. As with global warming, the basic requirement is for an extended, and reliable, data set.

The longest data record of ozone measurements comes from a network of ground-based stations referred to in Figure 3.11 – the so-called *Dobson network*, of which Halley Bay is a part. Although this network was extended in 1957, the distribution of stations remained quite uneven, with 42 out of 67 in northern temperate latitudes. Since 1979 the problem of spatial coverage had been much alleviated by instruments borne aloft on satellites (like the **Total Ozone Mapping Spectrometer – TOMS** – on board NASA's Nimbus 7 satellite), but here the data record was too short to permit the identification of any statistically significant trends. Overall, then, the early 1980s saw little convincing evidence that CFCs had *already* caused damage to global ozone levels.

Set against this background, the results from Halley Bay carried a double-edged message. On the one hand, they provided the first unequivocal signal of a real change to column ozone – albeit apparently restricted to Antarctica in springtime (September/October in the southern hemisphere, remember). On the other hand, the signal was so large and unexpected that its immediate effect was to challenge the validity of existing models: why did they fail to predict this dramatic decline?

▲   NASA's Nimbus 7 meteorological satellite carries a sensor from which global 'maps' of atmospheric ozone can be constructed.

▲   The Dobson spectrometer, which is used to measure ozone concentrations.

5.1   The ozone hole: why Antarctica?

Introduction

The results from Halley Bay have since been amply confirmed by other workers. Particularly telling are the computer-processed images from the TOMS data (see Plate 5), which show that the depleted region (less than 300 DU) extends over the entire Antarctic continent – and beyond. Other measurements, from satellites and balloons, have revealed that the depletion is mainly concentrated between 12 to 24 km in altitude – spanning much of the lower stratosphere at these latitudes. So the 'hole in the sky' is actually more like a *slice* out of the heart of the ozone layer: a striking example from 1987 is shown in Figure 3.16. Whatever happens to Antarctic ozone in the future, 1987 will undoubtedly remain a landmark year because it saw the first hard evidence for a link between ozone loss and chlorine chemistry.

The evidence came from a huge US-led experimental campaign during August and September – the period during which the ozone hole develops each year. The project involved some 150 scientists and technicians from several nations, based at Punta Areñas on the southern tip of Chile. Crucially, the team was equipped with two aircraft – a DC-8 and a modified U2 spy plane (an ER-2) – both capable of flying *into* the depleted region, but the latter at altitudes up to 18 km. As indicated in Box 3.1, it was instruments aboard the ER-2 that caught chlorine monoxide red-handed: in Watergate parlance, the 'smoking gun' of the CFC debate had finally been found.

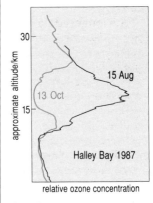

relative ozone concentration

▲   Figure 3.16
Between mid August and mid October 1987, some 95% of the ozone between 14 and 23 km altitude was destroyed over Halley Bay.

Box 3.1   Finding the 'smoking gun'

Schematic [record] of observations from the ER-2 showed that at ~18 km altitude, poleward of ~65°S the composition of the vortex was highly perturbed. As this chemically perturbed region (CPR) was entered, the concentration of chlorine monoxide (ClO) increased sharply over several hundred kilometres, reaching values some 10 times greater than those observed immediately outside and some 100 times greater than those at lower latitudes. In late August ozone concentrations were roughly constant across this boundary.

However, by the middle of September there was a sharp decline in ozone as the chemically perturbed region was entered . . . As well as the gross changes in ozone and ClO seen as aircraft flew into the CPR, there were also smaller-scale changes in ozone and ClO which [mirror one another]. This decline of ozone only in the region where the ClO concentrations were high provides a strong indication that chlorine chemistry is responsible for the ozone depletion.

Source: SORG, 1988, p. 9 and Figure 1.7.

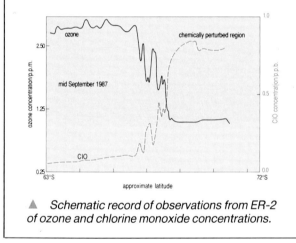

▲ *Schematic record of observations from ER-2 of ozone and chlorine monoxide concentrations.*

▲ *NASA's ER-2 – described as a 'rocket engine with glider wings' – carries instrumentation packed into two wing pods – and a lone pilot.*

What causes the hole?

At the time of writing (mid 1990), the consensus is that a sequence of stages is responsible for the peculiar efficiency with which chlorine destroys ozone over Antarctica.

First, there is the unique meteorology of the polar stratosphere. At the autumn equinox (the end of March), the Sun sets for six months at the south pole, and an area of darkness spreads over the polar cap. It gets very cold. Up in the stratosphere (*not* at ground-level, note), this rapid cooling sets up a pattern of very strong westerly winds that swirl around the pole – the so-called **polar vortex** (Figure 3.17), extending out to around 60°S. This 'structure' is extremely stable: it endures throughout the polar winter, weakens slightly with the return of sunlight in September, but does not finally break down until summer – usually some time in November. An important effect of the vortex is to isolate the air within it. In particular, it effectively blocks the circulation of ozone-rich air from the tropics, preventing it from moving further south than about 60°S for the 'darkside' of the year – the 'resistance' referred to in the caption to Figure 3.12 (Section 4.1). Now refer again to Figure 3.11. These circulation patterns

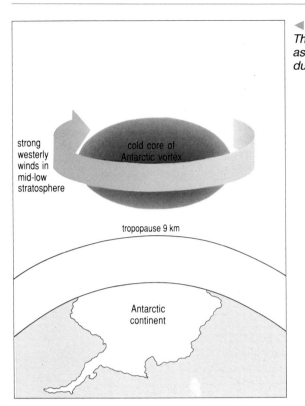

◀   *Figure 3.17*
*The Antarctic vortex forms
as air cools and descends
during the winter months.*

explain – in part, at least – why the amount of ozone *within the vortex* used
to hold steady (at around 300 DU) throughout most of the winter and
spring. Thereafter, the final dispersal of the vortex in early summer
allowed a rapid influx of air from lower latitudes – carrying in 'fresh' ozone
and thus increasing the amount, to some 400 DU. The vital difference –
again given dramatic force by the results from Halley Bay during 1987
(Figure 3.18) – is that now the ozone column is almost constant throughout
the winter, *but falls rapidly in the spring* – usually to less than 200 DU – before
recovering again in the summer.

The second key feature of the polar stratosphere is its odd chemistry.
Once again this stems from the isolation of the Antarctic vortex.
Eventually, its frigid core becomes cold enough (temperatures lower than
-80°C seem to be necessary) for icy particles to form – known as **polar
stratospheric clouds**, or **PSCs**. They have an ethereal beauty (see Plate 6),
but are believed to be deeply implicated in polar ozone loss. Full details of
their role are only now beginning to emerge, but the central point is clear:
they release chlorine from the holding tanks – remember those reservoir
molecules, hydrogen chloride and chlorine nitrate (Section 2.2) – that
normally keep its destructive effects in check. This seems to involve special
reactions that take place on the *surfaces* of the icy particles – 'surface
chemistry'* that converts the long-lived reservoir molecules into
compounds that are rapidly and efficiently broken up by sunlight. This
so-called *pre-conditioning* of the polar stratosphere apparently goes on as
long as PSCs are around. It sets the scene for a burst of active chlorine
radicals (Cl and ClO) *as soon as sunlight returns*. Once liberated, these
appear to engage in several different ozone-destroying catalytic cycles

*Just the same principle underlies
the catalytic converter that you
may have fitted to your car. Here,
the exhaust gases are passed over
a solid that promotes reactions to
give a less noxious spectrum of
products.

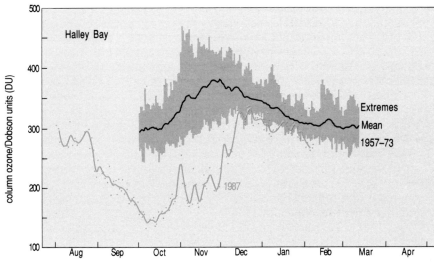

◀ *Figure 3.18*
Up to the mid 1970s,
column ozone values over
Halley Bay remained roughly
constant through to mid
October, before rising with
the influx of warm ozone-
rich air from lower latitudes.
The recent pattern is very
different.

(some of which also involve bromine atoms) – whence the sharp onset of accelerated ozone loss in September seen in Figure 3.18.

Neither the formation of PSCs, nor their role in perturbing the chemistry of the stratosphere was included in the models outlined in Section 4, so their failure to predict the ozone hole is not surprising. Indeed, with the benefit of hindsight, this failure takes on a certain inevitability. A 2–D model *cannot* fully simulate the complex meteorology of the polar vortex. Even a GCM would need to use parametrisation techniques to capture small-scale phenomena like the formation of PSCs. And without clouds in the model stratosphere, there is no a priori reason to invoke surface chemistry.

Activity 4

Look back at the history of ozone depletion over Halley Bay recorded in Figure 3.15. What other features of this record do you think the explanation summarised above needs to address?

You may have noticed several features, but the more prominent ones can, I think, be crystallised into two broad questions:

● Why was there a sudden onset of ozone depletion in the late 1970s?

● What causes the extent of ozone depletion to fluctuate from year to year – particularly marked being the strong swings apparent since the mid-1980s?

To these, I would add a third, related, question:

● What of the future?

The answers to these questions are still far from complete. Thus, it is clear that the late 1970s saw the Antarctic stratosphere cross some critical threshold. Part of this may have been induced by natural changes – in large-scale global circulation patterns, say – coming to favour a stronger, colder polar vortex, well-laced with PSCs. But without the inexorable build-up in anthropogenic emissions, there would have been little chlorine around to take advantage of this change.

This interplay between chemical and dynamic factors must also drive the year-by-year variability of the ozone hole. Thus, there is enough chlorine around already to wipe out virtually *all* the ozone in the Antarctic lower stratosphere (Figure 3.16), but what actually happens in a given year depends on the meteorological conditions that prevail: the stronger the vortex, and the longer its frigid core is maintained *after the return of sunlight*, the deeper and more sustained will be the ozone loss – as in 1987 (Figure 3.18), and again in 1989 and 1990. By contrast, 1988 saw a poorly formed, much distorted vortex that began to dissipate early – and the ozone hole was correspondingly less severe. At present, the detailed mechanisms whereby atmospheric dynamics set up conditions for the chemical depletion of ozone to occur are not well understood. Until they are, of course, it will remain difficult to incorporate these processes into computer models, and hence *predict* the severity and spatial extent of future ozone holes with any confidence – my third question.

Nevertheless, you should be clear that the *potential* for an ozone hole to appear each year will remain until chlorine levels fall below the threshold values achieved in the late 1970s. *Even if no more chlorine compounds are released into the atmosphere this will take many decades*. But whatever the prognosis for the Antarctic ozone hole itself, a broader question arises: can the processes at work there somehow enhance the perceived threat to the ozone shield as a whole?

5.2   Global implications

Q   Where else might you expect to find evidence of accelerated ozone depletion?

A   Above the north pole – the region most like Antarctica as far as climate goes.

An Arctic hole?

In fact the different distribution of land masses and oceans in the Arctic and Antarctica results in the north polar winter stratosphere being generally warmer than its southern counterpart. This has two important consequences. First, PSCs do form over the Arctic, but they are usually less abundant. Second, the circumpolar vortex is weaker, and may be disturbed, or even disrupted, during the winter by warm air pushing in from lower latitudes. As a result, the vortex and the PSCs within it rarely persist until sunlight returns.

Q   Why would this affect the severity of ozone depletion over the Arctic?

A   Substantial ozone depletion requires the PSCs to persist as long as possible *after* the return of sunlight – thereby maintaining the perturbed chemical composition.

At the time of writing, no ozone hole as such had been detected over the north pole in spring. However, there *is* evidence that the chemical composition of the Arctic stratosphere in winter can be as highly perturbed – in association with PSCs – as in Antarctica. So the region is primed for ozone depletion, even if no clear signal of major loss over the pole has so far been identified. The disturbing possibility is that this could be triggered by an unusually prolonged period of very cold winter temperatures – and records suggest that this does occur in some years.

Even without an ozone hole, the preconditioning of the Arctic stratosphere remains a cause for concern. For example, it is possible that the strong weather systems of the northern hemisphere could push the weak northern vortex off the pole – either bodily or in pieces – and out into sunlit regions, late in winter, but before the PSCs within it have evaporated. This could then lead to accelerated ozone loss over regions removed from the pole itself. The idea remains speculative – but it has been raised as one possible explanation for a disturbing report of unexpectedly large ozone depletions at middle and high northern latitudes during winter.

Worldwide ozone trends

In 1986 NASA (in collaboration with other US agencies, the World Meteorological Organisation (WMO) and UNEP) set up an international panel of scientists – the 'Ozone Trends Panel' – charged with a careful re-evaluation of all the available ozone data, from both ground-based and satellite instruments. Their conclusions were made public in March 1988 (shortly before the crucial results from Punta Arenas). Their key finding was that a thorough reassessment of the ground-based data – analysed this time over specified latitude bands and by season, not globally and annually as it had been before – did show statistically significant long-term downward trends. This shift in the way the data were analysed was undoubtedly influenced by the results coming from Antarctica. In brief, the analysis showed decreases in the range of 2.3 to 6.2% between 30°N and 60°N *for the winter months* (December to March) over the period 1969–1986 – the largest losses (some 7%) being in the higher latitude band (53–64°N), but with decreases of around 5% as far south as 40°N.* No significant trends were found for the summer period (May–August). Further reanalyses – including more recent data – have both confirmed the winter trends and suggested that the loss may be accelerating. Moreover, the observed losses – although broadly consistent with the *pattern* of seasonal and latitudinal changes revealed by the 'best' 2-D model calculations – are a factor of two or three times *larger* than the predicted decreases.

Q   Can you suggest why this report – albeit concerned with losses far less dramatic than those over Antarctica – nonetheless added weight to the call for more urgent action on CFCs? (Have a look at an atlas!)

A   To me, the reasons seem twofold. First, north of 40°N takes in most of Europe, the USSR, Canada and large tracts of the USA. Thus, actual ozone loss suddenly loomed large for much of the developed world – with its political structures sensitive to growing public concern about the environment. Second, this further – if less spectacular – evidence for an underestimate in calculated ozone depletion suggested that *extra* ozone-destroying processes may also be at work elsewhere in the stratosphere.

Although air pre-conditioned over the pole may be a factor here, no agreed explanation has yet emerged. Until it does, it remains a disturbing possibility that model calculations will continue to underestimate future ozone losses at all latitudes – and not just in the northern hemisphere. Unusually low levels of ozone have been reported from *mid-latitudes* in the

*The present Dobson network is inadequate to determine ozone trends in the tropics, subtropics or southern hemisphere outside of Antarctica.

southern hemisphere (over Australia and New Zealand, for example) at
various times in the late Austral spring and summer. This is taken as strong
evidence that ozone-poor air is transported away from the pole during the
breakdown of the Antarctic vortex, thus effectively 'diluting' the ozone
column at lower latitudes.

Activity 5

Make a summary of Section 5 for yourself by working through these
three questions:

Q1 Why did it prove so difficult to obtain convincing evidence that
    emissions of CFCs were damaging the ozone layer? How did the
    results from Halley Bay alter this situation?

Q2 Make a list of the key steps believed responsible for the ozone
    hole over Antarctica each springtime. Why does a similar hole not
    appear over the Arctic? (Or strictly, not as of 1990: you may be
    aware of developments since then.)

Q3 Suppose it is late 1996 (it may well be!). You open the paper and
    read: 'Ozone hole on the mend! The ozone loss over Antarctica
    was considerably less this October than it was last year . . .' What
    points would you include in your letter to the editor the next day?

Now try the following question:

Q4 The volcano El Chichón erupted in Mexico in March/April 1982.
    Column ozone fell to record lows at many Dobson stations in
    northern mid-latitudes in late 1982/early 1983. How might these
    observations, taken together, lend support to a suggestion that
    accelerated ozone loss may be caused by a fine mist – or aerosol –
    of sulphuric acid droplets known to pervade the low
    stratosphere? Here, the mechanism again invokes 'surface
    chemistry' in releasing active chlorine from its reservoirs, but on
    the droplets of sulphuric acid this time, not PSCs.

6   *Consequences of ozone depletion*

The most obvious cause for concern about ozone loss stems from its role as
a filter of the Sun's ultraviolet radiation. Figure 3.19 is a repeat of Figure 3.4
(the black curve), but compared this time with the pattern of radiation
received at the Earth's surface (the green curve). Concentrate on the uv
region. Notice that the band labelled *UV-C* (2.0–2.9×10^{-7} m) is virtually
eliminated by the atmosphere. This is just as well, because UV-C is lethal to
micro-organisms (whence its use in germicidal lamps), and can destroy
both nucleic acids and proteins: in the range from 2.4–2.9×10^{-7} m,
protection from UV-C is due entirely to absorption by ozone.

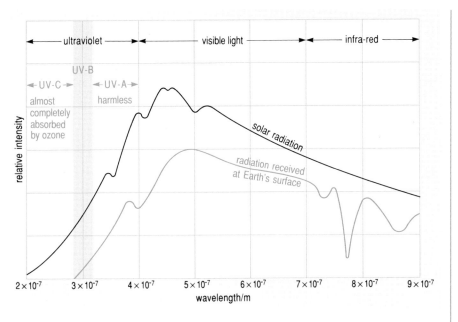

◀ *Figure 3.19*
Incoming solar radiation
(from Figure 3.4) compared
with that received at the
Earth's surface after passing
through the atmosphere.

More important as far as ozone loss is concerned is the band between 2.9×10^{-7} m and 3.2×10^{-7} m – known as **'biologically active' uv** or **UV-B**. Here the *attenuation* of the solar input evident in Figure 3.19 is again due to ozone, but the effect is less complete: a fraction of UV-B penetrates all the way to the ground.* Because of this, the proportion of UV-B reaching the surface should be highly sensitive to changes in the ozone column – *an increase of around 2% for each 1% loss of ozone* being the generally accepted figure. But these are calculated figures, and there is as yet little hard evidence that the real downward trends in ozone noted in the previous section have produced detectable increases in UV-B – with one notable exception: Antarctica in spring. Here, 1988 saw the first measurements of an increase in uv at the surface – radiation levels typical of the summer, but two months early – even though the ozone hole was relatively shallow that year.

UV-B is known to have a multitude of effects on humans, animals, plants and materials. Most of these effects are damaging – but few are sufficiently well understood at present for the impact of enhanced UV-B to be quantified.

6.1   *Human health*

The link between UV-B and the incidence of skin cancer is particularly emotive: here, there are two main strands of evidence. First, skin cancer is predominantly a disease of white-skinned people and the dark pigment – melanin – is known to be an effective filter of UV-B. The second strand comes from *epidemiology* – a study of the factors that influence the occurrence of the disease in human populations. These studies reveal a striking inverse correlation with latitude. Some typical data from North America are shown in Figure 3.20: similar patterns have been found within white populations in the United Kingdom, Norway, Australia and New Zealand.

*Indeed, analysis of UV-B that does penetrate (using Dobson's instrument) is the basis for daily measurements of overhead ozone concentrations from the Dobson network. This is where the 'map' in Figure 3.11 (Section 4.1) came from.

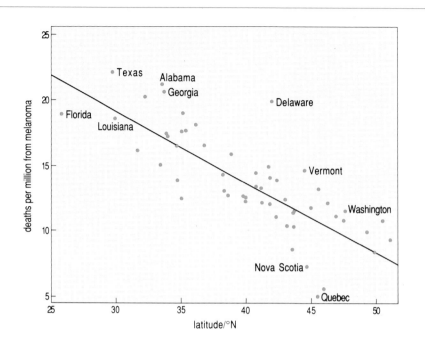

◀   Figure 3.20
The variation with latitude of
human death due to skin
melanoma among white
males in the United States
and Canada. Annual
averages for 1950–67.

Q   Why should this variation with latitude support a link between the incidence of skin cancer and the intensity of UV-B exposure?

A   The intensity of UV-B is greater near the equator, both because the Sun is more nearly overhead, so the radiation has a shorter path through the atmosphere, and because on average less ozone is found there (remember Figure 3.11).

Melanoma – the particular form of skin cancer reported in Figure 3.20 – is actually much rarer than other types (known collectively as *non-melanoma skin cancers*), but it is the most serious – with a substantial mortality rate unless diagnosed early: some 40% of patients die from the disease within 5 years. Incidence of the more common non-melanoma skin cancers is closely correlated with long-term UV-B exposure – occurring predominantly on light-exposed areas of the skin, in the elderly and in those who spend considerable time out-of-doors. These cancers are distressing, but can usually be treated successfully. By contrast, the epidemiology of melanoma is more complex: it affects relatively young people and, unlike other skin cancers, it has been increasing over the last few decades in all white-skinned populations studied. This, and the observed correlation with *indoor* working and social class, have led to the suggestion that melanoma is associated with intermittent, but intense, exposure to UV-B – the sort of exposure associated with sunshine holidays and other recreational activities.

Correlations like that in Figure 3.20 have been used as the basis for estimates of how ozone loss, and the attendant increase in UV-B, may affect rates of skin cancer. Possibly the best current estimate (but one still hedged with uncertainties) comes from the US Environmental Protection Agency (EPA). This suggests that every 1% decrease in column ozone will result in a 3% rise in the incidence of non-melanoma skin cancers – which translates into some 12–15 000 extra cases *a year* in the United States – together with a possible 1% increase in mortality from melanoma. To put

▲   A malignant melanoma
affecting the lower leg.

these figures in context, melanomas now kill an estimated 6000 people a year in the US: non-melanoma cancers – albeit some 20 to 30 times more common – account for roughly the same number of deaths.

Projecting the *global* toll in increased rates of skin cancer is even more problematic, partly because susceptibility to the disease is so dependent on skin type. On top of this, it is possible to take precautions against the adverse effects of uv exposure – and it is difficult to predict how such changes in personal behaviour may influence long-term trends.

Exposure to enhanced levels of UV-B can also have other directly harmful effects on the human body, the two most serious being a tendency to suppress the body's immune responses, and to cause damage to the eyes, especially in the development of cataracts. Although even more difficult to quantify, notice that these effects would touch all populations, with some consequences – possible increases in the incidence or severity of infectious diseases, for example – being particularly severe for people in tropical and subtropical areas.

6.2   *Terrestrial plants*

Plants are adapted to present levels of radiation, but rather little is known about their response to enhanced levels of UV-B. To date, most studies have focused on agricultural crops typical of mid-latitudes. Of the 300 or so species and cultivars screened for tolerance to UV-B, some two-thirds have been found to be sensitive – although the degree of sensitivity varies widely, even among cultivars within a given crop species. Typically, sensitive plants show reduced growth and smaller leaves: unable to photosynthesise as efficiently as other plants, they yield smaller amounts of seeds or fruit. In some cases, these plants also show changes in their chemical composition, which can affect food quality.

The limited data available so far suggest that increased UV-B levels may also affect forest productivity. Potentially more important, it is possible that subtle changes in plant growth induced by UV-B could upset the delicate balance in natural ecosystems – thereby changing the distribution and abundance of plants. Quantifying this effect remains a key area of uncertainty – as indeed do the more direct impacts on food production and forestry.

◄   *Loblolly pine trees irradiated with UV-B simulating 0%, 20% and 40% ozone depletion.*

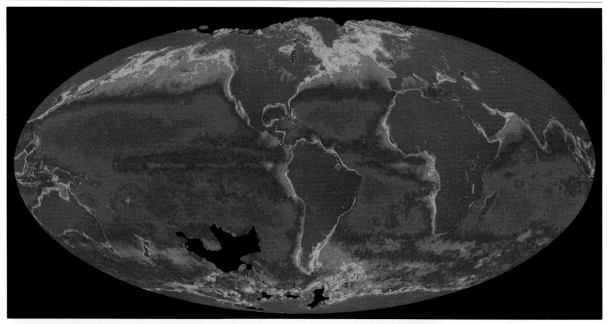

▲ Plate 1
A satellite remote-sensing image of the world ocean, over a period of 18 months. The image has been computer-processed, so the colours are not natural, to show plankton concentrations: yellow and orange areas have the most plankton, purple areas the least. Black indicates an area with not enough data for the image.

◄ Plate 2
A satellite remote-sensing image of the Exxon Valdez oil slick recorded on 7 April 1989, two weeks after the spill. The image has been computer-processed so the colours are not natural: oil shows up as pale green.

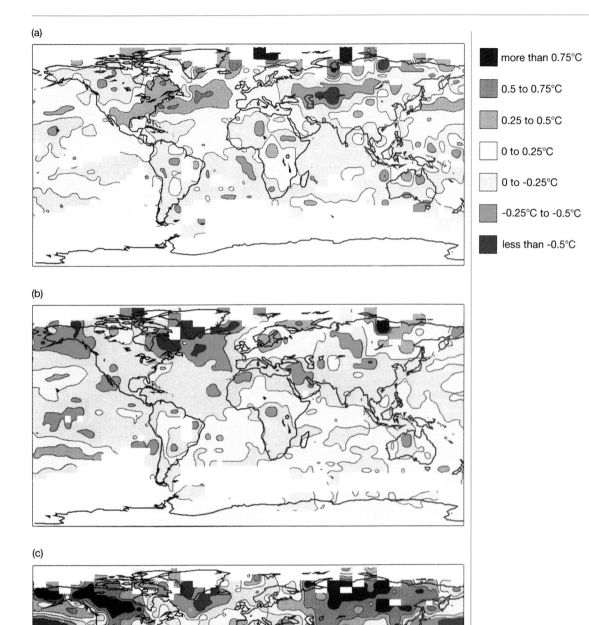

▲ Plate 3 Decadal surface temperature anomalies, relative to 1951–80, i.e. average difference over each decade from the mean value over the full 30-year period: (a) 1950–59, (b) 1967–76, (c) 1980–89. White areas show where there are insufficient data.

(a)

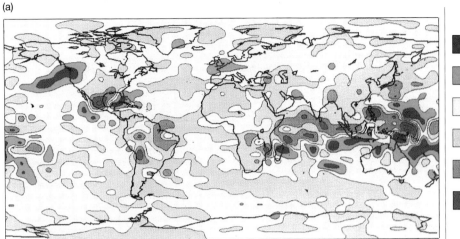

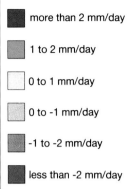

more than 2 mm/day

1 to 2 mm/day

0 to 1 mm/day

0 to -1 mm/day

-1 to -2 mm/day

less than -2 mm/day

(b)

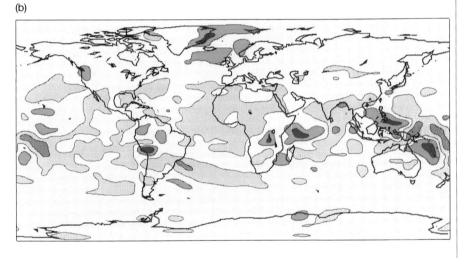

(c)

▲ Plate 4 Change in precipitation (smoothed 10-year means) due to doubling carbon dioxide for months December–January–February, as simulated by three high resolution models: (a) Canadian Climate Centre, (b) the Geophysical Fluids Dynamics Laboratory, and (c) the United Kingdom Meteorological Office.

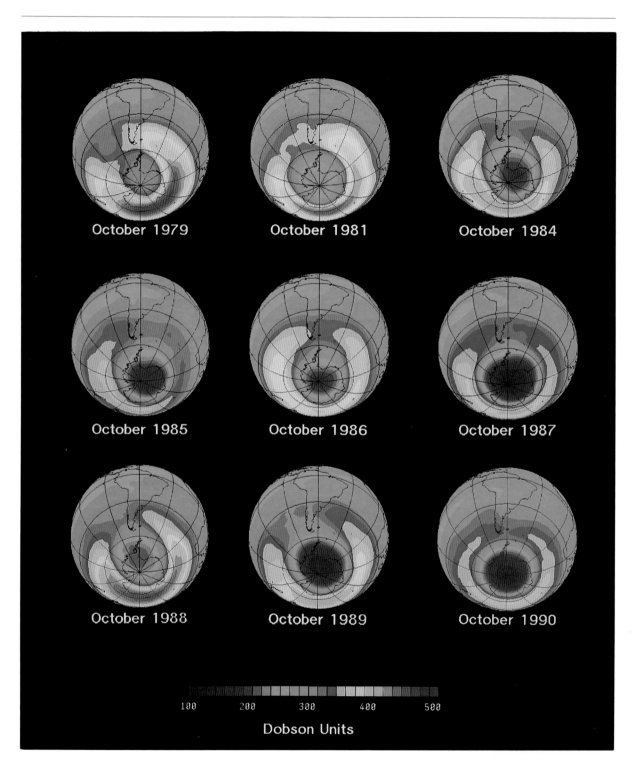

▲ *Plate 5 'Maps' of the ozone column (monthly mean total ozone) over the southern hemisphere for 1979, 1981 and 1984–90, based on data from the Total Ozone Mapping Spectrometer (TOMS) on board NASA's Nimbus 7 satellite. In the ozone 'hole' (purple) over Antarctica, the ozone abundance is roughly half that of a decade ago. This broader view confirms the variability in the degree of ozone depletion apparent in the ground-based data from Halley Bay (Figure 3.15).*

▲ Plate 6
Polar stratospheric clouds seen from the NASA DC-8 aircraft at nearly 39 000 feet in the polar regions north of Stavanger, Norway, during the Airborne Arctic Stratospheric Expedition in January/February of 1989.

◄ Plate 7
Coal waste being dumped into the North Sea from Easington Colliery, County Durham, whilst in the foreground a discharge pipe empties effluent from the mines into the sea. The beach is black with coal waste and the sea discoloured for several miles.

▲ Plate 8
'Coalbrookdale, by night',
Philip James de
Loutherbourg, 1801

◀ Plate 9
A vivid example of
desertification in
Burkina Faso.

◄ *Plate 10*
Smokestack effluent from a lignite (brown coal) power station in Bitterfeld, Germany. Air pollution from the combustion of lignite is a serious health hazard in eastern Germany and other former Soviet bloc countries.

▲ *Plate 11 Foaming effluent on a polluted stream near Zabrze, Poland. Zabrze is one of the towns of the Katowice district of Poland, an area which suffers from some of the worst industrial pollution found anywhere on Earth.*

▲ Plate 12 A 'self-build' biogas maker being filled with its essential fuel,
a mixture of cow dung and water, in Dhanawas village, Haryana State, India.

▲ Plate 13
This 'gasifier' is a good example of 'self-build' intermediate technology at work in Dhanawas village, India.

6.3   Aquatic ecosystems

Life in the oceans is also vulnerable to uv radiation. Although not as important as visible light or temperature or nutrient levels, there is evidence that ambient solar UV-B radiation is nevertheless an important limiting factor in marine ecosystems. The potential impact of any increase in UV-B will depend critically on the depth to which it penetrates – more than 20 m in clear waters, but only some 5 m or so in unclear (silty, say) water. These estimates are crude, because underwater penetration of uv is notoriously difficult to measure, but, if confirmed, they suggest that roughly half of all marine fishes, all nearshore flora and fauna (including coral reefs), and many of the living things in estuaries and lagoons could be at risk. Certainly, enhanced UV-B has been shown to damage a range of small aquatic organisms – zooplankton, larval crabs and shrimp, and juvenile fish – as well as slowing photosynthesis in phytoplankton.

Q   Why should damage to these small organisms be of particular concern?

A   They are at the base of the marine food chain, so any change here – in species composition, say – could have consequences higher up.

As was noted in Chapter 1, in many countries more than 50% of the dietary protein of the human population is obtained from the sea – so once again, the potential exists for a substantial *indirect* effect on human health. As with terrestrial ecosystems, too little is known for predictions of the overall biological consequences of ozone depletion to be made with any degree of confidence. However, there is a more immediate cause for concern – the ozone hole. Although the desolate, ice-covered continent of Antarctica is home to few land plants and animals, the southern oceans are some of the richest ecosystems on Earth – teeming with life that has evolved in the presence of little uv radiation. Some of these organisms – particularly the vital phytoplankton and the krill that feed on them – may be unusually sensitive to sudden increases in uv, especially when this happens just as they are emerging from the winter dark. Several research projects are now in place, but so far there is little consensus about the scale of the threat – with some investigators predicting minor effects, whilst others forecast a disastrous collapse of the entire southern ecosystem.

6.4   Climate

A further area of concern derives from ozone's other major role in the atmosphere. As ozone cycles through its round of creation and destruction, there is an overall absorption of solar radiation, which is ultimately dumped as heat into the stratosphere. This warms the stratosphere and produces the temperature inversion at the tropopause: indeed, there would be no stratosphere without the ozone layer. Thus any depletion of stratospheric ozone is predicted to cool this region, and hence change the temperature structure of the atmosphere to some extent. Furthermore, you know from the previous chapter that ozone also absorbs infra-red radiation, so any redistribution of the gas into the troposphere (as predicted in model calculations like those in Activity 3) will only increase ozone's input to the enhanced greenhouse effect. Since the latter introduces a temperature feedback to the chemical processes that control the ozone budget (Section 4.2), it should be clear that the possibility exists for extremely complex feedbacks between ozone depletion or redistribution and temperature, and hence atmospheric circulation. Once again, then, there is cause for concern, but little hard data. Thus, the upper stratosphere does appear to have cooled by a degree or two over the last decade, but how much of this can be attributed to anthropogenic effects as against natural changes remains unclear.

Added to this, existing GCMs are not yet sufficiently sensitive to incorporate the web of interactions outlined above, and hence predict their effect on climate. This inadequacy is particularly sharp when it comes to assessing the impact of the ozone hole. Here, the possibility certainly exists for a disturbing positive feedback effect.

Q   Can you suggest what this might be?

A   The severe depletion of ozone could cause significant cooling of the polar stratosphere, thus strengthening the polar vortex and increasing the abundance of PSCs – in short, producing conditions that would further enhance the loss of ozone.

There is evidence that the first step in this loop can occur: in 1987, for example, the temperature over Halley Bay at the beginning of December was some 15°C colder than is typical. But existing models cannot assess whether this local cooling could induce more widespread changes in atmospheric circulation – and hence perhaps a progressive strengthening of the vortex over the years.

6.5   Summary of Section 6

Rather little is as yet known about the physical effects or the ecological consequences of changes to the ozone layer. Nevertheless, awareness is growing of the types of damage that might ensue – not just directly to human health, crops and terrestrial and aquatic ecosystems, but also indirectly via possible disturbance to the climate. This, coupled with our lack of knowledge about the scale of the problem, has finally triggered international action to begin the process of healing our ozone shield.

Activity 6

In using epidemiological data to predict changes in the incidence of skin cancer, the argument goes as follows. Skin cancer rates depend strongly on latitude; this latitude dependence is assumed to be due to differences in the intensity of UV-B; thus the change of incidence can be calculated for a given change in UV-B, brought about by a given loss of ozone. During the early debate about CFCs, it was pointed out that there is another way of interpreting the data. This links the incidence of skin cancer *directly* with the fact that the ozone layer varies with latitude (Figure 3.11) – thinning by around 3 DU (i.e. some 1% of the average ozone column) for each 200 miles or so displacement towards the equator. Thus, on this basis, the chances of contracting skin cancer are increased identically by a perturbation producing a 1% depletion in the ozone column, or by moving 200 miles south. How would you respond to this argument?

7   Strategies for protecting the ozone layer: towards the Montreal Protocol – and beyond

The scientific basis for the original Montreal Protocol was the *theoretical* prediction that, should CFC and halon (Activity 2) emissions continue to grow for the next few decades, there would eventually be substantial damage to the ozone layer – essentially the situation outlined at the beginning of Section 5. Here we look at the terms of the Protocol and their shortcomings in the face of evidence that ozone loss has already occurred. But first, a look at the historical background to this seminal international agreement is in order.

7.1   The 'spray-can war' in the United States

The first step toward limiting the release of CFCs into the environment came with unilateral action in the United States. In May 1977 three federal agencies – the EPA, the Food and Drug Administration and the Consumer Product Safety Commission – issued a joint statement that set in train legislation to ban the use of CFCs as propellants in spray-cans by the end of 1978. This action was the culmination of a period of heated scientific and political controversy ignited by Rowland and Molina's initial publication. The debate raged throughout 1975 and into 1976. It focused on the aerosol industry because spray-cans necessarily involve complete release of the propellant gas: at the time, some 75% of CFC emissions worldwide were attributed to this source.

    Throughout this period, industry – both the giant chemical companies (notably Du Pont in the US) that produce CFCs, and the aerosol

**The spray can...
but does it matter?**

◀ *In the early 1980s, many argued that predictions of cancer and 'eco-doom' had probably been exaggerated.*

manufacturers themselves – contended that the 'burden of proof' rested
with the scientists who claimed that CFCs posed a threat. In particular,
they argued that a major industry should not be jeopardised – with the
attendant risks of unemployment and to the economy in general (this was
a period of worldwide economic recession) – on the strength of a
theoretical prediction, hitherto unsupported by observations on the real
atmosphere. Rather they advocated a 'wait and see' approach.

There is force to this argument – essentially a presumption of *'innocent
until proven guilty'*. But there is a counter view, namely that a legitimate
cause for concern about damage to the environment should evoke a verdict
of *'guilty until proven innocent'* – mirroring the principle routinely applied to
new drugs, for example, which are extensively tested for harmful effects
before being released for clinical trials. Of course, this begs the question of
what constitutes 'legitimate cause for concern', and who decides. In the
case of CFCs the issue was further compounded by the unusual stability of
the compounds. Those who argued for an immediate ban stressed that
this, together with the natural variability of the ozone column, meant that
monitoring the atmosphere could not provide an *'early* warning' of ozone
loss. Rather, by the time a clear signal was detected there would already be
enough CFCs effectively 'stored' in the troposphere to keep the damage
going for many decades – even if emissions were then halted at once: just
the circumstances we now find ourselves in.

The propaganda war was played out in the media, and in testimony
before committees of the state and federal legislatures. But in the end, the
US National Academy of Sciences (NAS) was effectively cast as the
'Supreme Court' in this environmental trial. Its report appeared in
September 1976: in brief, it supported the scientific case against CFCs
(confirming a 'legitimate cause for concern'), but stressed the uncertainties
in the calculations and the importance of further research. In policy terms it
recommended that 'non-essential' uses of CFCs should be drastically
curtailed (widely interpreted as a ban on their use in aerosols), unless new
findings emerged within two years to mitigate the threat: in short, a verdict
of 'guilty until proven innocent'.

7.2   *The international dimension: towards Montreal*

When the scare broke in 1974, the US accounted for over 50% of world
usage of CFCs. While acknowledging this position in its support for
unilateral action, the NAS report also stressed the global nature of the
problem, and the importance of encouraging other countries to adopt
similar restrictions. This call went largely unanswered. To take the United
Kingdom as an example, this was not because of any major differences
about the scientific assessment of the problem. On the contrary, a 1976
report from the DoE Central Unit on Environmental Pollution (Pollution
Paper No.5) produced much the same forecast of ozone depletion as its
American counterpart. But the tone of the report was far more cautious,
coming down against the 'need for precipitate action'. This reflected an
attitude prevalent among UK scientists that the United States was
overreacting in the urgency of its response. This, in turn, encouraged a
public debate that had a far more measured tone, and generally lower
profile, than that in the US.

The debate and the control strategy adopted by the US had its effect:
worldwide production of CFCs fell from the peak levels recorded in 1974,
and continued to decline throughout the late 1970s. This period also saw

further massive research programmes on both sides of the Atlantic. Once again the vehicle for providing policy-makers with a scientific assessment of the problem can be characterised as the 'expert committee' – under the auspices of the NAS (and later NASA) in the US, for example, and the DoE and Meteorological Office in the UK. Further parallel reports appeared in late 1979 – again reaching broadly similar scientific conclusions. But, equally, the disagreement about what action should be taken was again apparent.

The policy of 'cautious inaction' advocated in the UK report was broadly in line with the EC approach. Here a precautionary policy, amounting to a *voluntary* agreement to limit CFC production (but at a level allowing significant expansion), was about to be adopted. By contrast, the US report called for an urgent global ban on aerosol usage. It also pointed to the alarming growth in other uses of CFCs – a pattern that was to reverse the downward trend in worldwide production after 1982 (Figure 3.21). The US report prompted a further attempt at unilateral action by the EPA. But these were the last months of the Carter Administration, and the political climate in the US was about to take a sharp turn against the environmental lobby. This not only blocked the EPA's proposals, but also sought to prevent the agency from taking any further precautionary action in the absence of *international* agreement that it was necessary.

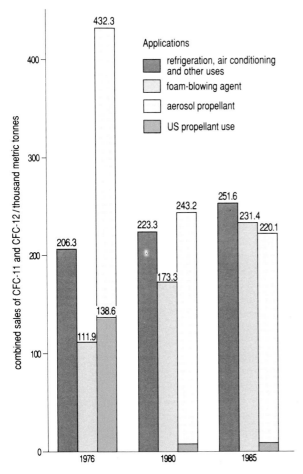

Figure 3.21
Estimates show how the decline in aerosol use of CFCs has been offset by increased demand in other sectors.

(Based on data supplied by CFC manufacturers to the Chemical Manufacturers Association, which do not reflect usage in the USSR, eastern Europe or China.)

The first steps toward achieving such an agreement were taken in 1981. Since 1977 UNEP had continued to issue regular bulletins which reviewed current research and forecasts of ozone layer depletion. In May 1981 it set up a working group of legal and technical experts charged with drawing up a draft 'Convention for the Protection of the Ozone Layer'. After long and difficult negotiations, this led to the **Vienna Convention**, signed by 20 nations in March 1985; it came into force in September 1988.

Take another look at Figure 3.13 (in Section 4.2). Given the ever more gloomy forecasts of the late 1970s, it is ironic that the negotiations for this convention took place during a period when this pattern of prediction was reversed.

Q   To what do you attribute the trend to *lower* estimates of ozone loss? (Refer back to Section 4.2 and Activity 3.)

A   In large part, to the growing understanding that emissions of other trace gases (notably methane and carbon dioxide) mitigate the effect of CFCs on the *total* ozone column.

Of course, as you have seen, the global figures mask an undesirable redistribution of ozone. But these forecasts – and more importantly, their downward trend – featured prominently in press reports during the early 1980s. Given this perception of a reducing threat, a major row between the US and the EC that erupted early in 1985 (each effectively wanting its own preferred control strategy incorporated in the UN code) and the timing (*before* news of the ozone hole first appeared), it is not surprising that the Convention is a somewhat anodyne document. It declared the signatories' determination 'to protect human health and the environment against adverse effects resulting from modifications to the ozone layer', and provided, *inter alia*, for the exchange of information and scientific data relevant to this determination. But, it had no regulatory powers at all – although it did provide for protocols to be adopted later.

7.3   *The Montreal Protocol*

The Protocol was agreed on 16 September 1987 and came into force on 1 January 1989, having been ratified by the required 11 countries representing two-thirds of global consumption. As originally agreed, it provided for a staged control of five CFCs (those listed in Table 3.2 in Section 3.1) and three halons (organic compounds containing bromine atoms, Activity 2). The overall effect would be to freeze consumption of the halons at 1986 levels in 1992, but to cut consumption of the CFCs to 50% of 1986 levels by the year 2000. *Production* of the CFCs was subject to less severe cutbacks, the intention here being to provide a surplus to meet the growing domestic needs of developing countries that became parties to the Protocol. Most such countries – notably China and India – were not represented at the negotiations. This provision – together with an Article exempting developing countries from controls on consumption for 10 years – was designed to encourage their participation in the Protocol, while discouraging the proliferation of CFC production capacity around the world.

The terms of the Protocol were an inevitable compromise between the conflicting national interests of the countries involved. Negotiations for a protocol began in earnest at the end of 1986 – a time, note, when the Antarctic hole had again heightened fears about the ozone layer, but no

hard evidence had yet emerged linking this phenomenon with chlorine chemistry. Straight away, the old split reappeared between the US (now backed by the Scandinavian countries) and the EC (and Japan). In fact, the US had hardened its stance, going into the negotiations with a call for immediate cuts in production, as part of a longer-term strategy leading to a virtual phase-out of CFCs. This position was later softened, not least as a result of infighting within the Reagan Administration. But at the time the strategy was resisted by several European countries; even here, the UK looked increasingly isolated from its Community partners – initially refusing to countenance any cuts at all.

By May 1987 a measure of compromise had been achieved – sufficient to allow a draft protocol to be drawn up. The terms were broadly similar to (if somewhat stronger than) those eventually agreed – but at the time, further progress seemed unlikely. Here, the UK position was crucial, with the prospect of its veto within the EC blocking approval of the second round of cuts.

Britain's retreat from this position came in August 1987. This U-turn has been characterised as a somewhat cynical move by the UK government, aimed at softening Britain's deservedly poor image on environmental issues but at virtually no cost to itself. Indeed, over 50% of the UK market for CFCs then went into aerosols, so major cuts in consumption could be achieved by the simple – and comparatively cheap – expedient of phasing out this usage. In addition, ICI – by far the major UK producer of CFCs – shifted its ground at this time, coming out publicly in favour of substantial cutbacks, provided the timetable was not too tight. An important factor here was undoubtedly the recognition that a schedule to phase out CFCs *worldwide* would provide an equal opportunity for companies to market substitute chemicals – newly developed compounds, production of which would be protected by patents (unlike the long established CFCs) and thus potentially highly profitable. Alongside these factors, a sustained campaign by environmental pressure groups, together with a hardening of attitudes among UK scientists, undoubtedly played their part.

With further compromises, the terms outlined earlier were finally agreed – but the *timing* of this agreement was extraordinary! Just two weeks later, the first results started coming in from Punta Arenas. The enormity of what is happening over Antarctica, together with the publication of the 'Ozone Trends' report in March 1988, prompted media coverage and public debate throughout 1988 and early 1989 – at a level to rival that of the mid 1970s in the US. Only this time, there was little controversy, public concern and action (in boycotting aerosols in the UK, for example) being matched at last by political will – culminating in a

◀   *Mostafa K. Tolba,*
Executive Director of UNEP,
addressing the Helsinki
Meeting in April 1989 . . .

◀   *. . . while, outside,*
Greenpeace broadcast its
message. Many
environmental pressure
groups argued for stronger
controls than those
eventually agreed in London
in 1990.

decisive shift in the international atmosphere behind much tighter controls. In the UK the most prominent feature of this period was the so-called 'Thatcher Conference' in London in March 1989 – actually hosted jointly by UNEP and the UK government. Public declarations apart, the real business had already started, was moved on two months later in Helsinki, and came to fruition in London in June 1990.

7.4   Beyond Montreal

A crucial feature of the Montreal Protocol is Article 6, which provides for a periodic review of its control measures 'on the basis of available scientific, environmental, technical and economic information'. The first such review took place in June 1990. It produced agreement to a strengthened set of controls that cover not only the original CFCs and halons, but also carbon tetrachloride and methyl chloroform (a situation that was foreshadowed in Section 3.1). At the time of writing, then, the terms are as follows (cuts generally refer to 1986 levels of consumption):*

● CFCs to be phased out by the year 2000, with cuts of 50% by 1995 and 85% by 1997

● halons to be phased out by 2000, with a 50% cut by 1995

● carbon tetrachloride to be phased out by 2000, with a cut of 85% by 1995

● methyl chloroform to be phased out by 2005, with a cut to 30% of 1990 levels by 2000.

The scientific input to this revised Protocol effectively shifted the focus of concern about ozone away from the long-lived CFCs and onto the short-lived compounds being developed to replace them. It seems appropriate to close this chapter with a brief look at this 'live' issue for the 1990s and at the other vital aspect of the negotiations in London: the financial mechanism designed to draw major developing countries – notably India and China – into a truly global agreement.

The role of 'transitional' substances

The scientific assessment for the 1990 review acknowledged the failings of existing computer models, and did not attempt to forecast future ozone losses in detail. Instead, it took the central problem to be the bleak prognosis for Antarctic ozone – and quite possibly for Arctic ozone as well – unless the total chlorine (and bromine) loadings of the atmosphere are first stabilised, and then progressively reduced toward the levels (estimated at some 1.5–2 p.p.b. for chlorine) associated with the first appearance of the ozone hole. Calculated projections of future chlorine loadings were used to identify the control strategies needed to achieve this objective within the foreseeable future: representative examples are included in Figure 3.22.

On this basis, the phase-out of *all* long-lived compounds and methyl chloroform agreed in 1990 should achieve a striking reduction in the

*There are some exceptions. CFCs and halons can still be used for essential medical applications where safe alternatives are unavailable (e.g. inhalant drugs). Halons can be used for firefighting in certain sensitive situations (e.g. in aircraft).

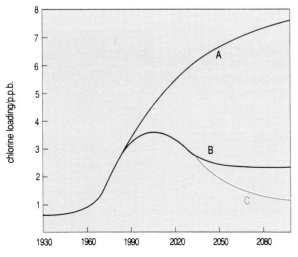

◄   Figure 3.22
Projections of future chlorine loadings of the atmosphere for different control strategies:

A and B – original and revised (1990) Protocol, respectively, both with 50% substitution of CFC markets by HCFCs.

C – total cessation of all anthropogenic emissions of chlorine compounds in 2030.

atmospheric abundance of chlorine (curve B) – especially when compared with the projected impact of the original Protocol (curve A). But even if all nations comply with the revised terms (as assumed in making these projections), notice that the chlorine loading is still predicted to be around 3 p.p.b. by the middle of the next century, thus committing the world to a seasonal recurrence of the Antarctic ozone hole for many decades to come. Yet stronger measures are needed to begin to reverse this pattern.

Here, the underlying problem was again foreshadowed earlier. Many of the compounds being developed as CFC substitutes are chemically very similar to the substances they will replace. In particular, the **hydrochlorofluorocarbons (HCFCs)** still contain chlorine (as well as carbon and fluorine), but the hydrogen in the molecule reduces the atmospheric lifetime, as it does in methyl chloroform (recall that a typical example, HCFC-22, was included in Table 3.2 in Section 3.1). Nevertheless, these shorter-lived compounds are capable of carrying chlorine into the stratosphere – just like the natural source gas, chloromethane – so some account must be taken of their contribution to the total chlorine loading. Curves A and B in Figure 3.22 do this in a fairly crude way by assuming that HCFCs (represented by HCFC-22 for simplicity) capture 50% of the CFC market and that all of their chlorine is 'available' for ozone destruction (an overestimate). Whatever the details, a comparison between these projections and the green curve in Figure 3.22 certainly adds force to the argument that emissions of HCFCs should also be subject to tight controls – and the sooner, the better. Particularly telling here is the rapid recovery of chlorine levels toward the desired 2 p.p.b. 'threshold' once these short-lived compounds are themselves banned.

Moves to extend the Protocol to cover HCFCs proved unsuccessful in 1990 – not least because of warning noises from the chemical industry that this could make investment in their production difficult. But the parties did approve a declaration that characterised HCFCs as *'transitional' substances*, and called for their 'prudent and responsible' use, prior to their phasing out between 2020 and 2040. An agreement along these lines should be incorporated into the Protocol at the next review due in 1992.

Q   Do the **hydrofluorocarbons (HFCs)** present a similar problem to the HCFCs? Note that HFC-134a (see Activity 2, Section 3.2) is a typical example.

A   No, as the name suggests, HFCs contain neither chlorine nor bromine – implying an ODP of zero, like HFC-134a.

It is important that concern about substitute compounds should not be allowed to delay the rapid abandonment of CFC-based technologies. On the other hand, at the time of writing the newly-developed chemicals – be they HCFCs or HFCs – are still being tested for their toxicity and broader environmental impact, including any potential contribution to global warming (some *are* potent greenhouse gases) – and, indeed, to tropospheric pollution as well. Hopefully, concern about *all* these compounds – short- and long-lived alike – will fuel the adoption of 'containment' strategies in all sectors of the industry, and thereby cut *emissions* to the atmosphere. In the 'coolant' industry (refrigeration, air conditioning and so on), for example, this means containing the CFCs – *or their substitutes* – within the equipment during its lifetime (by regular maintenance and repair to prevent leakage), and then capturing and recycling or safely destroying the chemicals when it is finally scrapped.

OBSERVER David Austin

AND, FOR YOUR POLAR PROTECTION, IT IS ENTIRELY CFC- FREE!

One further issue for the 1990s is the extent to which all major sectors need, in fact, be dependent on new chemicals with properties closely matched to those of the original CFCs. The issue is important, because it touches on the crucial question of how much it will cost to implement the Protocol worldwide. HCFCs and HFCs are more complex and difficult to make than the CFCs: they will be patented, and will be more expensive – perhaps 2 to 5 times the price on current estimates.

Economic implications: the funding mechanism

Many factors contribute to the 'incremental costs' associated with phasing out old CFC technologies. Such costs will vary widely from country to country – depending on differences in national development, on the scale of CFC and halon producing and using industries, and so on. Whatever the differences between individual nations, however, a broad distinction can be drawn between the developed world and the developing countries.

At present North America, Europe and Japan together account for some 80% of the total consumption of the controlled chemicals – a pattern that reflects the historical usage. Thus, prime responsibility for existing ozone depletion clearly rests with the developed world. On the other hand, improvements in living standards in many developing countries include plans that could easily change this pattern. Here, refrigeration is the largest and fastest-growing application of CFCs – just the sector that is currently assumed to be totally dependent on the new, more expensive chemicals.* Because of this, all economic assessments to date show that refrigeration will account for a major fraction of the incremental costs for most developing countries – with some estimates as high as 90% of the total.

Estimates like this were central to the negotiations in London in 1990. Out of that debate came a major advance – agreement to a financial mechanism under which developed countries will meet the incremental costs that developing countries incur in complying with the Protocol. This is intended to cover all aspects of the process of technology transfer, including access to the necessary technical expertise, patents, training and so on, as well as the direct costs of converting existing production facilities or of establishing new ones, or of simply importing CFC substitutes. The heart of the mechanism is a special 'multilateral fund' – set at an interim level of $240 million for the first three years – to be financed by contributions from developed countries (probably on the basis of an agreed UN scale of assessments). The fund is overseen by a committee made up of representatives drawn in equal part from the developed and developing world – but no permanent membership (despite claims to that effect by the US on the strength of its 25% contribution to the fund). With this agreement has come the crucial participation of both India and China.

Activity 7

Make a summary of Section 7 for yourself by noting down the key stages in achieving international agreement to phase out CFCs. To what extent were decisions taken at each stage influenced by evidence of damage to the ozone layer? What other influences were at work?

*In fact, alternative technologies do exist that can use far cheaper chemicals, like propane – or even water – as coolants. This is an area worth watching.

8   Conclusion

As of June 1990, it seems certain that release of all long-lived chlorine compounds should cease by the year 2000, a quarter of a century after the alarm was first raised. That same period will have seen a major shift in international attitudes to global environmental problems – a shift in which some would claim that the ozone hole over Antarctica has played no small part. Certainly, it is shocking to recognise that damage to this remote and pristine environment could be caused by such everyday activities as getting rid of an old fridge, or using an underarm deodorant. And once the link was established, the international community *appeared* to react quickly and decisively – as did the public at large. But had it actually waited too long?

There is no simple answer. However, the long debate about CFCs – marked by calls for a better scientific understanding of the problem, more accurate forecasts of long-term ozone depletion, and so on – surely carries an important message when set against the sudden and wholly unexpected loss that did occur. The atmosphere is a complex and finely-balanced system. Tamper with it, and it may respond in a gradual and more-or-less predictable way. Or it may not. Under these circumstances, the notion of 'scientific certainty' takes on a different cast – especially when a built-in time-delay means that the problem, once manifest, is not easily reversed.

Clearly, these points apply with equal – or greater – force to the problem of global warming and climate change. Here, much remains to be understood. Nevertheless, a consensus is growing that the time for 'cautious inaction' is past. And there is an important precedent in the Vienna Convention: there, for the first time, nations agreed in principle to tackle a global environmental problem *before* its effects were felt, or even scientifically proven. Hopefully, the international cooperation manifest in then agreeing to phase out CFCs will spill over into the debate about global warming – but the measures required are likely to prove a lot more costly, and more difficult to orchestrate, as you will see in the next chapter.

References

MOLINA, M.J. and ROWLAND, F.S. (1974) 'Stratospheric sink for chlorofluoromethanes: chlorine atom-catalysed destruction of ozone', *Nature*, Vol. 249, pp. 810–12.

REDDISH, A. and RAND, M. (1991) 'The environmental effects of present energy policies', Ch. 4 in Blunden, J. and Reddish, A. (eds) *Energy, Resources and Environment*, London, Hodder and Stoughton/The Open University (Book Three in this series).

SILVERTOWN, J. (1990) 'Earth as an environment for life', Ch. 2 in Silvertown, J. and Sarre, P. (eds) *Environment and Society*, London, Hodder and Stoughton/The Open University (Book One in this series).

SORG (1988) *Stratospheric Ozone 1988, Second Report*, London, HMSO.

Further reading

Two very readable books on this subject are:

DOTTO, L. and SHIFF, H. (1978) *The Ozone War*, New York, Doubleday.

GRIBBIN, J. (1988) *The Hole in the Sky*, New York, Bantam.

Rather more technical, though still fairly accessible to non-specialists, is a series of reports produced by the UK Stratospheric Ozone Review Group, all published by HMSO.

- *Stratospheric Ozone 1987, First Report*
- *Stratospheric Ozone 1988, Second Report*
- *Stratospheric Ozone 1990*

UNEP has also produced a short account of its role in achieving the phase-out of CFCs:

UNEP (1989) *Action on Ozone.*

The following book gives an excellent survey of the background and significance of the Montreal Protocol, by the chief US negotiator:

BENEDICK, R.E. (1991) *Ozone Diplomacy: new directions in safeguarding the planet*, Cambridge, Mass., Harvard University Press.

Authoritative updates on the status of polar ozone and worldwide trends, and on further revisions to the Protocol will appear in *New Scientist.*

Answers to Activities

Activity 1

The desired effect is achieved if hydrogen (H) first attacks ozone (O_3), forming the hydroxyl radical (OH), and then this collides with another oxygen atom (O) – freeing the hydrogen for further destruction. In symbols:

$$O_3 + H \rightarrow O_2 + OH$$
$$O + OH \rightarrow O_2 + H$$

Activity 2

Q1 (a) Since SSTs fly within the stratosphere (Section 1), nitric oxide from their engines would be expected to add to the normal stratospheric burden of NO – and hence enhance ozone destruction via the catalytic cycle in equations 2 and 3.

(b) To be a problem, some of the NO produced at ground-level would have to be carried up into the stratosphere. But NO is a very reactive molecule (as suggested by its role in the catalytic cycle) – with a very short lifetime in the troposphere. In fact, this reactivity makes NO a pollutant of the *lower* (rather than upper) atmosphere, its presence in vehicle exhausts etc. leading to nitric acid (a component of acid rain – *Reddish and Rand* (1991)) and photochemical smog.

Q2 The ODP of zero must mean that the molecule (as suggested by its name) does not carry ozone-destroying catalytic species – notably chlorine and bromine – into the stratosphere. (See also Section 7.4.)

Q3 From the cycles in the text and in Section 3.2, the following would be a good guess:

$$O_3 + Br \rightarrow O_2 + BrO$$
$$O + BrO \rightarrow O_2 + Br$$

Note: BrO or OBr are equally acceptable.

Q4 Of the compounds listed in Table 3.2, halon-1301 has an atmospheric lifetime comparable with those of CFC-12 and CFC-113. Each of these carries more than one Cl atom per molecule, yet rates an ODP little different from 1.0. By contrast, the halon has an ODP of 12.3, but carries only a single Br atom. This suggests that Br atoms must be more efficient at destroying ozone than are Cl atoms. Other evidence confirms this.

Activity 3

(a) (i)   If the different families did *not* interact, then the column ozone change in a given multiple perturbation should be just the *sum* of the changes produced by the appropriate collection of single perturbations. For example, from the left-hand column of Table 3.3, the package: 'increase total Cl to 8 p.p.b., *and* N_2O by 20%, *and* double CH_4' should produce a change of:

$$(-5.7 - 1.7 + 2.9)\% = -4.5\%, \text{ that is an ozone loss of } 4.5\%.$$

But the actual loss when this multiple perturbation is run is less than this – just 2.8%. In fact, both the nitrogen and hydrogen families interfere with the chlorine family, due, in part at least, to formation of the reservoir molecules – chlorine nitrate and hydrogen chloride.

(ii) The effect of temperature feedback can be seen by comparing the two multiple perturbations in the right-hand column. Here the only difference is the amount of carbon dioxide – and the only effect that it has is to change the temperatures of troposphere and stratosphere.

(b) I would make the following points:

●   These results come from one study – using a particular 1-D model, together with a set of assumptions, both about the unperturbed atmosphere and about the future emissions of source gases. All of these features would need to be spelt out in detail – and their validity assessed – if such a study were to form the basis for policy-making. In this context, predicting emissions of CH_4, N_2O and CO_2 are still subject to large uncertainties.

●   Emissions of CH_4 and CO_2 only mitigate the effects of CFCs on the *total* ozone column: a substantial *redistribution* of ozone is still predicted to occur – the likely effects of which are taken up in Section 6. However, enhanced ozone-production in the troposphere (Figure 3.14c) is certainly undesirable.

● *All* of the source gases are also greenhouse gases: a strategy to protect ozone based on *necessary* continued and growing emissions of all these gases would be madness!

Activity 4

(See the main text.)

Activity 5

Q1 The central problem was the natural variability of the ozone column which meant that long-term monitoring was required in order to detect the small, but statistically significant, downward trend in ozone levels that CFC emissions were *expected* (on the basis of model forecasts) to cause worldwide. By contrast, the results from Halley Bay were quite unequivocal – with ozone concentrations well outside the range previously recorded (Figures 3.15 and 18). Their impact was twofold. First, they generated widespread concern – sufficient to support the crucial international campaign (Box 3.1) that furnished proof of a link with CFCs. Second, they shaped the re-analysis of existing long-term data records by the Ozone Trends Panel.

Q2 There are two key ingredients:

● First, the unique meteorology of the Antarctic stratosphere. The loss of sunlight leads to strong cooling, which in turn produces the polar vortex – a sort of containment vessel that both isolates and cools the air within it. At temperatures below about -80°C, icy particles – polar stratospheric clouds (PSCs) – can form.

● Second, the special chemistry that takes place on the surface of the PSCs. This releases chlorine from its 'inactive' reservoir molecules into a form ready to produce a burst of active radicals once sunlight returns – whence the rapid and deep ozone depletion in early spring.

● The hole is 'healed' each summer by the influx of warm, ozone-rich air from lower latitudes once the polar vortex dissipates.

The lack (so far) of a northern hole is mainly attributed to the winter stratosphere usually being warmer over the Arctic – so producing a weaker vortex, that is generally disrupted before sunlight returns. However, the region is pre-conditioned for ozone depletion: dispersal of this air may contribute to the unexpectedly large ozone losses observed over high northern latitudes in winter.

Q3 You may want to fill in some of the background outlined under Q2, but the crucial point to stress is the interplay between chemical and dynamic factors that drives the year-by-year variability of the ozone hole. You should cite the fluctuations apparent in the late 1980s (and any subsequent records) to support your case.

Q4 The timing suggests a link – but is not proof of one, nor that any link is necessarily causal. However, El Chichón did inject large amounts of sulphur dioxide into the low stratosphere – and sulphur dioxide is the main precursor of sulphuric acid in the atmosphere, so the eruption should have added to the normal aerosol level: there is evidence that it did. If droplets of sulphuric acid can act in a similar way to PSCs (and laboratory measurements suggest they can), then this could provide a mechanism leading to enhanced ozone depletion at any latitude.

Activity 6

The argument seeks (quite deliberately at the time it was propounded) to obscure the crucial distinction between changes in the ozone column *averaged over the entire Earth* (as predicted by a given 1-D model calculation, say) – and *natural variations* – here with latitude, but equally well from month-to-month, or year-to-year, at a given location. Hopefully, you spotted the analogy with temperature changes – raised in Chapter 2. Thus for example, a drop of some 3°C in the global average temperature would plunge the Earth back into a glacial period. But changes of this magnitude from day-to-night, or day-to-day, are commonplace – as are similar differences in the average annual temperature between one place and another, each deemed to be habitable.

　　To return to the ozone problem – a 1% depletion over the entire globe means that *everywhere* would be subjected to higher levels of uv-radiation. The link with skin cancer would then predict an increase in such cancers unless *everyone* (or at least all the white-skinned people) moved to higher latitudes (thereby effectively cancelling the change) – or took other precautionary action.

　　Note that to concentrate on skin cancer also ignores all the other possible consequences of enhanced uv – to human health, but also to crops, and terrestrial and aquatic ecosystems, which cannot so easily be shifted around. Here, overall ozone depletion superimposed on the natural variations could expose organisms to levels of UV-B higher than ever before experienced – a situation that already appears to be occurring in springtime in the oceans around Antarctica.

Activity 7

In brief, the chronology is as follows:

1974　Molina and Rowland publication.

1978　US bans use of CFCs as propellants.

1979　EC adopts precautionary policy – voluntary agreement to limit CFC production.

1981　UNEP sets up working group to draft a framework convention for the protection of the ozone layer.

1985　Vienna Convention signed.

1987　Montreal Protocol agreed.

1990　Revised Protocol with phase-out by 2000.

Only the final stages of this process were influenced by direct evidence of ozone loss – following news of the ozone hole (May 1985) and its subsequent deepening (especially in 1987), and publication of the *Ozone Trends* Report (1988).

To me, the major influences at work throughout the process appear to have been:

●　The scientific assessment of the scale of the problem and the urgency of doing something about it – and hence the attitude of the scientific community.

●　The industry – both directly (for example, during the 'spray-can war' in the US), and through its influence on policy-making both nationally and internationally (as in, for example, input to the technical and economic assessments that underpin reviews of the Protocol).

- Environmental agencies (e.g. the EPA in the US) and pressure groups (e.g. Greenpeace, FoE etc).

- Governments' policy-making processes, including the reassessment of national interest (as in, for example, the UK U-turn in the negotiations for Montreal, the recent participation of India and China, and so on).

- International organisations, notably UNEP – in placing the issue on the international agenda, and keeping it there (especially during the early 1980s), and achieving cooperation between developed and developing countries.

- The media and public education, especially during the mid 1970s in the US (but not in the UK!) and then again, worldwide, in 1988/89.

- The growing power of consumer pressure, for example in boycotting aerosols, support for local recycling schemes and so on.

1   Introduction

It took a long time for the risk of global warming to be established as an important issue on the international political agenda. It was in 1896 that the scientist Arrhenius first suggested that carbon dioxide emissions associated with industrial production might lead to an increase in average global temperatures. Yet it wasn't until 1979 that the First World Climate Conference, where government representatives and scientists discussed the risks of climate change due to human activities, was held.

The global climate monitoring and large-scale development of climate models necessary for a serious scientific assessment of such risks only really got under way in the early 1960s. However, as discussed in Chapter 2, by the late 1980s a scientific consensus had emerged that 'greenhouse gas' emissions may already have increased global temperatures by 0.3 to 0.6°C and, if existing trends continued, would probably further increase these temperatures by 3°C or more over the next century. Such warming would lead to enormous human, ecological and economic costs, raising the question of how global warming could be prevented or limited. On the basis of the accumulating scientific evidence, scientists and environmental pressure groups became increasingly active in their attempts to promote a wide debate about how to prevent global warming.

However, as with the problem of stratospheric ozone depletion discussed in Chapter 3, it took more than the steady accumulation of scientific evidence to force the risks of global warming to international attention. Unfortunately, there was no direct equivalent for global warming of the dramatic discovery of the 'ozone hole' over the Antarctic. The fact that seven of the ten years in the 1980s were amongst the warmest since records began, and that there were unexpected droughts in the United States and severe storms around the world in 1988, lent warnings about global warming a popular credibility that they had previously lacked. But these events could have been a consequence of the natural variability of the climate. Reliable empirical indications of global warming are not likely to be apparent until the late 1990s at the earliest.

The risks of delaying preventive action until then are extreme. Thus many scientists were grateful that the droughts, storms and heatwaves generated attention for the more substantial scientific evidence of climate change. Those promoting international action took the opportunity to encourage governments to give the problem serious attention, and prayed that a few cool summers in the early 1990s would not result in renewed public complacency.

As usual, inevitable scientific uncertainties about the effects of greenhouse gas emissions on the global climate have been used as an argument for delaying preventive measures. However, in a way the uncertainties have also helped to promote international consensus. If the likely effects on regional climates were more definite, any regions that expected to benefit from the changes might be inclined to obstruct preventive action. As it is, although some regions would be more vulnerable to the effects of global warming than others, all are faced with a real risk of catastrophe.

Thus at an international conference in Toronto in 1988 to discuss climate change, involving representatives and scientists from 48 states, there was a remarkable consensus about the scale of the risks of global warming. The agreed statement called upon all governments to meet an initial target of 20% reductions in global carbon dioxide emissions by the year 2005, as a prelude to further reductions in greenhouse gas emissions in the twenty-first century.

After the Toronto conference, the Intergovernmental Panel on Climate Change (IPCC), convened under the auspices of the World Meteorological Organisation (WMO) and the United Nations Environment Programme (UNEP), were given the task of coordinating preparatory work for an international response to the threat of global warming. Three subcommittees prepared reports on: the science of global warming; its potential social, economic and ecological impacts; and possible policy responses. These IPCC reports provided an essential basis for the Second World Climate Conference held in Geneva in November 1990.

At the end of this Geneva conference, 137 countries formally agreed that the risk of global warming was sufficiently well-established scientifically to justify an urgent international response to the problem. The Ministerial Declaration from the conference stated:

> We agree that the ultimate global objective should be to stabilize greenhouse gas concentrations at a level that would prevent dangerous anthropogenic interference with climate . . . We stress, as a first step, the need to stabilize, while ensuring sustainable development of the world economy, emissions of greenhouse gases.   (7 November 1990)

At the conference Japan, Canada, Australia, New Zealand, the European Community and six other west European states made unilateral commitments to stabilise or reduce greenhouse gas emissions by the end of the century. Negotiations for a global response to the risk of global warming began in February 1991, with the aim of preparing an agreement for signing in Rio de Janeiro in 1992 at the United Nations Conference on Environment and Development.

Thus international discussions on policy responses to global warming focused on *preventive* measures, rather than *adaptation* or *technical fixes*, in the terms introduced in the final section of Chapter 2. In view of the potentially devastating impacts of global warming, this focus is very welcome. In practice, however, the pressures to opt instead for delay and piecemeal adaptation will remain powerful for the foreseeable future. Note, for example, that the 1988 Toronto initial target of 20% *reductions* in greenhouse gas emissions by the year 2005 was watered down at the 1990 Geneva conference to the aim of *stabilising* global emissions at 1990 levels over a similar but vaguer timescale. As we shall see, effective preventive action would require social and economic reforms and international co-operation on an unprecedented scale. Unfortunately, governments and peoples tend to be more influenced by short-term interests than by the uncertain requirements of long-term planning. Nevertheless growing awareness of environmental issues, and developing international co-operation in tackling them (for example, in agreeing to phase out CFC production), give some grounds for optimism.

This chapter aims to examine what could be done to limit or prevent global warming, and to explore the prospects for, and obstacles to, gaining agreement on substantial international responses. It can only aim to be introductory. The issues are complex. In any case, the process of responding to the risks of global warming is bound to continue for decades to come.

2 Negotiating an international response to global warming

Q   Review Chapter 2 and list:
   * the main greenhouse gases
   * their relative contribution to global warming in the 1980s
   * their main anthropogenic sources.

A   The key points are summarised in Table 4.1 and Figure 4.1.

Table 4.1   Greenhouse gases and their main anthropogenic sources

Carbon dioxide (CO_2)	Fossil-fuel burning
	Wood fuel
	Deforestation and land use change
	Cement manufacture
Methane (CH_4)	Releases from gas, oil or coal production or transmission
	Enteric fermentation from ruminants (e.g. cattle, sheep, goats)
	Wetland rice cultivation
	Landfill waste sites
	Burning and decay of biomass
Chlorofluorocarbons (CFCs)	Used for solvents, refrigerants, aerosol spray propellants, foam packaging etc.
Nitrous oxide (N_2O)	Fertilisers
	Fossil-fuel burning
	Tropical deforestation and wildfires
	Land conversion for agriculture
Also, gases involved in generation of low-level ozone:	
Nitrogen oxides	Fossil-fuel burning
	Biomass burning
Carbon monoxide	Fossil-fuel burning
	Biomass burning
Non-methane hydrocarbons	Evaporation of solvents and liquid fuels

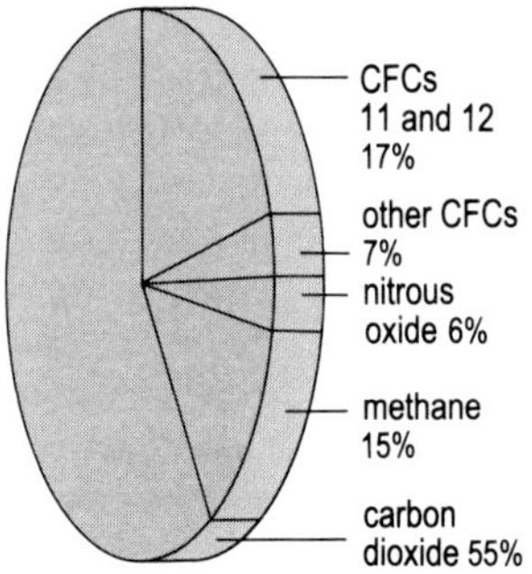

▲   *Figure 4.1*
Estimated contributions of each greenhouse gas to global warming in the 1980s. Tropospheric ozone may also make a significant contribution, but this cannot be quantified at present.

CFCs 11 and 12 17%
other CFCs 7%
nitrous oxide 6%
methane 15%
carbon dioxide 55%

2.1   Introduction

The IPCC scientific assessment of climate change, accepted at the 1990 Geneva Conference, updated and broadly confirmed the results of the SCOPE report discussed in Chapter 2. If current trends continue, the IPCC report anticipated an average global warming over the next century at a rate of some 0.3°C per decade, with associated major changes in regional climate patterns and sea-level rises averaging about 6 cm per decade. There remained some uncertainty in these estimates but likely values are between 0.2 and 0.5°C per decade and 3–10 cm per decade respectively.

If we aimed to stabilise the atmospheric concentrations of greenhouse gases at 1990 levels, the IPCC report shows that radical measures would be needed: see Table 4.2. For example, carbon dioxide emissions would need to be reduced by over 60%. Even if such reductions could be achieved immediately (which is obviously impossible), average temperatures would be expected to continue to rise for some 20 to 30 years, due to long atmospheric lifetimes of several greenhouse gases (see Table 4.3 and Figure 4.2) and to the great heat capacity of the oceans. They would not return to roughly their 1990 levels until the middle of the next century.

Table 4.2
Emission reductions required to stabilise atmospheric concentrations at current (1990) levels

Carbon dioxide	>60%
Methane	15–20%
Nitrous oxide	70–80%
CFC-11	70–75%
CFC-12	75–85%
HCFC-22	40–50%

Note: The stabilisation of each of these gases would have different effects on climate.
Source: IPCC.

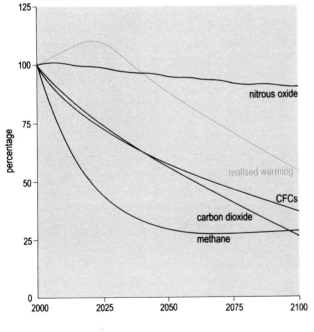

◀   Figure 4.2   The atmospheric response to a sudden cut-off in all anthropogenic greenhouse gas emissions. 100% is defined as the year 2000 atmospheric concentration, and 0% as the pre-industrial concentration. The 'realised warming' line indicates the estimated resultant changes in global warming. Note that this is an entirely theoretical exercise, to illustrate the implications of the atmospheric lifetimes of the greenhouse gases. Even if all humans were suddenly to vanish from the face of the Earth, CFCs stored in packaging and refrigerators, for example, would continue to be emitted, as would methane from landfill waste dumps, domestic animals, mines and such-like. Indeed, as can be seen, even in this calculation the researchers assumed that total methane emissions would not return to pre-industrial levels.

Table 4.3   Greenhouse gases: atmospheric characteristics

	Carbon dioxide	Methane	CFC-11	CFC-12	Nitrous oxide
Current rate of change per year	1.8 p.p.m. (0.5%)	0.015 p.p.m. (0.9%)	9.5 p.p.t. (4%)	17 p.p.t. (4%)	0.8 p.p.b. (0.25%)
Atmospheric lifetime (years)	(50–200)*	10	65	130	150

Notes: p.p.t. = part per trillion (10^12).

*The way in which CO$_2$ is absorbed by the oceans and biosphere is not simple and a single value cannot be given.
Source: IPCC.

As discussed in Chapter 3, by 1990 substantial international agreements had already been achieved on reducing CFC emissions, as a result of concern about depletion of stratospheric ozone. However, international negotiations to limit emissions of other greenhouse gases only began in 1991, and promised to be much more difficult to achieve. Whereas the elimination of CFC production only involves the development of a few chemical substitutes and the reform of an industry worth at most a few billion dollars per year, emissions of the other greenhouse gases are an intrinsic by-product of basic activities in contemporary human society, relating to energy production and use, industrial production, agriculture and the exploitation of forests: see Figure 4.3. Thus, any effective policy to prevent or limit global warming will challenge countless established practices and powerful interest groups.

This section examines alternative overall approaches to achieving effective global action and identifies some of the key issues that will need to be addressed.

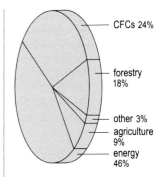

▲   Figure 4.3
Estimated contribution of different human activities to global warming in the 1980s.

2.2   Approaches to an international convention on global warming

It is possible to distinguish two broad approaches to an international agreement. One is to aim to achieve an **umbrella convention**, in which rules governing national behaviour on all important aspects of the problem are specified in one agreement. The other aims only to establish a **framework convention** containing an agreement on basic principles and objectives, and an agreed framework within which subsequent protocols detailing specific obligations can be negotiated.

A prime example of an umbrella convention is the new Law of the Sea, discussed in Section 4 of Chapter 1. This sought to regulate access to, and exploitation of, ocean resources. Because the negotiations sought to define detailed rules and regulations for most key aspects of the problem in one final agreement, they were extremely complex and protracted.

In the context of global warming, the 'umbrella convention' approach would be to aim for an agreement dealing with all the different gases involved in global warming and all the different types of sources of emissions. An ultimate target for global emissions of greenhouse gases

---

Box 4.1   *Labelling groups of states*

There are difficulties in finding any precise and convenient way of labelling groups of states. In this chapter, the countries of the world are frequently grouped into OECD countries, the 'third' (or 'developing') world, and the USSR and eastern Europe. The member countries of the Organisation of Economic Co-operation and Development (OECD) are roughly synonymous with the developed capitalist market economies (western Europe, the United States, Canada, Japan and Australia), and the OECD is used as a label for

these. The USSR and eastern Europe are treated separately, because in spite of recent reforms, their economies remain deeply conditioned by decades of state socialist central planning. Combined with the 'OECD', these states comprise the 'developed' world. The 'third' world, or 'developing' world, is taken to include all the rest of the states in the world. These obviously span very poor countries like Bangladesh, oil-rich states in the Gulf, and fairly industrialised states such as China and Brazil.

would be agreed, with a series of interim targets to be achieved by specified dates. For example, states could agree to reduce global carbon dioxide emissions by 60% of 1990 levels by the year 2050, with interim targets to stabilise emissions at 1990 levels by 2000, and to achieve 20% reductions by 2020.

After provisional acceptance of such global targets, negotiators would aim to agree specific obligations for each state. The key challenge would be to find a way of dividing the burden of achieving the global targets that all states would find acceptable and fair. This question of *equity* is highly contentious, and agreement would be hard to achieve. One superficially equitable proposal would be for each country to be obliged to make equal percentage reductions in its greenhouse gas emissions. However most states would argue that this would be unjust. It would:

- 'freeze-in' unequal levels of economic development
- ignore questions of responsibility for the threat of global warming
- impose unequal burdens on states.

Historically, developing countries have contributed relatively little to the risk of global warming, being responsible for only about 15% of world greenhouse gas emissions between 1870 and 1986. Although some 75% of the world's population lives in the third world, the developing states jointly contributed only about one third of global greenhouse gas emissions in the 1980s: see Figure 4.4. Developing countries argue that it would be unjust for them to be obliged to make the same percentage cuts in emissions as the developed states who are primarily responsible for the problem.

Moreover, the Ministerial Declaration of the 1990 Geneva Conference recognised that 'developing countries have as their main priority alleviating poverty and achieving social and economic development and that their net emissions must grow from their, as yet, relatively low energy consumption to accommodate their development needs.' As Figure 4.5 shows, carbon emissions per head of population from burning fossil fuels in developing countries typically are small compared with more economically developed regions, though developed countries themselves

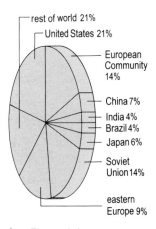

▲   Figure 4.4
Estimated regional contributions to global warming in the 1980s.

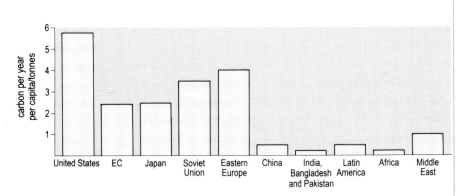

▲   Figure 4.5   Carbon emissions from fossil-fuel burning per head of population. This graph shows the number of tonnes of carbon emitted per capita in the late 1980s from fossil fuels only. If emissions from deforestation or other sources were to be taken into account, the per capita emissions from some countries, notably Brazil, would increase greatly (see Figure 4.8).

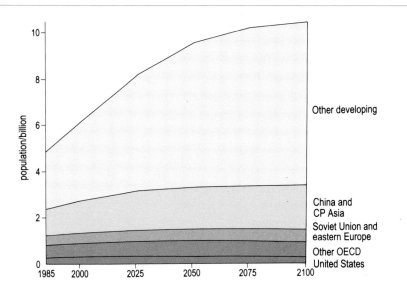

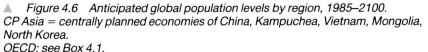

▲ *Figure 4.6   Anticipated global population levels by region, 1985–2100.*
CP Asia = centrally planned economies of China, Kampuchea, Vietnam, Mongolia,
North Korea.
OECD: see Box 4.1.

vary a great deal – from the very high levels of emissions in the United
States and eastern Europe to the much lower levels in western Europe and
Japan. Even using more energy-efficient methods, economic development
in the third world is bound to involve some increase in such per capita
emissions. Combined with rapid population growth in developing
countries (shown in Figure 4.6), this means that third world governments
are almost certain to insist that they be allowed some scope for increasing
their greenhouse gas emissions *above* 1990 levels.

   However, an effective international agreement would have to impose
some limits on the growth of third world greenhouse gas emissions, which
were growing at over 5% per annum in the late 1980s. Developing
countries' share of global emissions is projected to increase rapidly for the
foreseeable future: see Figures 4.7(a) and (b). In the late 1980s China, India
and Brazil were estimated already to be responsible respectively for 7%,
4% and 4% of global warming (shown in Figure 4.4).

Activity 1

On the basis of the information provided so far in this chapter,
compare the anticipated carbon dioxide emissions from the
developing world in 2025 with:

(a) global carbon dioxide emissions in 1990;

(b) the level to which global carbon dioxide emissions must be
reduced to stabilise atmospheric concentrations of carbon dioxide at
1990 levels (and thus avoid further global warming from this gas).

(c) Repeat this exercise in relation to emissions from developing
states in Asia alone.

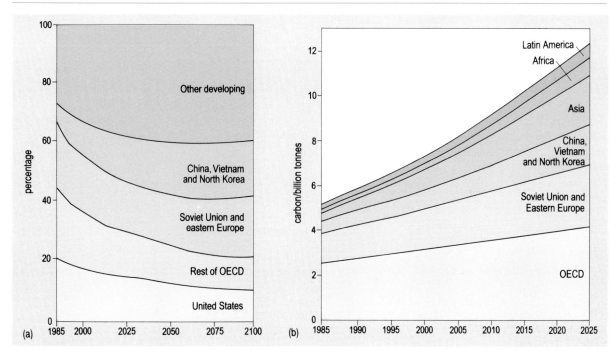

▲   Figure 4.7   Projections of greenhouse gas emissions by region.

(a)   Projection of percentage share of greenhouse gas emissions by region, 1985–2100 (making plausible
assumptions on the basis of trends in the late 1980s).

(b)   Estimated carbon dioxide emissions by region, 1985–2100.

For these reasons, negotiators might aim to reduce the rate at which
developing states increase their greenhouse gas emissions to 1–2% per
year until 2020, say, while imposing substantial reductions in the emissions
permitted from the developed world. As Table 4.4 shows, if the overall
objective was to achieve global emissions reductions of 20% below 1990
levels, this would imply an agreement by the developed states to cut their
emissions from fossil fuels to 40–75% below 1990 levels – a challenging
undertaking!

The task of obtaining agreement from the developed *and* the
developing world to international constraints along these lines would be
daunting even if it was widely accepted to be just and fair. The precise
percentages involved would be the subject of long negotiations. So would
the borderline between developing and developed states: the classification

Table 4.4   Implications for developed and third worlds of targets for reductions in fossil-carbon emissions by 2020

Third world emissions	Percentage reductions in emissions required from developed world by 2020 (cf 1990 levels)		
% annual growth	50% global reductions	20% global reductions	0% global reductions
0.0	69% cut	28% cut	0% cut
1.0	84% cut	43% cut	15% cut
2.0	–	73% cut	36% cut

Source: Developed from a table in Eastwood, P. (1991) *Responding to Global Warming*, London, Berg Press.

carbon per year per capita/tonnes

0   1   2   3   4   5   6

Canada	
United States	
Australia	
The Netherlands	
United Kingdom	OECD countries
West Germany	
France	
Italy	
Japan	
Sweden	

East Germany	
Soviet Union	
Czechoslovakia	
Poland	Soviet bloc countries
Bulgaria	
Romania	
Yugoslavia	

United Arab Emirates	
Brazil	
Saudi Arabia	
Costa Rica	
Colombia	
Mexico	
Indonesia	Developing countries
Venezuela	
Thailand	
The Philippines	
Nigeria	
China	
India	

Figure 4.8   Estimates of per capita greenhouse gas emissions for selected
countries, 1987 (tonnes of carbon).
(Existing data are for East and West Germany before reunification.)

of countries like Turkey, the Soviet Union, Iraq, South Africa, Argentina,
Taiwan or Malaysia might prove controversial. However, this whole
approach would be criticised if it did not take into account the wide
variations in responsibility, burden and level of economic development
within the groups of developed and developing nations. In many ways, the
variations within the 'developed' and 'developing' groups of states are as
great as the differences between them. For example, it has been estimated
that in 1987 East Germany, Brazil and the United States each emitted
over 4 tonnes of carbon per head of population, compared with less than 2
tonnes per head in Bulgaria, Indonesia and Japan: see Figure 4.8 (and also
Figure 4.5). Every country is different, reflecting variations in economic
development, energy efficiency, natural resources, geography, climate,
and patterns of industrial development, agriculture and forestry.

    Thus Japan could object to being treated in the same way as other
developed states. As a relatively late developer, it is less responsible for
global warming. Moreover, it has already gone further than most OECD
states in its energy-efficiency programmes: its energy use in 1990 was less
than in 1973 although its GNP had increased by some 45%. A further 30%
cut would be more costly and difficult for Japan to achieve than for the
United States or the Soviet Union, both of which are relatively inefficient
users of energy, as shown in Figure 4.9. Furthermore, Japan could argue
that it was unjust for it to be obliged to make large reductions in emissions,
while Brazil is allowed to continue with its massive carbon emissions

(largely a result of the burning of the Amazon forests). In response, Brazil might point out that Japanese corporations are the main organisers and beneficiaries of cutting rainforest in South East Asia. (The complexities of such global economic relationships are explored further in Chapters 5 and 6.) Similarly, very poor countries like Ethiopia, Zaire and Bangladesh might object to being subject to the same constraints as relatively wealthy and industrialised states such as Chile or Argentina.

In order to overcome these objections, it would be tempting to aim to negotiate separate emission targets for each country. In each case, the different factors affecting each country's greenhouse gas emissions would somehow be taken into account, and an equitable target agreed according to criteria related to their level of development, degree of responsibility for the problem, and to the costs they would have to bear in adjusting to reduced emissions targets.

The prospects for achieving an effective agreement along these lines seem remote. Every country would try to find reasons why their targets should be less severe than the average. For example, the United States would doubtless argue (indeed it already has) that its large land area means that it deserves a relatively large energy quota for transport. States such as Finland and Soviet Union would argue for a special allowance for heating relative to warmer countries. Countries such as China would point out that they are more dependent on coal for energy than countries like France, Norway or Israel, which can generate much of their energy from nuclear, hydroelectric, tidal and solar power schemes (which do not emit greenhouse gases).

Every country is a special case. The negotiations would be enormously complicated, and the potential for disagreement, haggling and delay seems boundless. The problems would be exacerbated by scientific uncertainties. Worse still, every country would have a strong incentive to concentrate on

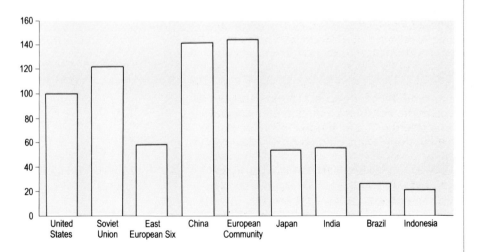

▲ *Figure 4.9   Fossil-carbon emissions per unit (renormalised) GNP, late 1980s. US = 100; GNPs renormalised on the basis of purchasing power parity. Note that a comparison on the basis of conventional exchange rates would show even greater disparities, but these renormalised data arguably provide a more accurate representation of the situation.*
East European Six = East Germany, Poland, Bulgaria, Romania, Hungary, Czechoslovakia.

finding reasons why it could not feasibly cut greenhouse gas emissions, in order to bolster its negotiating position, instead of looking for opportunities to make such cuts.

For these reasons, it was widely agreed by the end of 1990 that *flexibility* should join *equity* as a guiding principle of any international approach to limiting global warming. Useful unilateral measures by states, commercial organisations and other social groups and individuals should be encouraged. Moreover, groups of 'like-minded' states should develop agreements amongst themselves to limit emissions. For example, in October 1990, the European Community agreed to limit total carbon dioxide emissions from member-states at 1990 levels by the year 2000. The distribution of the burdens involved in meeting this target were then negotiated between member-states, with countries like Germany, Denmark, France and the Netherlands accepting more radical limits in order to make up for the less ambitious targets declared by states like the United Kingdom.

However, the problem with relying entirely upon such a unilateral process is that there may be other groups of states that are 'like-minded' in their reluctance to limit their greenhouse gas emissions significantly. These groups could include most third world countries, together with nations like the United States and Soviet Union – thus ensuring that rapid global warming continues. Moreover, many states may only be willing to accept the costs involved in reducing greenhouse gas emissions if they are assured that most other states, particularly their main competitors, are having to bear similar costs.

Thus the key international challenge is to find an approach to international negotiations that:

● is unlikely to be rejected as inequitable by major states or groups of states

● is sufficiently flexible to avoid getting seriously bogged down or discouraging useful unilateral actions

● will nevertheless develop real international constraints on greenhouse gas emissions.

It is in this context that the governments at the Second World Climate Conference at Geneva in November 1990 called for 'negotiations on a framework convention on climate change [to] be framed in such a way as to gain the support of the largest possible number of countries while allowing timely action to be taken'.

Such a framework convention would confirm that global warming poses a major threat requiring substantial reductions in greenhouse gas emissions as soon as is 'reasonably' possible, and would possibly include global targets for limiting emissions. It would formalise the IPCC process for improving understanding of the science and impacts of global warming and for identifying the policy options to deal with them. It would provide for improved monitoring and analysis of climate conditions, and probably for some international structure to provide assistance to poor countries in limiting their greenhouse gas emissions.

Most importantly, the Convention should establish a process for negotiating subsequent protocols, which would aim to establish specific limits or obligations on states relating to various aspects of the problem, such as carbon emissions from fossil fuels, deforestation, agricultural practices, and landfill management. It might also outline the general principles on which such protocols would be based.

International negotiations to protect the ozone layer, as described in Chapter 3, offer a good example of the effective use of this 'framework' approach. The 1985 Vienna Convention specified no detailed targets or regulations concerning CFC emissions. Rather it established the destruction of the ozone layer as an issue of international concern, confirmed that CFC emissions were primarily responsible, and established general goals for reducing these emissions. This Convention, then, provided a framework for negotiations leading to the specific obligations of the 1987 Montreal Protocol, which were then tightened considerably at the London meeting in June 1990. Arguably the more flexible 'framework convention' approach was more effective than an attempt to move immediately to an 'umbrella convention' to ban CFC production would have been: the latter approach could have been more easily stalled or bogged down.

On the basis of this experience, a framework convention on global warming could be expected to increase international and domestic political pressures for action. By helping to create a general expectation that greenhouse gas emissions would be limited in the near future, it could encourage large bureaucracies and corporations to begin to accommodate themselves to the anticipated future environment and to plan to reduce their direct or indirect greenhouse gas emissions. Moreover, more states may be willing to take unilateral actions to reduce greenhouse gas emissions as they become more confident that other states are likely to follow in due course. In the process, the specific targets discussed at negotiations of subsequent protocols might then appear to be more achievable and less disruptive.

A number of experts have suggested that some specific obligations should be included in the global warming convention itself, in order to achieve as rapid an international response to the problem as possible. For example, in 1990 W. Nitze (who had earlier represented the United States at IPCC meetings) suggested that a convention should include:

- initial ten-year targets for limiting global greenhouse gas emissions

- a requirement for every OECD country within ten years to stabilise its emissions at the levels they were when the convention came into force

- an obligation for every state to ensure no net deforestation and to reduce the ratio of its carbon dioxide emissions to its GDP by 2% per year

- each state would also have to publish and regularly update a detailed strategy to achieve its targets.

These proposals were designed to tighten the immediate obligations accepted by states, while avoiding measures that would lead to difficult and prolonged negotiations. Many other experts doubted whether Nitze's proposals achieved the right balance. If such proposals seemed to be seriously delaying agreement, the framework approach would be to dilute them in the interests of achieving rapid agreement on an international convention, and then to return to the difficult issues later.

We will examine possible protocols specifying obligations on states to limit greenhouse gas emissions in Section 4. Before that, the next section will discuss the ways in which states can actually reduce their emissions, whether by unilateral action or as part of their international obligations.

3   The scope for limiting greenhouse gas emissions

3.1   Introduction

Greenhouse gas emissions result from such a wide variety of activities that no single reform or narrowly focused strategy can adequately address the problem. Rather, improvements must be sought on a large number of fronts. Nevertheless, it is necessary to identify priority areas, where there is scope for major and relatively cost-effective reductions in greenhouse gas emissions. In order to analyse the problem further, it is convenient to consider separately each of the following areas:

- energy production and use
- industrial production
- forestry
- agricultural practices.

3.2   Energy production and use

Introduction

Energy production and use is presently the largest single factor contributing to global warming: during the 1980s this sector accounted for almost half of anthropogenic greenhouse gas emissions (shown in Figure 4.3). Of these gases, carbon dioxide from burning fuels is the most significant – responsible for some 76% of the global warming due to the energy sector: see Figure 4.10. Also, methane is produced from burning fuels and from coal-mines and oil and gas facilities. Some nitrous oxides and tropospheric ozone are also indirectly produced.

During the period 1950–1985, global energy consumption increased by nearly a factor of four, while carbon dioxide emissions tripled: see Figure 4.11. OECD countries use most energy, but the relative share of the rest of the world is increasing. If the trends during the 1980s were to continue, total carbon dioxide emissions would increase by almost 250% between 1985 and 2025, by which time the third world would be responsible for almost half of the global total (see Figure 4.7). Methane production would also increase greatly, but trends are even harder to evaluate because of lack of reliable data.

Given this background, what is the scope for reducing greenhouse gas emissions from energy production and use? This section will review the situation in OECD countries, the Soviet Union and eastern Europe, and the third world.

Energy efficiency

There is general agreement among experts that substantial improvements in energy efficiency and conservation could be achieved in the near and medium term, making a major contribution to limiting greenhouse gas emissions. New energy-efficient technologies and designs are emerging or already available (*Olivier, Elliot and Reddish*, 1991). According to the IPCC

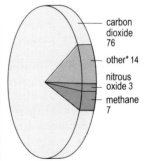

carbon
dioxide
76

other* 14

nitrous
oxide 3

methane
7

▲   *Figure 4.10
Contribution to global
warming of greenhouse
gases emitted as a result of
energy production and use
during the 1980s.*

**Primarily tropospheric
ozone due to CO, NO$_x$ and
volatile organic compounds
(VOCs).*

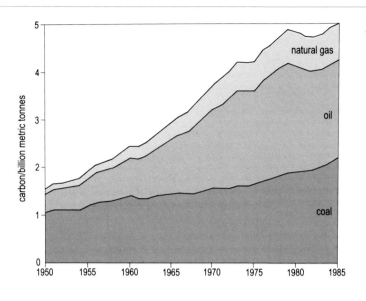

Figure 4.11
Global fossil-carbon
emissions, 1950–85.

reports, vehicle efficiency improvements of 50–100% are readily available. Indeed, some prototype cars have been developed that are capable of 25–32 km per litre (70–90 mpg) in urban areas, compared with a typical 9–12 km/l (25–35 mpg). The energy efficiency of existing residential and commercial buildings could typically be improved by 25–50% at reasonable cost. Conversion efficiencies for existing coal-powered electricity production stations could be improved by 15–20%, while emerging technologies could be used to make new power stations up to 60% more efficient than existing facilities. Energy efficiency in industry could be improved by from 15% to over 40% (depending on the industry) using presently available technologies.

Furthermore, energy demand could be greatly reduced by *structural* changes in the way we use energy. For example, passenger cars and lorries account for about 83% of the total energy use in the transport sector in typical OECD countries. Significant energy savings could be achieved if more freight was carried by rail, or a larger fraction of people shared cars or used public transport or worked from home. Similarly, much of the energy generated in power stations is wasted as heat released into the environment from cooling towers. Wider use of 'combired heat and power and district heating' would greatly increase efficiency.

Major improvements in energy efficiency are thu technically achievable. For example, a World Resources Institute study estimated that US carbon dioxide emissions in 2020 could be 40% lower than 1987 levels if energy-efficient technologies and practices were adopted, even allowing for continued economic growth. Most OECD states are more energy-efficient than the United States, but average reductions in carbon dioxide emissions of 20–40% could probably be achieved through these means. However, technical feasibility is not the only issue. In practice the take-up of energy-efficient technologies and designs is notoriously slow and partial.

At present prices, many energy-efficient technologies are still uneconomic compared to their cheaper but less efficient competitors. This problem is exacerbated by the many direct or indirect state subsidies for energy users, encouraging wasteful practices: in 1984 energy subsidies in the United States alone totalled $44 billion.

Nevertheless, in most areas of energy use, introducing many energy-efficient technologies would be cost-effective in the medium or long term. Often, however, the capital is not available to purchase and install them. Even when there are no financial constraints, other factors may come into play. There is widespread ignorance, and even well-informed consumers, investors or managers tend to be unwilling to buy cost-effective energy-efficient technologies unless the 'pay-back' period is rather short. Many studies have shown that market forces alone will lead only to gradual improvements in energy efficiency. To achieve rapid progress, governments must take action.

This is even more true in the Soviet Union, eastern Europe and the third world than it is in OECD states. There are characteristic differences between these countries and the OECD states, which affect their prospects of achieving major reductions in greenhouse gas emissions from changes in energy use. In 1989 the United States alone was responsible for more carbon emissions from burning fossil fuels than the whole of the Soviet Union and eastern Europe combined: see Figure 4.12. But in terms of emissions per head of population, these latter countries were profligate. The eastern European states emitted almost twice as much carbon from fossil fuels per capita than EC countries or Japan. The Soviet Union was almost as bad (see Figure 4.5). Needless to say this was not because of higher standards of living in the Soviet Union and eastern Europe; rather it was due to extremely inefficient use of energy. The Soviet Union and east European states emitted more than twice as much fossil carbon per unit of economic activity as EC countries or Japan (see Figure 4.9). (See Plate 10.)

This implies that there is even greater scope in the Soviet Union and eastern Europe than in OECD countries for major reductions in carbon dioxide emissions through improvements in energy efficiency and economic reforms. If the Soviet Union and east European economies were only to achieve the energy intensity of the west European economies in the late 1980s, energy savings of some 66% would be achieved and carbon dioxide emissions would fall correspondingly. However, it is important to appreciate the scale of capital investment and economic restructuring that would be necessary for such energy savings to be achieved.

In the Soviet Union and eastern Europe most energy has traditionally been used for industrial purposes: see Figure 4.13. Enormous capital investment would be required to replace their industrial plant with modern, more energy-efficient facilities. Similarly, although poor insulation and design of buildings is common throughout the region, vast capital expenditure would be needed to improve this situation. However, the necessary capital resources are scarcely available domestically. In the early 1990s all these countries are in severe economic difficulties and most

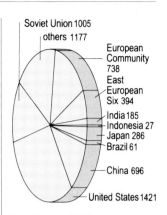

▲　*Figure 4.12*
Fossil-carbon emissions from commercial energy consumption by region, late 1980s (millions of tonnes of carbon).

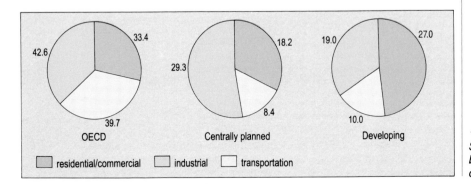

◄　*Figure 4.13*
Structure of energy demand by region, 1985 (energy demand in exajoules).

The Nowa Huta steelworks near Cracow, Poland. Processes and plant at the works are technologically redundant: the steelworks is a replica of the US Pittsburgh plant built in the 1930s and itself out of date by the Second World War.

east European states are heavily in debt. The only available major source of outside capital and technology is from the OECD countries. Investment to improve energy efficiency in the Soviet Union and eastern Europe would be a very cost-effective way for the OECD states to limit global warming. However, for reasons of economic and political competition, there might be considerable resistance in the west for the massive government investment and aid programmes required.

Ironically, in the early 1990s, it is western automobile companies that have taken a lead in investing in eastern Europe. Traditionally the transport sector in the Soviet Union and eastern Europe has accounted for a much smaller proportion of total energy use than in OECD countries (see Figure 4.13). This is primarily because there are many fewer cars and lorries. It would be disappointing if the market reforms in eastern Europe and the Soviet Union were to undermine their one important area of energy efficiency relative to the west – their heavy reliance on public transport and rail.

As far as developing countries are concerned, widespread poverty and rapid population growth mean that they have little option but to aim to achieve rapid economic development. Historically, the early stages of industrialisation have tended to be highly energy-intensive. Establishing basic industries such as steel-making, aluminium processing or cement production entails a rapid increase in energy (usually fossil-fuel) consumption. Energy intensity is sharply rising in most of the rapidly industrialising countries of Asia. Many regions of the third world are still mainly agrarian. If most of the third world attempts to achieve economic growth through the traditional path of heavy industrialisation, the implications for global warming will be grave.

In those countries that have already developed an industrial infrastructure, the plants are typically outmoded and very inefficient in their use of energy. Improvements in energy efficiency could therefore allow scope for development without corresponding increases in greenhouse gas emissions. Third world countries that are still at the very early stages of industrial development could theoretically adopt best-available technologies from the beginning.

However, even more than the Soviet Union and eastern Europe, third world countries lack the capital and technical expertise to invest in new efficient technology. Indeed, massive third world debt resulted in a net capital transfer of some $30 billion per annum from the developing states to OECD countries in the late 1980s. This capital transfer cannot but greatly hinder progress towards energy efficiency improvements in the third world. This debate is taken further in Chapters 5 and 6 below, with particular reference to the sustainability of different models of development.

Changing fuels and energy sources

It is possible to limit greenhouse gas emissions by changing the fuels we use for energy as well as by limiting energy use. Of the fossil fuels, coal produces the most carbon dioxide per unit energy generated: see Figure 4.14. Substitution of natural gas for coal could reduce carbon dioxide emissions from a power plant by between 40 and 45%.

The scope for fuel-switching varies greatly from one country to another. China, for example, is bound to continue to rely heavily on coal, because of its shortage of foreign currency and lack of major fossil-fuel reserves other than coal. However, many countries have much scope for such substitution, including the Soviet Union which is the world's largest producer of natural gas and has large natural gas reserves. Indonesia has large natural gas as well as coal reserves.

However, the carbon dioxide reductions would be partially offset by increased seepage of methane into the atmosphere from leaky gas pipelines. Even the claimed leakage rate of about 1% in OECD countries would be significant, since methane is such a potent greenhouse gas. In fact there is some doubt about these claims, and in any case in the Soviet Union and third world leakage rates are certainly far greater than 1%. Furthermore, throughout the world natural gas is also often allowed to vent into the atmosphere at oil or gas production sites, or is flared (to produce carbon dioxide). Measures need to be taken to eliminate these practices, though flaring is preferable to venting in terms of the lower potency of carbon dioxide as a greenhouse gas.

Just as nitrous oxide (and sulphur dioxide) can be removed from the emissions from coal-fired power stations to reduce acid rain, it is technically possible to remove up to 90% of carbon dioxide itself from such emissions. However, the technology would almost certainly be expensive and require considerable energy inputs, leading to an overall reduction in the conversion efficiencies of power plants. There are also problems with storing the vast quantities of fixed carbon dioxide that would be collected.

Replacing petrol with methanol and ethanol as automobile fuels could result in a net reduction in carbon dioxide emissions provided they were produced from plant materials. Compressed natural gas would be 'clean' fuel in relation to sulphur dioxide and nitrogen oxides, but not in terms of carbon dioxide. However, widespread use is bound greatly to increase leaks of methane into the atmosphere.

Another important approach is substantially to expand the role of energy sources that do not involve greenhouse gas emissions: nuclear power, hydroelectrical power, solar, wind, wave, tidal and geothermal

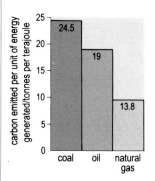

Figure 4.14
Carbon emissions per unit of energy generated for coal, oil and natural gas.

▲   *Natural gas being flared near a Saudi Arabian off-shore oil rig, producing carbon dioxide.*

energy. (These energy sources and their potential role in energy production are discussed in *Olivier, Elliott and Reddish* (1991).) Some countries already rely heavily on such energy sources. For example, France supplies 18% of its electricity needs through hydro-electric power and some 70% through nuclear power. The result of this is that the French per capita consumption of fossil fuels for electricity generation in the late 1980s was barely 8% of those of Germany or the United Kingdom.

The scope for expanding the role of 'renewable' energy sources varies from country to country, due largely to geographical and climatic factors. The development of the technologies associated with them has sadly been relatively neglected until recently, leaving several of the renewable technologies far from fully developed. In the United Kingdom, official estimates of their potential contribution to electricity generation vary between about 18% and 28% by 2025: some outside experts think that the potential could be even greater. Renewable energy sources could make equal or greater contribution in other OECD and third world countries.

In contrast, a great deal of capital has been invested in nuclear power. Nuclear power generation does not involve the emission of any greenhouse gases, except indirectly through the construction programme and fuel cycle. However, the trend at the beginning of the 1990s was away from reliance on nuclear power. It has its own associated environmental, health and security problems, and has not typically proved to be economically competitive. Nevertheless, heightened awareness of the risks of global warming, and also acid rain, has led to a reconsideration of the nuclear option.

Strategies for government action

It is clear that there is considerable scope for achieving reductions in most states' greenhouse gas emissions from the energy sector, but that these will only be achieved gradually unless there is determined government action. There are debates about whether states should focus on market mechanisms or regulation to achieve rapid progress. In practice, a combination of both of these seems likely to prove most effective.

Market systems do respond to price changes. For example, the major energy-price rises in 1973 and 1978 led to great improvements in energy efficiency in all OECD states. In Japan, where there was also a major government energy-efficiency programme, energy use throughout the 1980s was less than in 1973, even though Japan's economy had grown very substantially.

Government use of market mechanisms to reduce carbon emissions from energy use could begin with the removal of many of the subsidies for energy users, and then move on to increase substantially energy prices by increasing taxes on energy use. This could be justified in terms of the 'polluter pays' principle: energy prices should take into account the true social and environmental costs of energy production and use. To limit global warming, the priority is to reduce the use of energy from fossil fuels. Thus a **carbon tax** has been proposed, where tax levels on different types of energy are calculated according to the amount of carbon dioxide or methane emissions they involve. By 1990 Finland and the Netherlands had respectively introduced carbon taxes of $6 and $7 per tonne of carbon in the fuel.

It might be argued that additional taxes are socially or economically undesirable. However, it would be possible to make corresponding reductions in income or corporation tax, or to increase state support for economically vulnerable and disadvantaged groups, perhaps in the form of grants for insulation or energy-efficient technologies.

Such an approach would have the benefit of penalising inefficient energy use, encouraging reductions in energy demand and a switch to less polluting fuels, without reducing a country's overall disposable income or investment capital. It would use governmental fiscal policy to limit greenhouse gas emissions, but would rely on market mechanisms to achieve the energy-efficiency improvements in an efficient and flexible way. To be effective, however, the new energy or carbon taxes would have to be substantial enough to cause major (and often painful) adjustments in many sectors of the economy and society.

Non-fiscal measures could also play a vital role, such as strict energy-efficiency standards for new appliances, equipment, automobiles and buildings. Public information campaigns or grants for energy conservation would also help. Another approach is to change the regulations governing the electricity industry to promote energy conservation. This is becoming successful in parts of the United States, where the utilities are allowed to profit on all energy *saved* as a result of their energy-efficiency programmes for their customers, as well as on the electricity generated.

3.3   Industrial activities

Non-energy sources of greenhouse gases associated with industrial activity were responsible for about 27% of global warming in the 1980s (see Figure 4.3). In this category CFCs are the main culprits, accounting for some 24% of global warming. Production of most of these is due to end by 2000, though atmospheric concentrations are not expected to fall to 1990 levels until the second half of the next century.

Biogas emissions from buried waste are also a significant and growing source of greenhouse gases. Landfill refuse sites release significant quantities of methane and carbon dioxide into the atmosphere: leakage from landfills contributes about 8% of total global methane emissions (see Figure 4.15). Recovery of this methane to burn for power could limit global warming in two ways – by reducing emissions of methane and also by displacing the use of coal in electricity generation. Such schemes should

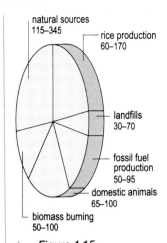

▲   *Figure 4.15*
Estimated emissions of methane by source, late 1980s (millions of tonnes of carbon).

◀   *An environmental scientist testing for methane and carbon dioxide gases at a vent in a landfill site where domestic and industrial waste is buried.*

therefore be encouraged, but it would be unrealistic to expect more than a small proportion of the gas from landfills to be recovered before the end of this century. Meanwhile, the huge quantities of waste produced each year by modern society continue to increase.

The third significant source of greenhouse gas emissions in this category is as a chemical by-product of the cement production process. This accounts for about 2% of current global CO_2 emissions, and since about 1950 has been growing at an average annual rate of 6%. Since carbon dioxide is an inherent part of cement manufacture, the only way to slow emissions here is to limit cement production and increase energy efficiency at the plants. In OECD countries measures to reduce demand for cement may be modestly successful, but the prospects for such reductions in the rest of the world seem remote.

3.4   Forestry

Forests store 20 to 100 times more carbon per unit area than croplands and play a critical role in the Earth's carbon cycle. As they are cleared for timber and to make space for agriculture, large quantities of carbon are released into the atmosphere as a result of fire or decay. Humankind has been deforesting the planet for thousands of years. Until the early twentieth century, this was mainly in the temperate regions, such as Europe and North America. More recently, it has been concentrated in the tropics. In the late 1980s, deforestation in the third world accounted for roughly 18% of global warming (see Figures 4.3 and 4.16). Each year, between 11 and 15 million hectares of tropical forests are cleared – an area larger than Austria.

Temperate forests are essentially now in balance in terms of carbon cycling: the annual forest growth rates roughly balance the timber harvests and forest clearances. Thus one approach to reduce carbon dioxide emissions would be to halt and reverse the deforestation in the third world, particularly of tropical forests, and to introduce widespread reforestation programmes in the temperate zones of the northern hemisphere. Overall, however, some 3.9 million hectares of new forest would be needed each year to compensate for just 1% of emissions from OECD countries.

Reforestation in the third world could offset a relatively large proportion of developing countries' emissions. However, it should be

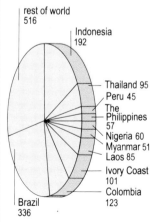

rest of world
516

Indonesia
192

Thailand 95
Peru 45
The Philippines 57
Nigeria 60
Myanmar 51
Laos 85
Ivory Coast 101
Colombia 123

Brazil
336

▲   Figure 4.16
Estimated net emissions of carbon from tropical deforestation in 1980 (millions of tonnes of carbon).

A reforestation programme in Sechura, Peru.

understood that tropical deforestation is partly driven by poverty and by population pressures to increase agricultural land. Targeted development aid therefore could play an important role in halting such deforestation.

3.5   Changing agricultural practices

Agriculture contributes to global warming through methane production as a result of rice production and enteric fermentation in domestic animals. These respectively probably account for 20% and 15% of global methane production (see Figure 4.15). Use of nitrogenous fertilisers is estimated to account for up to 17% of global sources of nitrous oxide. Overall these sources are probably responsible for more than 9% of global warming.

Changes in water management and other practices could help to limit methane emissions from rice production. But rice is a staple food for a large proportion of the world's population, and it seems realistic only to aim to stabilise global emissions in this area of activity. Similarly, although good management can reduce fertiliser use in each farm, and fertiliser use may be reduced in developed states, the possibility of preventing some global increase in the use of fertilisers in the medium term seems small.

Cattle are responsible for some 76% of annual methane emissions from agricultural animals, with a further 20% coming from other ruminants such as sheep, goats and camels. There is no way of preventing methane emissions from livestock, though feed and management practices can reduce them. The main way to achieve major reductions in this source of methane would be to reduce the overall numbers of ruminants and rely on crops for a higher proportion of world food supplies, or to switch between types of animal – for example, sheep produce about 20% less methane per unit of animal product than cattle. However, even dramatic changes would only change the rate of global warming marginally.

Activity 2

Review this section and summarise its main points. Compare your notes with those given at the end of the chapter.

4   Negotiating specific international obligations to reduce greenhouse gas emissions

4.1   Introduction

Assuming that a framework convention on global warming has been achieved along the lines discussed in Section 2, what are the prospects for achieving agreement on subsequent protocols, detailing specific obligations for states to reduce greenhouse gas emissions? In principle each protocol should focus on particular aspects of the problem. The discussion in Section 3 shows that it is in the energy sector that there is typically most scope for substantial reductions in states' greenhouse gas emissions, with forestry being the next most important area. Constraints relating to these two sectors are both most urgent and also most 'cost-effective' in their potential for limiting global warming. International agreements to promote good agricultural, industrial and waste management practice, from the global warming perspective, would also be useful. But specific ceilings for states' emissions from such activities would be particularly hard to negotiate or to verify, in view of the uncertainties involved.

In relation to the energy sector, negotiators could in principle focus on establishing obligations for each state to meet targets relating to energy demand, energy efficiency or fuel-switching. Such an approach, however, has the disadvantage of being both too partial and too specific. Differences between states' systems of energy production and use would make it hard to set targets that would be accepted as equitable or effective. Instead, by the end of 1990, expert attention was becoming focused on specifying limits on all carbon emissions from fossil-fuel combustion. However, the United States and a number of other developed states made it clear in 1989, and at the 1990 Geneva conference, that they wanted limits on deforestation to be discussed in parallel negotiations if fossil fuels were to be singled out in a protocol.

4.2   Limiting fossil-carbon emissions

The category of carbon emissions from fossil fuels covers several of the most important and rapidly growing greenhouse gas emissions. It includes some sources of methane and all important carbon dioxide emissions due to human activities apart from deforestation. Limits on fossil-fuel combustion would also help to reduce emissions of gases such as nitrous oxide and, indirectly, tropospheric ozone. The category is broad enough to involve a substantial proportion of greenhouse gas emissions from every country, so it does not seem to single out a particular group arbitrarily. Yet it is narrow enough to avoid direct linkage with the political and scientific complexities of aiming to regulate deforestation, leakage from landfills, or agricultural practices.

It is also possible to estimate fossil-carbon emissions for each state relatively reliably, using standard published economic statistics: emissions from deforestation, landfills and agricultural practices are much harder to estimate reliably. There is thus the prospect of being able to monitor compliance with any agreement achieved.

Activity 3

In view of the information provided in this chapter and Chapter 2, comment upon the likely differences in attitudes of the governments of the United States, the Netherlands, Bangladesh, Saudi Arabia, China and Brazil towards the singling out of fossil-carbon emissions for early regulation.

As shown in Table 4.2, the IPCC estimates that global carbon dioxide emissions would have to be reduced by more than 60% below 1990 levels in order to stabilise atmospheric concentrations of the gas. However, an initial protocol on fossil-carbon emissions would almost certainly have to focus on achieving less dramatic interim targets in order to be negotiable: for example, to reduce global fossil-carbon emissions to 20% below 1990 levels by 2020. Table 4.4 indicates that this would be roughly compatible with average reductions of about 40% in the developed world, and an annual increase of about 1% in emissions from the third world: a very challenging but achievable target.

   Once such a target has been provisionally agreed, negotiations must focus on agreeing specific obligations on states to achieve it. This means that negotiators would have to grapple with the problems which were discussed in Section 2.

Activity 4

Review Sections 2 and 3, and briefly list the main issues and difficulties for such negotiations. Compare your answer with the one given at the end of the chapter.

One of the main conclusions that can be drawn from the discussion in Section 2 is that any attempt to negotiate specific ceilings for each state is almost bound either to get bogged down indefinitely or to result in limits that are so high as to be ineffective in limiting global warming. A number of alternative approaches have been proposed which seem to offer more felxibility and clarity of principle, by using market mechanisms as well as international regulations.

   For example, international 'carbon taxes' could be established – an extension of the approach discussed in Section 3.2 in the context of national strategies. Such an international tax could either be used to raise funds to assist the third world with the investments required to cut emissions, or to raise the international energy price to encourage energy efficiency.

   Even a small carbon tax could raise vast amounts of capital. A worldwide tax of $1 per tonne of carbon in fuel used would, for example, only raise the price of coal by about 2%, but it would have raised some $6 billion per year in the late 1980s. This would certainly have funded a major programme to monitor carbon emissions and climate change and to provide relevant technical assistance to the third world.

   However, such a low tax would make such little difference to energy prices, and thus would not in itself encourage energy efficiency. To begin to have a real impact, the tax would need to be of the order of $30 per tonne of carbon. Applied internationally, this would raise well over $100 billion. Even supposing that the problems of agreeing on how to administer and allocate such vast sums could be overcome, it seems doubtful that developed states would agree to such an enormous capital transfer. On balance, therefore, although an international carbon tax might be a feasible way of raising the money to help fund technology transfer to the third world, it is unlikely to be used as a mechanism for cutting carbon emissions themselves.

An alternative option for limiting emissions by increasing energy prices would be to agree to limit the amount of fossil fuels that can be produced. Just as OPEC aims to keep oil prices high by limiting production, a system of production quotas and production permits for all fossil fuels could be introduced.

Q   Think about the implications of such an approach and comment on how it would be likely to be received internationally.

A   The energy-producing industries and energy-exporting states would probably look upon such an approach favourably: it would increase the profit margin for their products. However, therein lies the problem. If it was effective, energy prices would increase greatly and energy production – the very activity that one wants to discourage – would become immensely profitable. The process of allocating production quotas would be extremely controversial, and the incentives to break quotas or engage in 'black market' dealing would be great. Moreover, energy importers, particularly in the third world and eastern Europe, would be particularly hard hit by such a regime, a situation which would be hard to justify.

One market-based approach that seems more promising is that of **marketable carbon emission permits**. This could take a number of forms, but they all involve controlling emissions through a system of permits which can be interchanged between countries or companies without central direction. For example, each country could be granted 'permits' for a certain amount of fossil-carbon emissions each year. If it did not need to use all its permits for itself, it could sell the remainder to other countries that wanted to emit more carbon than their own allocated permits allowed. Thus energy-efficient countries, or low energy users, could raise extra capital by selling their permits to less efficient or higher energy users. All the incentives for each country would be to reduce its emissions. Overall emission levels would be limited by the total number of permits issued each year.

The main issue for negotiation would be how to allocate permits each year. To be negotiable, it would have to be equitable. But there is a choice between basing the scheme on the principle of either **equity of burden** or **the 'polluter pays'**. An example of the former approach would be to allocate permits in a way that is related to countries' present annual emissions. However, this would reward countries that are already emitting high levels of fossil carbon, and are primarily responsible for the problem itself. An example of the second approach would be to allocate permits according to each country's population, allowing each year a given amount of fossil-carbon emissions per capita. Since the third world typically has low emissions per head of population, each year they would be able to sell a large fraction of their permits to the developed countries. In order to ensure that this large capital transfer is used to invest in energy-efficient technologies or less polluting energy sources, the trade could be in appropriate technology and specialist expertise rather than money.

This approach seems to meet most of the key criteria for a just and effective regime to reduce fossil-carbon emissions identified in Sections 2 and 3. There are, however, no straightforward options. For example, this scheme could encourage states to increase their populations: a very undesirable outcome. An amendment to reduce this risk would be to allocate permits according to a state's *adult* population. A further problem relates to the Soviet Union and eastern Europe. On its own, the above approach would involve a net transfer of capital *away* from these countries: an undesirable effect for the reasons discussed in Section 3. Some additional source of international funds for the Soviet Union and eastern Europe would probably have to be arranged, in order to counteract this effect (perhaps under a separate arrangement with the EC and other OECD states).

In spite of such amendments, even this flexible approach would be difficult to negotiate. Any effective protocol must require major reforms within virtually every country and involve international agreements to transfer capital from the developed to the developing world on an unprecedented scale. Furthermore, even if a protocol is agreed to reduce global fossil-carbon emissions to 20% below 1990 levels by 2020, this would only limit the rate of global warming. Much more radical measures would have to be agreed subsequently in order to stabilise atmospheric concentrations of carbon dioxide and methane.

4.3   Forestry

There was great international concern about the destruction of the tropical rainforests even before the problem of global warming rose high on the political agenda; this concern related to the loss of many species of life, soil erosion and the role of the forests in the Earth's climate. In the 1980s a Tropical Forestry Action Plan was launched and the International Tropical Timber Organisation aimed to encourage sustainable management of these forests. At their 1990 Houston Summit, the seven leading industrialised

states declared that they are ready to begin negotiating a separate forest agreement aimed at curbing deforestation and protecting biodiversity. It was hoped that this agreement would be ready in 1992.

Such a negotiating process might therefore proceed in parallel with talks on a global warming convention. In any case, as discussed above, the United States and other developed states have made it clear that they expect international action to prevent tropical deforestation in parallel with agreements to reduce fossil-carbon emissions. One possibility would be an obligation on governments to ensure no net loss of forest in each of their states. However, this obligation would have to apply to all regions – not only the tropics. For example, in 1989 President Sarney of Brazil argued that the United States was in no position to criticise Brazil for destruction of the Amazon forests when the United States was itself subsidising destruction of the last remaining primeval rainforest in the Pacific Northwest. Moreover, temperate forests were largely destroyed in the present developed states while they were in the process of industrialising.

Fortunately such an obligation is now accepted in principle by OECD states. Some of these countries, such as the United States and Australia, have declared major tree-planting initiatives: an option that has its attractions for politicians ever aware of photo-opportunities. A forestry protocol might therefore go beyond a 'no net loss' approach, and set targets for increasing the global forest area. Adherence to national targets could be monitored reliably using satellite photographs. There might also be agreements to prevent the destruction of established forests, involving labelling of sustainably harvested wood and restrictions on the use of hard and mature woods.

5   Summary

Any effective strategy for limiting global warming will involve difficult and potentially costly adjustments, particularly for the developed world. It may be technically possible to reduce greenhouse gas emissions by 40% or more by 2020 while still allowing slow economic growth. In practice, however, such reductions will not be achieved without determined action by governments, by raising energy prices and by tightening regulations. Such actions would be painful for many powerful sections in society, and thus politically controversial.

Unilateral national and regional measures to cut greenhouse gas emissions have a potentially valuable role to play. But they do not provide a long-term solution. To limit global warming, global action is needed. Any effective international agreements will have to operate over a long period, and must be accepted as just and equitable.

Account must be taken of the need for the third world to develop economically to meet the legitimate needs of its population (while encouraging a reduction in the rate of population growth). Thus, cuts in greenhouse gas emissions must be concentrated in the developed world. There is nevertheless great technical scope for development policies in the third world to be much more energy-efficient, and to involve practices that would limit greenhouse gas emissions. However, to achieve such savings, capital and expertise is needed that developing countries typically do not possess in large amounts. The same applies in the Soviet Union and eastern Europe which are very energy-inefficient, but lacking in capital and modern technology. Again the only major source of capital and technology are the OECD states.

Achieving any international agreement is going to be very difficult, and there are no easy options. Some of the most obvious and superficially attractive approaches are in fact very problematic and unlikely to result in an effective agreement. For this reason, a flexible approach involving a framework convention on global warming, with specific obligations on states being established in a subsequent series of protocols seems more appropriate than aiming for an all-inclusive umbrella agreement. A number of possible approaches to limiting global fossil-carbon emissions were briefly analysed. All have their problems, but one of the most promising would involve 'marketable carbon emission permits'.

The debate is complex, and will continue for a long time to come. This is inevitable, but time is not on our side. The prospects for preventing global warming in the coming decades are not good. But we could substantially limit it, provided we are determined to act fast. The primary obstacles are not technical; they are above all political disputes about how economic costs are to be distributed. A political and economic perspective on environment and development issues is the subject of the final two chapters.

References

INTERGOVERNMENTAL PANEL ON CLIMATE CHANGE (1990) *IPCC First Assessment Report, Volume 1, Policymakers' Summary*, August; Working Group One Report, *Scientific Assessment of Climate Change*, June (published as Houghton, J., Jenkins, J. and Ephraums, J. (eds) (1990) *Climate Change: the IPCC scientific assessment*, Cambridge, Cambridge University Press); Working Group Three Report, *Formulation of Response Strategies*, June.

OLIVIER, D., ELLIOT, D. and REDDISH, A. (1991) 'Sustainable energy futures', Ch. 5 in Blunden, J. and Reddish, A. (eds) (1991) *Energy, Resources and Environment*, London, Hodder and Stoughton/The Open University (Book Three in this series).

NITZE, W. (1990) *The Greenhouse Effect: formulating a convention*, London, RIIA.

Further reading

The following were some of the more readily available texts which were particularly useful in the preparation of this chapter or can be recommended if you want to read more about this topic:

EASTWOOD, P. (1991) *Responding to Global Warming: an examination of the prospects for effective action*, London, Berg.

GRUBB, M. (1989) *The Greenhouse Effect: negotiating targets*, London, RIIA.

GRUBB, M. (1990) *Energy Policies and the Greenhouse Effect* (Volume I), RIIA/ Dartmouth.

LEGGETT, J. (ed.) (1990) *Global Warning: the Greenpeace report*, London, Oxford University Press.

NITZE, W. (1990) *The Greenhouse Effect: formulating a convention*, London, RIIA.

See also the IPCC publications listed in the References.

Answers to Activities

Activity 1

(a) From Figure 4.7(b) it can be seen that global carbon dioxide emissions in 1990 were estimated to contain about 5.9 billion tonnes of carbon, and emissions from the developing world in 2025 were anticipated to be about $12.4 - 7 = 5.4$ billion tonnes. Thus the emissions from the developing world alone in 2025 are expected to be $(5.4/5.9) \times 100 = 91\%$ of the global emissions of carbon dioxide in 1990.

(b) According to Table 4.2, carbon dioxide emissions in 1990 would have to be reduced by more than 60% in order to stabilise atmospheric concentrations of carbon dioxide at 1990 values: that is to less than 40% of $5.9 = 2.36$ billion tonnes of carbon. If existing trends continue, by 2025 emissions from the developing world alone would thus be $(5.4/2.36) \times 100 = 228\%$ higher than the level required to prevent atmospheric concentrations of carbon dioxide going beyond 1990 levels.

(c) From Figure 4.7(b), carbon dioxide emissions in 2025 from Asia are expected to contain $11 - 7 = 4$ billion tonnes of carbon. This is $(4/5.9) \times 100 = 67.8\%$ of the level of global emissions in 1990, and $(4/2.36) \times 100 = 169.5\%$ of the emissions levels required in 1990 to stabilise atmospheric concentrations.

Activity 2

It is in the energy sector that there is typically most scope for substantial reductions in states' greenhouse gas emissions. Rapid and extensive take-up of energy-efficient technologies and practices could rapidly allow OECD countries to reduce their fossil-carbon emissions by 20–40% while still allowing for limited economic growth, particularly if accompanied by fuel-switching to natural gas or non-fossil-fuel power sources. In the Soviet Union and eastern Europe the potential gains are even greater. In the third world economic growth and industrialisation make it hard to avoid some annual increase in fossil-fuel emissions over the next 30 years, but such measures could reduce this growth from over 5% at present to between 0% and 2%.

However, although many of these measures would be beneficial even without the threat of global warming, substantial and rapid gains are unlikely to be achieved in most states without concerted government action, through removal of energy subsidies and varying combinations of regulations and changes in fiscal policy. Moreover, substantial capital investment and technical expertise will be required. In the Soviet Union, eastern Europe and the third world, such resources are in very short supply. Without substantial investment from OECD states, the potential for limiting greenhouse gas emissions from these countries will not be realised.

Apart from CFCs, production of which are being phased out by international agreement, forestry is the next most important area where significant measures could be taken to limit global warming. These are to halt and reverse tropical deforestation programmes and carry out large-scale reforestation programmes throughout the world. Improved management of waste and agricultural practices could also make a significant contribution to reducing greenhouse gas emissions from some countries and regions, but the prospects for reducing global emissions from such practices in the foreseeable future are poor.

Activity 3

The United States is responsible for some 21% of global greenhouse gas emissions (see Figure 4.4), and has one of the highest per capita emission rates in the world (Figure 4.8). Similarly, Saudi Arabia and the Netherlands have high per capita emissions (Figure 4.8). Thus all these states could expect to be disproportionately affected by a protocol that imposed substantial global reductions of fossil-carbon emissions, particularly if each state's ceiling was based on per capita emission quotas rather than equal percentage cuts. As a relatively high proportion of these countries' greenhouse gas contributions come from burning fossil fuels, they would all have an interest in emphasising the importance of agreeing protocols covering other areas of activity, such as deforestation.

Moreover, as rich states, they could also expect to be asked to transfer resources to the developing world and the Soviet Union and eastern Europe on a large scale, to fund energy efficiency and other improvements. In this context, unilateral adaptive measures to the impacts of global warming could come to seem less costly to these states than effective international preventive measures. These temptations would probably be strongest in the United States (with its particularly high carbon emissions) and Saudi Arabia, which has a strong interest also in maintaining global demand for fossil fuels, since its economy depends almost entirely on exports of these. The Netherlands was amongst the first unilaterally to commit itself to some (moderate) limits on its greenhouse gas emissions, and as a low-lying country adaptive measures (such as sea defences) would be relatively costly.

Bangladesh, China and Brazil all have relatively low per capita emissions of fossil-carbon (Figure 4.5). As developing countries, they would expect to be allowed to increase these at least gradually in any internationally agreed protocol, and also to receive resources from the OECD states to fund energy-efficiency improvements. Brazil would have a strong interest in encouraging the international community to focus on limits on fossil-fuel burning, because if all sources of carbon emissions were taken into account, it would have to be treated as one of the world's largest emitters, both in absolute and per capita terms.

In contrast, China depends particularly heavily on coal for its fuel, so any effective protocol on fossil-fuel emissions would threaten to be more costly for it than for much of the rest of the developing world. So China would have an interest in arguing for different treatment than Brazil, for example, perhaps expressed in a desire for a significant part of the burden of reducing greenhouse gas emissions to be focused on reversing deforestation. As a coastal state that is highly vulnerable to climate change and rises in sea-level, Bangladesh would have every interest in promoting immediate preventive global action of all sorts. As an extremely poor country with very low carbon emissions per capita (Figure 4.5), it would expect to be allowed to continue to increase its annual fossil-carbon emissions by any protocol, and would look to foreign aid to provide the resources for improving energy efficiency and such like.

Activity 4

The key challenge would be to find a way of dividing the burden of achieving global targets for reducing fossil-carbon emissions that all states would find acceptable and fair over a long period (since the process of limiting global warming will be a long-term one). Arguments about equity would appeal to principles such as: equal rights to economic development; 'the polluter pays' (the burden of tackling the problem should fall on those who are responsible for the problem); and equality of burden in tackling the problem.

Any just agreement would have to allow the developing world substantial scope for continued economic growth, and impose the greater part of the burden for limiting global warming on the developed world. But the dividing line between these two worlds is blurred, and would become controversial if it became important in the allocation of burdens.

Moreover, the differences within each of the developed and developing groups of states in relation to greenhouse gas emissions are in many respects almost as great as the differences between them. Thus there would be arguments that any just international agreement would have specifically to take into account the special circumstance of each state – a recipe for endless delay and haggling. Realistically, any negotiable approach to limiting fossil-carbon emission must be flexible as well as equitable. To be effective, it must also provide for a transfer of capital, new technologies and expertise from the OECD states to the third world, the Soviet Union and eastern Europe.

1   Introduction

In February 1990 *The Guardian*, a serious newspaper raising and reflecting public concern in the United Kingdom, led with an editorial entitled 'In search of a greener politics'. Here is an extract from that editorial:

> As Europe's political barriers come down, there is suddenly a sense of a common human destiny, of people making elementary connections in place of the artificial boundaries of ideology and repression. It is no coincidence that this revolution has emerged alongside a world-wide concern with environmental degradation. Indeed, a significant impulse behind change in eastern Europe has been fury at the physical ruination of the environment. The Green movement seeks to re-establish connections that have become fractured between [people and their] surroundings. So does Green philosophy provide the framework for a completely new order that will save the world?
>
> Environmental concern operates on different levels. It is local: the traffic gridlock around London; the sulphurous smogs from eastern European chimneys; Chernobyl; Bhopal; or the deadly spume of chemicals in the Adriatic. It crosses national boundaries through acid rain and the destruction of species in pursuit of profit. And environmentalism is above all stratospheric. It predicts imminent catastrophe through global warming caused by too much carbon dioxide being pumped into the atmosphere. Green politics says that [humankind's] greed and selfishness are to blame and that the consumer society and economic growth itself must be halted if the very planet is not to perish.   (*The Guardian*, 5 February 1990*)

* The full text of this article is given in the Appendix on page 286.

Almost twenty years earlier the renowned environmental campaigner, Edward Goldsmith, prefaced a 1972 edition of the journal, *The Ecologist*, with the following remarks:

> The principal defect of the industrial way of life with its ethos of expansion is that it is not sustainable. We can be certain that sooner or later it will end, whether against our will, in a succession of famines, epidemics, social crises and wars; or because we want it to.

These words heralded a new publication, co-written by Goldsmith and others, entitled *A Blueprint for Survival*. This was published in 1972 as a set of radical proposals for what was regarded as the need for immediate action on the environment. It provoked a widespread debate at the time amongst politicians and scientists.

You might have the same almost contradictory reactions as I did after reading these two extracts. My immediate thoughts ran something like this:

> 'So much has happened recently on the political and environmental front, that it is difficult to take it all in. It certainly does provide some

cause for hope that at last we are beginning to come to terms with some of the major environmental issues of the time.

'Then again, very little has really changed when it comes to looking after the environment; in fact in many ways things have got worse. The script may have developed a bit, the actors may have changed (although not all of them), but, beneath the storyline, fundamentally we are no nearer to tackling global environmental problems.'

Well, both responses can be justified, depending on your point of view as to how you interpret events unfolding on the international scene – politically, economically, socially, environmentally. What we are particularly concerned to understand here is how our level of *awareness* on environmental issues both relates to and is affected by our *analysis* of them, and how this in turn can result in *action* which may have political, economic and social dimensions.

1.1   *Overall objectives*

The first part of this book has dealt with two complex matters of environmental concern which demand analysis at global level – the oceans and the atmosphere. It has been proposed that responses and policies to ensure, say, more equitable management of the ocean's resources, or to mitigate the causes of global warming, require initiation and co-ordination also at a global level. The main problem for most of us is how to make sense of the issues in terms of the 'environment' as we experience it – in our own 'local' surroundings. And if we are concerned, can we do anything to alleviate the world's major environmental problems? This chapter considers the global context within which environmental problems occur, and speculates on possible futures in terms of the potential for making alternative choices about the world we might wish our children to inhabit. Of paramount importance is the need to demonstrate how far local and national environmental issues can be linked to the global.

The principal objective of these concluding chapters is thus to move from an awareness of the issues raised in the series to a critical analysis of them at a global level. This will contribute to our understanding of what constitutes an 'appropriate response' to environmental problems from the nations of the world. Whose problems are they? Where does the responsibility for action rest? We may talk in terms of global problems but can we realistically expect global action or even global solutions? Is local or national action more feasible?

In seeking to assess the relationship between 'problems' and 'actions', these chapters consider environmental issues from the standpoint of political economy and critically examine the idea that environmental problems are really problems of development. We will be asking whether the 'real' debate about the environment concerns the nature of political and economic systems within which the problems occur, and which indeed may determine the manner in which such problems are defined.

1.2   *Achievement of objectives*

Chapters 5 and 6 deal with a great many issues. Environmental issues, in particular, are often controversial and emotive. Social scientists would argue that totally objective, 'value-free' enquiry is impossible, so whilst I attempt always to take a balanced view, do not be surprised if some of my underlying values creep through my analysis. As far as possible I will demonstrate the strengths or weaknesses of one argument against another, in terms of how comprehensively it seeks to explain an issue with the evidence available. I hope, on the information presented, that you will be able to make your own assessment and come to your own conclusions about possibilities which exist.

'Only connect' observes E. M. Forster in *Howard's End* (1910). This present chapter seeks to make some important connections by providing in Section 2 an *historical context* for looking at global development issues. It starts by taking the theme of the 'conquest of Nature' and seeing what this has meant historically in terms of the relationship between economic development and the use and abuse of environmental resources (Sections 2.1 and 2.2). Section 2.3 then raises questions about different responses to progress, particularly in the nineteenth century. Sections 2.4–2.6 trace the development of industrial capitalism and global economic growth over a 200-year period, particularly in the United Kingdom, specifically emphasising the links between the development of capitalism in the west, and colonialism and underdevelopment in the third world. Section 2.6 shows how criticism of industrial capitalism developed from a number of diverse sources in the nineteenth century and led to the establishment of political movements, the most potent of which was Marxist socialism. The section concludes by examining the relationship between war, conflict and economic change in the first half of the twentieth century.

This may lead you to ask the following two questions:

● *Why history?* Many social scientists (myself included) wish to underline the importance of *historical processes* in our consideration of issues such as global environmental problems. The points outlined above should help us to make some important connections with a view to clarifying our understanding of these issues.

● *Why now?* It is less a matter of giving you new material, more of setting a context for summarising some of the principal areas discussed previously. This means making the history brief and selective, whilst maintaining relevance.

The *second part* of the chapter – Section 3 – is concerned to look at contemporary global development issues, using the framework established in the first part. It establishes a critical context for analysing these issues by posing a debate between two conflicting *ideologies* (that is, major sets of ideas/beliefs) on development and progress – capitalist and Marxist – and asks an initial question about whether sustainable development is achievable within either (Section 3.1).

The next two subsections then take a more detailed look at two case studies which show that both Marxist-inspired and capitalist modes of development have severely damaged the environment. In Sections 3.4 and 3.5 discussion on responses to development, change and environmental degradation is developed by looking at the growth of environmental concern over the past 20–25 years, as a preliminary to the detailed consideration of sustainable development in Chapter 6.

Central to this chapter, then, is a critical examination of two contrasting and conflicting models of development – capitalist (market economy) and Marxist (centrally planned economy) – and of their relative capacities to provide for a future which is sustainable, and literally 'does not cost us the Earth'. Can capitalism, in modified form, provide the basis for a secure future? Or does it require some form of centrally planned system? Or is there *another* way? This is perhaps the key question.

2   *Global development: an historical overview*

2.1   *A greener politics?*

If we are going in search of a 'greener' politics we need to be clear just what that entails. The quotations at the start of this chapter provide a useful frame of reference. Economic growth, consumerism, greed, selfishness: these have all become associated with the process of development in the industrialised world. The environmental effects are manifest locally, nationally and globally.

So is the 'culprit', then, that particular model of development we know as capitalism? But during this century the centrally planned economies, particularly those in the Soviet bloc, have overseen the ruination of their environments. And surely there is as much if not more environmental degradation to be found in many of the less developed or developing countries of what is usually called the 'third world'? What about deforestation, for example, and the related problems of soil erosion, desertification and silting – problems which afflict countries as diverse as the Ivory Coast, Nepal, Java and China? We cannot simply 'blame' capitalism, because environmental problems occur in other types of societies as well.

Our way forward here is conveniently prescribed by Edward Goldsmith when he states that 'the industrial way of life with its ethos of expansion . . . is not sustainable.' We shall be returning to his ideas and more particularly the concept of sustainable development later in this chapter and the next. For the moment the concept of **sustainability**, or **sustainable development**, provides us with an ideal vehicle for linking awareness to analysis to action. A working definition is:

> Development which ensures continuing growth and progress for humankind, whilst arresting and changing those processes which cause irreversible damage to the environment.

It is a theme which is currently (in 1991) high on the political agenda of many countries in both the developed and the developing world. To understand why, we shall need to take a step back into history: to trace the various strands of thinking, both convergent and divergent, which have culminated in what for the cynical observer might have become the latest political bandwagon, but what for us is an important means of integrating a wide range of themes: historical processes, economic development, underdevelopment and uneven development, environmentalism, equity and resource use, ecology and politics. For there is nothing new in the concept of sustainability: it is the political economic context within which it is seen to operate which is of paramount importance here.

2.2   *The 'conquest of Nature'*

Many contemporary environmental thinkers like Goldsmith have equated the continuing quest for economic growth with the idea of the 'conquest of Nature'. *Brown* (1990) introduces some contrasting ideas on the natural world, developed in their historical context.

Q   If you have read Book One of this series, can you recall how he categorised these ideas?

A   He identified four significant 'traditions': Stewardship, Imperialist, Romanticist and Utilitarian. He showed how each of these traditions has developed and has been handed down to us, and how each has had an impact on contemporary attitudes to environment and resource use; but two have been dominant: Imperialism and Utilitarianism.

By *Imperialism* is meant the spirit of Empire and conquest, and the dominant attitudes to development which accompany it. So, for example, economic imperialism would refer to the dominant influence of a particular economic system, that of capitalism, on the world economy. *Utilitarianism* is the ethos, attributed particularly to Jeremy Bentham in the nineteenth century, of achieving the greatest good for the greatest number through the utility of actions. This is often referred to as working for 'the common good'.

Stewardship, which sees human beings as being in a position of special privilege and responsibility in relation to the rest of Nature as stewards or managers, is not a strong western tradition, but it is a persistent one. Within it, we are able to trace the origin of the word 'conservation', back to seventeenth-century France. In 1669 Colbert, Chief Minister to Louis XIV, reorganised the administration of the French national forests. To replace the feudal system the various forest regions or 'conservations' were put under the supervision of government officers, who were known as 'conservateurs' to regulate use and introduce a system of overall control. The objective was to achieve a *sustained yield* of the diverse products of the forest. They could be considered therefore, as some of the earliest 'resource conservationists'. Stewardship remains an important conceptual prop for many contemporary environmentalists.

Romanticism is also a persistent tradition, and developed particularly in nineteenth-century Britain when the Romantic movement accorded an intrinsic value to Nature, and particularly to wild Nature. It represented the very antithesis of Imperialist thinking, whereby Nature was considered as having no value except in its relation to the needs and wants of humans; Nature was to be subdued and subordinated. Utilitarianism valued Nature in so far as it could give pleasure as an amenity for people.

Although Stewardship and Romanticism have certainly been significant in shaping some of our current attitudes to environment (for example, the Romantic movement played an important part in shaping the conservation movement), the Imperialist and Utilitarian traditions have retained an overriding influence, linked as they have been to political and economic considerations and requirements, even though both are becoming increasingly questioned.

At the turn of the century a movement in the United States gave some commentators of the day cause for optimism that a genuine concern for resource use was being given political expression. It has been called a 'conservation movement', implying that there was some consensus about the future use and management of natural resources in the United States. A brief examination of this movement is instructive, because it serves to illustrate how a concept – **conservation** – which would appear superficially to engender commendable principles, can lend itself to varying interpretations and use, depending upon who is doing the interpreting and the using. Now read Box 5.1.

Box 5.1   The conservation movement in the USA

In the 'American Declaration of the Conservation of Natural Resources' of 1908 Gifford Pinchot, who was much influenced by the writings of American naturalist George Perkins Marsh, amongst others, and who was himself involved in the Forestry Service, stated a basic principle of conservation:

> . . . that resources (in the widest sense of the word) must be developed for the benefit of posterity. Let us conserve the foundations of our prosperity for the material base of our civilisation is threatened with exhaustion.

Significantly, the Declaration was endorsed and given a seal of political approval by the then President, Theodore Roosevelt. The movement as envisaged by Pinchot and his followers essentially embraced a *conservationist* ethic of good *Stewardship* wherein policies should seek the 'common good' within a basically Utilitarian framework. Whilst there is undoubtedly an undertone of progressive thinking in Pinchot's writings, incorporating at least implicitly ideals of greater equity in the use of resources, the words of the Declaration reflected the strongly materialist basis to the general movement.

More fundamentally perhaps, and certainly from the point of view of our interest in these events, the US 'movement' was never really that, in that it never embodied an overall consensus of ideas about the process of development and how to contain and to manage it. It evolved right out of nineteenth-century ideas of progress, measured predominantly in terms of technological development and achievement. It demonstrated a realisation that there were limits to the seemingly boundless expansion which characterised the drive westwards by capitalists during the latter part of the nineteenth century, and that what had been achieved should not be forfeited.

The movement was never united. If the Declaration attempted to echo the sentiments of Pinchot and his supporters, the reality was far more imperialist in its execution. The 'technocratic' interpretation, adhering to a 'Gospel of Efficiency' which embodied a reflection of the spirit of applied scientific rationality that was abroad in the land, was predominant. An opponent of Pinchot's wrote some time later that this problem was fervour without direction: 'Conservation neither arose from a broad popular outcry, nor centred its fire primarily upon the private corporation.' Indeed, corporations often supported conservation policies, while the people just as frequently opposed them.

To those who were in positions of power – the politicians, the captains of industry – the movement was above all a scientific movement. Its role in history arose principally from the implications of science and technology in modern society. To those who perhaps claimed a greater vision, stressing social as well as political and economic meaning for the movement, this approach was no more or less than protecting the rationalised self-interest of the strong in society. It was about the 'conquest of Nature'.

Activity 1

If you have studied *Sarre* (1990), try to recall some of the discussion in that chapter. From your knowledge of that and your reading of this case study, note down what benefits the ideas developed in the American Conservation Movement might have produced, in the way in which resources are used and managed today, for example in relation to ideas of sustainability, both in the United States and in the United Kingdom. Compare your answer with the one given at the end of the chapter.

2.3   *Different responses to 'progress'*

A recurrent theme is that in the past, and particularly over the last one hundred years or so, there has been a variety of responses to the 'threat' to the environment of **development** in various forms. We have already noted the diversity of ideas which emerged from one short but significant episode in US history, but on what processes of development are we most obviously focusing and at what level: local, national, global?

It is quite apparent that there was considerable destructive intervention in the natural environment globally prior to industrialism. This has been well brought out by *Simmons* (1990) and can be traced back at least to neolithic times: the destruction of forests, overgrazing and farming malpractice had all produced major environmental disasters long before the advent of modern forms of industrial production.

There is a persistent strand in some English literature – as well as in the contemporary writings of a number of 'radical Greens' – which urges a return to some form of pre-industrial rural idyll. This strand of romanticist thinking has been diagnosed and analysed by Raymond Williams:

> In a large part of the ecological movement as it developed, there was an in-built tendency to contrast the damaging industrial order with the undamaging, natural pre-industrial order . . . In its false contrast of physical conditions, and its characteristic evasion of social and economic conditions, this weak but popular case altogether misses the point.   (Williams, 1982, p. 6)

Williams is making an important point here, that if you only pick up the physical appearances, you are likely to miss all the central social and economic questions, and it is one to which we will be returning shortly. It is nevertheless the case that the new processes of production introduced in Britain through the Industrial Revolution brought a new threat to the physical environment in terms of the scale for potential damage and destruction. (See Plate 8.) And of course this potential has been realised in large measure, both at a local level, and ultimately at a global level. Raymond Williams quotes an account by James Nasmyth, the inventor of the steam hammer, on the 'impact of his iron workings at Coalbrookdale, circa 1830':

> The grass had been parched and killed by the vapours of sulphureous acid thrown out by the chimneys; and every herbaceous object was of a ghastly grey – the emblem of vegetable death in its saddest respect. Vulcan had driven out Ceres.   (Nasmyth in Williams, 1982, p. 4)

Since the early days of industrialisation in Britain there have been scores of commentators who have set down their thoughts and feelings about the disastrous legacy being delivered through a relentless drive to 'conquer' the Earth. The metaphor of 'conquest', is very much equated with the ethos of imperialism. From Cobbett's *Rural Rides* (1830) to the novels of Charles Dickens (1812–1870) to the contemporary alarums of Goldsmith and others, images are presented of varying degrees of social deprivation and environmental pollution and degradation, brought about by the 'unbridled forces of industrial capitalism'. None was more damning in his writings than the German philosopher Friedrich Engels. In *The Conditions of the Working Class in England* he painted a vivid picture of urban and industrial squalor in Manchester in the 1840s, when the ethos of expansion was at its height. In 1848 he and Karl Marx issued the *Communist Manifesto*. His radical political persuasions did not prevent Engels falling into the 'all was fair in the garden until the Industrial Revolution came along' trap. He wrote of a pre-industrial golden age of rural bliss where:

> The workers enjoyed a comfortable and peaceful existence – children grew up in the open air of the countryside, and if they were old enough to help their parents' work this was only an occasional employment, and there was no question of an eight or twelve hour day.   (Engels, 1848; 1970 edn)

Summary of 2.2 and 2.3

An examination of different attitudes to 'Nature' in an historical context
can assist understanding of contrasting approaches to environment and
resource use in the present day.

The dominance of Imperialist and Utilitarian values, as manifest in
ideas of progress measured primarily in terms of industrialisation and
economic growth, has been challenged historically within the traditions of
Stewardship and Romanticism, and is being challenged increasingly today.

2.4   *Industrial capitalism and global development*

The process of industrial development which started in Britain with the
initial stages of the Industrial Revolution around 1750 will be considered in
this section. This will enable us to understand development essentially as
an historical process in relation to the use and exploitation of resources, to
appreciate how the system known as industrial capitalism came to have
such a dramatic impact upon the global economic scene; and to
understand the connections between a dominant economic system (that is
capitalism) and trade, colonialism and underdevelopment.

The process which transformed Britain from an agrarian, trade-centred
society to a fully industrialised one took place over a long period of time,
extending back into the early eighteenth century, and indeed beyond. By
1750, England, if not Scotland and Wales, was already a *monetary* and a
market economy. It was a **monetary economy** because products were sold for
money and not exchanged for other goods, and it was a **market economy**
because nearly everything was produced to be sold. The development of
the market economy meant that communities, regions or even the country
as a whole did not have to be self-sufficient in what they produced. People
could consume things they did not produce themselves, but obtained from
both national and international sources. In 1750 largely self-sufficient
peasant communities had long ceased to exist in England.

This is a very significant point, particularly in relation to the role of
industrialisation in modern agricultural or developing economies (to be
discussed in Chapter 6). In mid-eighteenth-century England an agrarian
system which had already been revolutionised through invention and
technical development could produce sufficient supplies of food with a
reduced input of labour, supplemented by imports from abroad, to enable
increasing numbers of people to concentrate in towns. Absolute shortages
of food, as a result of bad harvests, ceased to occur. The market regulated
prices in times of short supply, and had an integrating effect on the whole
economy, and the process of exchange allowed for an advanced division of
labour that was mobile and not tied to the land. This provided a sound
basis for the Industrial Revolution – a revolution in economic production,
based upon resources and technological innovation.

The economy was not transformed overnight. But the transformation
was revolutionary because it involved fundamental change not just in the
means of production, but in social and economic relations. The Industrial
Revolution certainly changed attitudes to the use of resources, had major
environmental effects, and irreversibly changed the relationship between
society and its environment. These changes reflected the dynamism and
growth of the economy through successive phases of industrialisation
during the latter part of the eighteenth century, and the nineteenth

century. A new form of society emerged, **industrial capitalism**, based on the new form of production.

It was *industrial* because the basis for wealth in the new system arose out of *production* rather than from trade. It was *capitalist* because capital took over the basic economic process of production. Of course, capital existed before the Industrial Revolution: the basis of trade had always been capital. In this new system industrial capital made its profit from organising production rather than trade, by employing workers to make products which could be sold for more than it cost to have them made. So what was revolutionary about this evolving system was that the process of production was run to make a *profit*.

▲ *Barrow-in-Furness Haematite Works, c. 1875.* The industrialisation process required great capital investment.

Box 5.2   An analytical point

Industrial capitalism is an economic system that operates through the pursuit and accumulation of capital for profit. Profit is the 'motivating force' that drives the system and produces growth, in a progressive process of reinvestment and increasing productivity, which is also linked to technological development and change. These two interconnected themes – profit accumulation and technological advancement – are not necessarily contradictory, but they can be used for undertaking

fundamentally different analyses of the impact of industrial capitalism. Emphasising profit can lead to a critical consideration of capitalism, as was undertaken by Marx and Engels in partricular (see Section 2.6). Focusing on technological innovation can stress the benefits of capitalist expansion, reinforcing the classical economic belief that a 'free market' economy – that is an economy which operates with a minimum of state intervention – works in the best interests of everyone. This is an important analytical distinction, the relevance of which will be developed further in Sections 3.4 and 3.5 and in Chapter 6.

The path to full industrialisation in the UK was by no means a smooth one. It was subject to frequent periods of crisis, both economic and social. During the 1830s and 1840s, marked by a protracted period of severe economic crisis (brought about principally because the industrial base was narrowly dependent on one sector of the textile industry, cotton) and of considerable social and political unrest (notably the Chartists' revolt), a second major phase of expansion occurred, based upon a revolution in transport, the railways. This highlights an important recurring theme about the capitalist economic system, its ability to ride out economic and political storms, and to reassert itself yet more strongly. Eric Hobsbawm, in *Industry and Empire* (1968), describes this development as appearing:

> . . . to be several generations ahead of the rest of the economy, and indeed 'railway' became a sort of synonym for ultra-modernity in the 1840s, as 'atomic' was to be after the Second World War. . . . [Here] was a new transport system, a new means of mobilizing capital accumulations of all kinds for industrial purposes, and above all, a vast new source of employment and a gigantic and lasting stimulus to the capital goods industries of Britain.   (Hobsbawm, 1968)

As important at this time was the increasing impact of British 'railway expertise' on a global scale, in particular in the major stimulus brought to the export of capital goods for the construction of railways abroad. This global development had a dual purpose: to secure access to raw materials and food for Britain's industrial society, and to satisfy the incessant search for markets in which to sell the factories' products. The figures in Table 5.1 demonstrate the growth of railways globally.

To a great extent the railways were built with British capital, usually by British contractors, using British materials and equipment. What we see here is a remarkable period of expansion globally, with industrialisation in the west transforming, in particular, Germany and the United States into major industrial economies to rival the British, and ultimately to surpass it, and the opening up of previously undeveloped areas: the North American prairies, the South American pampas, the south Russian steppes, and the laying of the foundations of tropical and sub-tropical economies based on the exports of mined and agrarian products.

This major expansionist phase, and the re-orientation of the British economy, are keys to understanding the development of contemporary global economic structural relationships. It is above all about the driving force of capitalism, allied to a dominant imperialist ideology – that is an overriding set of beliefs about the inevitable indomitability of **economic growth** and advancement, and its structural consequences in terms of a 'western industrial *hegemony*' – the concept of domination or leadership

Table 5.1   *World railway mileage opened, per decade (to nearest 1000 miles)*

Year	United Kingdom	Europe (excluding United Kingdom)	America	Rest of World
1840–50	6 000	7 000	7 000	–
1850–60	4 000	13 000	24 000	1 000
1860–70	5 000	27 000	24 000	7 000
1870–80	2 000	37 000	51 000	12 000

▲   The construction of the railways in the nineteenth century brought vast new
areas into the global economy: (top) laying the Union Pacific Railway in North
America, 1869; (below) the opening of the Madras railway in India, 1856.

directly related to economic power. (Note that the word 'imperialist' here
takes on an altogether more political and economic connotation than just
'dominion over Nature'.)

This development process had different impacts upon the industrial
countries and the 'underdeveloped' world. In the former, industrial
capitalism, initiated in the United Kingdom, was being carried on and
extended based upon technological innovation and improvement. In the
latter it meant the construction of a global system of transport, based upon
the railway and improved shipping, to facilitate the exploitation of
resources and their transport to the major markets in the industrialised
world. It is to this latter set of circumstances that we now turn.

2.5 Colonialism and underdevelopment

Britain had been an imperialist power since the seventeenth century, but the last quarter of the nineteenth century saw the rise of a 'new' imperialism, which was both economic and political. Allen (1981) sees this as directly linked to capitalist development: 'Colonialism . . . stems from the expansionist character of capitalism, the drive to seek out new sources of profit through the conquest of the non-capitalist world.'

The continents of South America, Africa and Asia offered a number of sources of profit: they provided new sources of raw materials for manufacturing production, new markets for the products of capitalism, and a source of cheap labour to produce goods for sale in the domestic market. This process had been foreseen by Adam Smith a century earlier, in *The Wealth of Nations* (1776), in relation to an international division of labour.

When the great internal markets of western Europe and North America started to falter in the economic depression of the 1870s and 1880s, the imperialist drive of other industrial nations gathered momentum, and ended the virtual British monopoly in the undeveloped world. Globally, a discernable 'core and periphery' was evolving in terms of economic development, imperialist exploitation and resource use. So the rest of the world, largely dominated by European empires before the Industrial Revolution, continued to be dominated by a new form of economic imperialism which also incorporated the North American continent. Clearly this 'relationship' as it developed was unequal, and has important consequences which we shall be looking at later, when we come to deal with the links between development and environment in a contemporary context.

For the present the connection between colonialism, **underdevelopment** and **uneven development** needs to be understood.

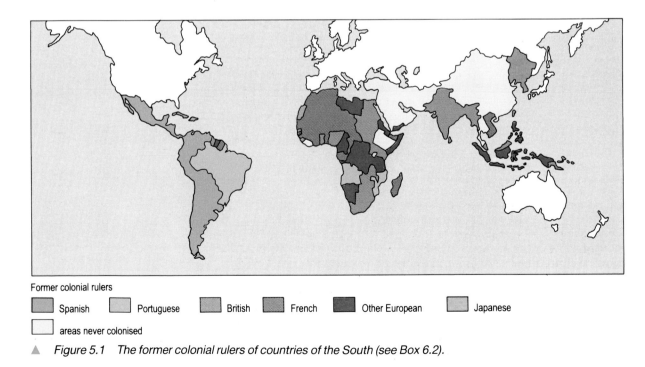

Former colonial rulers

☐ Spanish   ☐ Portuguese   ☐ British   ☐ French   ☐ Other European   ☐ Japanese

☐ areas never colonised

▲   *Figure 5.1   The former colonial rulers of countries of the South (see Box 6.2).*

Box 5.3   Development and underdevelopment

These are both value-laden terms, capable of wide interpretation. The sense in which development is most commonly used, and hence the starting-point for our consideration of the term here, is economic development: a combination of economic growth and the assumed benefits this brings in terms of human progress and improvement. **Gross National Product (GNP)** and **Gross Domestic Product (GDP)** are relatively crude measures or indicators of economic development, and relate to the economic system which dominates international economic relations – capitalism. So, the way most of us view 'development' in the industrialised world is in terms of the way we have experienced that process ourselves, in the context of capitalist economic development.

The concept of 'underdevelopment' is one developed by Marxist thinkers in particular. If we only use capitalist indicators as measures of 'development' then clearly many areas of the world are going to be considered as 'underdeveloped'. Also, most developing countries are economically dependent upon the developed nations, in terms of aid and as a market for their products, which are often in the form of 'cash crops' for which they do not always receive a 'fair market price'. This is due to the trade agreements like GATT (General Agreement on Tariffs and Trade) which work in favour of the developed nations. Such a situation keeps many countries in a state of underdevelopment, because they are unable to generate sufficient currency internally to sustain economic growth.

'Development projects' are funded by international financial institutions like the World Bank and the IMF, but many of the benefits of the schemes accrue to the developers themselves. (Such an example is the Carajas Iron Ore Project in Amazonia in the case study in Section 3.3.) To describe the relationship of economic dependency between the developed 'capitalist' countries and the developing world, some writers talk in terms of a 'core' and 'periphery'. Of course, a number of developing countries are developing strong and vibrant economies, like Thailand for example, and so we have to be careful about many very broad generalisations. This is the problem social scientists encounter when they use terms like 'development' and 'underdevelopment'.

The growth of trade between colonial powers and the colonies was highly skewed in favour of the former, and prejudicial to the latter's development. Capital accumulated in the colonies was not retained there, but provided merchant capital for extending trading relationships between the developed and underdeveloped nations. The accumulative and exploitative logic of capitalism led to the destruction of local economies, which became 're-oriented' to the requirements of the colonising nations. Indigenous technical skills and craft industries suffered greatly in the wake of the more advanced technologies. In short, the economic development of the advanced nations was at the expense of locally oriented, indigenous development in what became termed the 'third world' countries, and led directly to their underdevelopment. See Figure 5.1 and Box 5.3.

2.6   Political movements and individuals: from Marxism to populism

At this juncture it is instructive to pause in order to take a more measured view of some of the growing number of 'voices of discontent' about the adverse consequences of industrialisation and development in Europe, since their messages of protest, of 'finding another way' are still with us today, some strongly, others more falteringly. Some come to us in the form of connected political or social movements, like Marxist socialism, others by way of traditions of thinking which have also been influential, though less through the medium of orthodoxy and dogma. For example, we could use the umbrella term of **'populism'*** to embrace a range of thinkers –

* The belief in the right and ability of ordinary people to play a major role in governing themselves.

philanthropic, romantic, political – who, in one way or another, have offered alternatives to large-scale industrialism. These alternatives focus on the importance of individuals co-operating together, working with and not against Nature, with an emphasis on small-scale development. Some of the more cherished principles of today's major environmental pressure groups can be said to derive from their writings, although the search to give meaningful political expression to their aspirations may often involve wrestling with the more 'orthodox' political traditions. One pertinent illustration is the current trend amongst some proponents of radical economic and social change to forge a link between *socialism* and *ecology* to construct a new kind of 'green politics'. We will be looking at this in Chapter 6.

We must be wary, nevertheless, of overstating the connections between the thought-provokers of one hundred years ago and today's environmental thinkers. Our concern is to establish the significance of historical processes in allowing us a greater insight into the most pressing contemporary issues. For this purpose I propose to discuss briefly the relevance of one of the more influential political movements of the nineteenth century, Marxism, to current environmental problems, and the contributions of two important writers from quite different backgrounds who, for convenience, we can place under the populist umbrella: William Morris (1834–96), an Englishman, born rich by inheritance, a master craftsman, poet and socialist, and Peter Kropotkin (1842–1926), a Russian anarchist, who did much of his writing in exile in London.

Marx and Engels

Engels' critical observations on the worst excesses of industrialisation in terms of the appalling living conditions in the rapidly expanding industrial towns in Victorian Britain have already been referred to in Section 2.3. What specifically separates out the major influence of Marx and Engels and the revolutionary socialist tradition from other movements of the time is the emphasis on poverty. To them the central problem of society was poverty which was inevitable with the particular social and economic relations of production within capitalism – the two-class system of *capitalists*, who owned the means of production, and *workers*, who were employed by the capitalists as wage labourers. It was therefore necessary to restructure the productive processes, with the objective of increasing output and ensuring its more equitable distribution by handing over ownership of the means of production to the workers. For Marx and Engels industrialisation was a progressive force, whose full realisation was being impeded because of the struggle between class interests within capitalism.

In the second half of the nineteenth century the threat to natural resources from development was not readily foreseen, yet much of Marxist thinking at this time appears to be laced with references in the opposite direction: extending humankind's dominion over Nature, mastering Nature, conquering Nature. The irony, as Raymond Williams (1982) explains, is that here we have 'a classic rationale of imperialism in just that expanding phase. That's where the metaphors of conquest and mastery come from. They form the whole internal ethic of an expanding capitalism [as we have already noted]; to master it, to conquer it, to shift it around to do what you want with it . . .', and to push people around as well.

Many observers would see the disastrous environmental consequences of decades of centralised control in the Soviet Union and the countries of eastern Europe as a damning indictment of Marxist thinking. It is certainly contestable to what extent it is possible to link the theorising of Marx and Engels to what has actually occurred in the eastern bloc since the 1917 revolution, and this theme is taken up in a later study. Certainly, contemporary neo-Marxist thinking does have an important contribution to make to the debate about environment and underdevelopment, as discussed in Chapter 6. It is also incorrect to leave you with the impression that Marx and Engels had nothing 'positive' to say about our relationship with Nature. Indeed Engels wrote a text entitled *Dialectics of Nature* in which he argues that we shall never understand the ethos of expansionism if 'we fail to remember that we ourselves are part of nature, and that what is involved in this mastery and conquest is going to have its effect on us. . .' (quoted in Williams, 1982). This is an important point to which we will also be returning in Chapter 6. In another essay 'The Part played by Labour in the Transition from Ape to Man', Engels comes arguably close to expounding a conservationist ethic:

> Let us not, however, flatter ourselves overmuch on account of our human victories over nature. For each such victory nature takes its revenge on us . . . we are reminded that we by no means rule over nature, like something standing outside nature, but that we . . . belong to nature, and exist in its midst, and that all over mastery of it consists in the fact that we have the advantage over all other creatures of being able to learn its laws and apply them correctly.   (1970, p. 12)

William Morris

In William Morris we find a very different revolutionary fervour, nurtured at Oxford University, where he was greatly influenced in different ways by the works and writings of Thomas Carlyle and John Ruskin. From Carlyle he acquired his hatred of the Utilitarian and imperialist values of capitalism, which were ultimately to take him from the romantic 'poetic' yearnings for a pre-industrial way of life to a revolutionary socialist conviction which culminated in the founding of the 'Socialist League' in 1885. From Ruskin, Morris was to gain a new outlook on the role of creative satisfaction in labour, which was to underline his most decisive and important contribution to socialist thinking, his critique of the abstract idea of production.

It was his own practice as a craftsman that gave him a clear insight into what work on physical objects really means. As Williams (1982) puts it: 'Instead of the simple capitalist *quantum* of production, he began asking questions about what *kinds* of production.' Morris himself wrote: 'Have nothing in your home which you do not either believe to be beautiful or know to be useful.' This translates into a criterion of the types of production that puts human need above the consumerist dominance of capitalist marketing. In challenging the notion of production as an end in itself, Morris was in effect throwing down the gauntlet not only to laissez-faire capitalist thinking, but also to conventional socialist thinking.

Two quotes from lectures given in 1881 and 1879 respectively serve to highlight Morris's rejection of Utilitarianism and imperialism:

> Civilisation . . . has let one wrong and tyranny grow and swell into this, that a few have no work to do, and are therefore unhappy . . . Of all countries ours is the most masterful, the most remorseless; in pushing forward this blind civlisation . . . for our parts, we think that the remedy is to be found in the simplification of life, and the curbing

of luxury and the desires for tyranny and mastery that it gives birth to . . .   (1881; in Thompson, 1976, p. 254)

To further the spread of education in art, Englishmen in India are . . . actively destroying the very sources of that education – jewellery, metal work, pottery, calico-printing, brocade weaving, carpet-making – all the famous and historical arts of the great peninsula have been . . . thrust aside for the advantage of any paltry scrap of so-called commerce.   (*The Art of the People*, 1879; *op. cit.*, p. 260)

Morris's ideas have remained both influential and persistent, but have not been sustained in the way in which, say, Marxist socialist thinking has. One reason might be that his solution of 'simplification' implies almost a regression to a pre-industrial way of life. Another rests in the nature of centralist versus non-centralist movements at this particular time in history.

Peter Kropotkin

A number of commentators have seen Peter Kropotkin and his followers as the forerunners of contemporary environmentalists, and have argued that the anarchists were the first 'true ecologists'. It is certainly the case that Kropotkin foresaw the severe social and environmental problems that we now see as consequences of industrialisation and global development.

Interestingly, we can trace here the historical connections between what has more often been regarded as an apolitical science, ecology, and political movements towards the end of the nineteenth century. The German biologist Haeckel coined the term **ecology** during the 1860s, and he subsequently became involved in the widespread socialist movement in Europe. (See *Silvertown* (1990) for a full discussion of this term.) At about the same time Kropotkin became an anarchist, and employed the theories of ecology extensively in his writings.

In his text *Fields, Factories and Workshops* (1899), seen by some as one of the essential texts of the ecological tradition, he dealt with many issues of central concern to ecologists today. In particular he argued for the reversal of the trend towards political and economic centralisation, stressing that policies about human needs should emanate from the level where people come together in direct personal and working relationships, the 'grassroots' level, and not the level of the state or the industrial corporation. Wastefulness of industrial and agricultural production disturbed him, and he was convinced that England could be made agriculturally self-supporting through effective conservation of fertility. The integration of agriculture and industry was a major consideration, with an emphasis on small-scale production units spread throughout the land. Kropotkin was also a fierce critic of the Darwinian competitive view of evolution. He contended that one of the most potent forces in evolution and in sustaining the balance of nature was co-operation, and that the struggle for existence was the struggle against adverse circumstances rather than within species. His central contribution was to relate a political creed, anarchism, to the movement for conserving the environment, through concrete proposals for industrial and agrarian reform.

Again, the views of Kropotkin and the nineteenth-century anarchists have been influential, and are perhaps gaining a new pre-eminence with the increasing concern for global environmental crises. Yet, as we saw with William Morris, there has not been a sustained political movement to counter capitalism. That has been the domain of Marxist doctrine.

Activity 2

Summarise the three views presented above, noting down major differences and similarities between them. How do the ideas of these four thinkers link to modern-day movements and ideas? Compare your answers with those given at the end of the chapter.

2.7   *War, conflict and change*

By the turn of the century, when some British and American philanthropists were already questioning deeply the whole process of industrialisation and economic growth, and followers of Marxist socialism were girding their loins for a major political onslaught, most particularly in Russia, a pattern for global economic development for the 1900s had been established, although it was not to remain settled for long. A major consequence of the depression of the 1870s and 1880s, when there was a slump in capitalism's traditional markets, was the emergence of a *competing group* of industrial and economically advanced powers.

A new dimension had entered international politics. The process of imperialism saw the industrialised powers of Europe – Britain, Germany, France – and the United States establishing regions of imperial influence against potential competitors, often in advance of any perceived economic benefits. This underlines the political as well as the economic motives for colonialist expansion. Significantly, after a long period of relative peace, the great powers moved into an age of world wars.

The two World Wars affected the balance of economic power amongst the industrialised nations of the world, saw the emergence of new powers, and had a major impact on the whole structure of industrial capitalism and global economic relationships. The First World War reduced the productive output of all the industrial powers, and, following a short period of stabilisation, the great slump of 1929–32 reduced it even further (except in Japan and the Soviet Union). This major crisis in global capitalism had been accurately predicted by Marxism, but their ultimate prediction, its complete demise, failed to occur, although to economic thinkers like John Maynard Keynes it certainly appeared to be under severe threat. His criticism that the 'free' market system had spawned the crisis became the economic orthodoxy of the post-Second World War era, and 'saved' capitalism by establishing the **mixed** or **welfare economy**, which involved direct intervention in the market by governments (for example, by guaranteeing a subsistence income to the unemployed).

Between the Wars world trade slumped, both in manufactured and primary products, international flows of capital dried up, and everywhere trade barriers went up. The 'liberal' economic processes set in motion in the United Kingdom 150 years earlier, within the 'free enterprise, classical economic' doctrine of Adam Smith, no longer appeared capable of steering the capitalist ship.

After the Second World War the global economic picture looked very different from that of fifty years earlier, although some important 'themes' remained intact, particularly those of **economic dependency** and the inequitable distribution of resources. The modern industrial state (that is outside the centrally planned economies) was all about the implementation of scientific technology, mass production methods, industrial production for the 'mass market' and government intervention. Even more significantly, industrialism was increasingly about **economic concentration** (of a large proportion of output or employment in a small number of firms), **monopoly capitalism** and the growth of the multinational or transnational corporations.

The global map saw a number of economic power blocs in the United States, western Europe, the Soviet bloc and Japan, a newly revolutionised China, and through the 1950s and 1960s third world countries emerging from their period of colonialism to become nation-states in their own right. But, as we shall see in Chapter 6, colonialism did not disappear, it evolved into a 'neo-colonialist' web of uneven economic relationships into which financial loans (from the developed world) and debt have become inextricably woven. This situation of economic dependency has a fundamental bearing on global environmental issues, on world security, and on the whole debate about sustainable development.

2.8   *Summary*

Thus far this chapter has taken an essentially historical approach to the consideration of what is a very contemporary issue, environment and development, in order to underline the significance of *historical processes* in helping to broaden our understanding of current global development issues. Here is a summary of the principal themes which I shall be developing in the subsequent analysis:

● The political and economic context for achieving sustainable development is of critical concern for us, even though sustainability is not a new concept.

● There was a pragmatic response to perceived limits of expansion in the United States at the turn of the century, which was essentially political and scientific.

● There have indeed been varied responses to industrialisation and development from the romantic and idealistic to the social and political.

● These found their greatest expression in the Britain of the mid to late nineteenth century, as a reaction to the development of industrial capitalism.

● Criticism has been particularly focused on capitalist industrialisation and its specific economic relations of production, but 'radical' alternatives under Marxist socialism have also had major social and environmental consequences.

● There are important links between industrial capitalism, colonialism and underdevelopment.

● There are important links between global economic development, environmental degradation and national security.

● The search for alternatives to large-scale industrialisation has involved many prominent and influential thinkers of quite different political persuasions like William Morris and Peter Kropotkin.

● If 'alternatives' are being sought, they have to be seen in terms of looking forwards, not backwards, and looking beyond the physical repercussions of development to the social, economic and political implications.

● The debate is centred in the relationship between economics and ecology, and ecology and politics.

3   Global development: a contemporary view

3.1   Sustainable development: a context for analysis

The second part of the chapter aims to establish a critical context for
analysing contemporary environmental problems by building upon the
historical themes already discussed. Specifically, it looks at the political and
economic context within which a sustainable form of development might
be achieved – one that puts environmental issues at a premium. It does this
by probing more deeply the concept of sustainability, and by evaluating
two contrasting case studies of 'environmental misuse': the first illustrates
the impact of a **centrally planned** (Marxist-inspired) **economy** on the
environment in the USSR, and the second focuses on the destruction of the
tropical rainforest within the structure of a market economy. The overall
aim is to raise questions about the potential for either 'model' of
development – Marxist or capitalist – to adapt to the requirements of a
sustainable future, and about the scope for possible practical alternatives.

A fairly basic definition of 'sustainable development' was given in
Section 2.1. You may recall the point made in the case study on the US
Conservation Movement (in Box 5.1) that implicit in the use of terms like
'conservation' and 'sustainability' is the view that some sort of consensus
exists as to their meaning and interpretation. But the term 'sustainable
development' is capable of wide interpretation. The essence of the concept
is encapsulated in the Report of the United Nations World Commission on
Environment and Development (1987), entitled *Our Common Future* but
often referred to as 'The Brundtland Report' (the Commission was chaired
by the then Prime Minister of Norway, Gro Harlem Brundtland). It states:

> **Sustainable development** is development that meets the needs of the
> present without compromising the ability of future generations to
> meet their own needs. It contains within it two key concepts:
>   ● the concept of needs, in particular the essential needs of the
> world's poor, to which over-riding priority should be given;
>   ● the idea of limitations imposed by the state of technology and
> social organisations on the environment's ability to meet present and
> future needs.   (Brundtland Report, 1987, p. 43)

This definition contains at least four serious implications:

(a) a concern about the relationship between resource use, population
growth and technological development and advancement;

(b) a concern about the production and the distribution of resources of
food, energy and industry amongst the developed, developing and
underdeveloped nations of the world;

(c) a concern about uneven development, about the gross imbalances
between the rich and poor nations, about economic dominance and
ideological differences.

(d) a concern about environmental degradation and ecological disaster.

Overall, it exposes a concern which focuses on human *need* rather than
human want. As such it effectively offers a fundamental challenge to the
materialist and consumerist values of much of the developed world, but

does it offer a challenge to industrialisation, to industrialism as such, or only to industrialism in certain forms? What, for instance, is the ethical or moral position for those in the environmental movement who are telling the underdeveloped world that it is forbidden the benefits of an industrialised society? Brundtland stated bluntly: 'It is both futile and indeed an insult to the poor to tell them that they must remain in poverty to protect the environment'.

To what extent *is* economic growth an adequate measure of development, anyway? To deal adequately with these crucial questions is to begin to grasp the complexities of the relationship between global economic development and environmental degradation. What lessons might we learn from taking a closer look at two contrasting examples of environmental degradation in a centrally planned and a free market economy?

Earlier I referred to the contrasts between the centrally planned, state-controlled economy and the market-oriented, private enterprise economy of the 'free' world. Marxism's principal concern was poverty, the basic cause of which was the economic relationship of the factors of production within capitalism. This ensured the maintenance of an often impoverished working class who only had their labour to sell, and the mutual though highly unequal interdependency with the owners of the means of production, the capitalists. The Marxist solution was revolutionary economic change, which wrested the means of production from the capitalists and put them into the hands of the proletariat, with the objective of increasing productivity and ensuring the equitable distribution of the products catering for human need, thus alleviating poverty.

This simplified and 'traditional' account derives from its origins; Marx was after all writing about economic and social relations of a century or more ago. Nonetheless, the political, economic and social repercussions of the implementation of his philosophy endure to the present day. This raises obvious questions about the durability of Marxist thinking since Marx was concerned above all about the human condition. Of more immediate interest, now that the political barriers have tumbled in eastern Europe, is an examination of the degree of physical ruination of the environment brought about under Marxist-inspired state socialism (see Plates 10 and 11). The reformist philosophies of 'glasnost' and 'perestroika', introduced by Mikhail Gorbachev in the mid 1980s, have enabled western observers to gain a detailed impression of the extent of environmental damage in the Soviet Union and the Warsaw Pact countries. In the following case study we can take a look at why it happened, and what political reform might mean for the environment in the future.

3.2   *Environment and the centrally planned economy: the world after Chernobyl*

The nuclear disaster at Chernobyl in the Soviet Union, in April 1986, has afforded an opportunity to assess in greater depth than ever before the impact of a centrally planned economy on the environment. It is becoming increasingly evident that communism – or at any rate the Soviet version of communism – is having to face up to a fundamental reappraisal of its long-standing ideological commitment that technological development and achievement are more important than the environment. Communism's achievement in the USSR is an environment which has been exploited for decades; but it is not overstating the case to say that ecology is taking over from the economy as a top priority for Soviet planning in the 1990s. Chernobyl and its aftermath is posing basic questions about that model of development, not just from without but from within.

How has this situation come about? Are we talking about a damning indictment of all centrally planned systems of control and management, or a particularly bad example of its implementation within a highly doctrinaire and dogmatic regime in the Soviet Union? For when we talk about tackling global environmental problems, is not one line of argument to be pursued that there is a need for some form of centralisation or internationalisation in terms of control and legislation? Engels, as we have seen, argued that communism alone could 'save' Nature (from the exploitative demands of capitalism, he meant), but nevertheless the emphasis was on production, and the slogans used after the 1917 Revolution were all about conquering Nature and the necessity for rapid economic development to combat poverty. Such exigencies were given full rein under the repressive totalitarianism of the Stalin era: 'Stalin's genius . . . will make it possible to master the forces of nature in the USSR', went the rhetoric (Pryde, 1972). 'The irresponsible use and resulting deteriorated condition of Russia's resources is a consequence of the capitalist economic system.' Stalin's great 'Plan for the Transformation of Nature' saw the party and the Soviet government doing everything possible to transform Nature, to do away with deserts, and to attain a further big rise in agricultural productivity. Embodied here were the ideological assumptions that natural resources would invariably be exploited in a capitalist economy, but that under a form of state-planned economy they would necessarily be utilised in the wisest possible manner.

The reality was somewhat different. In the late 1980s a number of Soviet scientists estimated that some 16% of the total area of the USSR should be declared an ecological disaster zone. Within the rapidly transforming Soviet Parliament a political forum is being established for concerned environmentalists, with the backing of Mr Gorbachev who in 1989 appointed a new Environment Minister, Mikhail Vorontsov, a non-party member. Environmental problems have been put firmly on the political agenda as a question of survival. Two particular examples illustrate the scale of the problem: the Aral Sea and the steel town of Magnitogorsk.

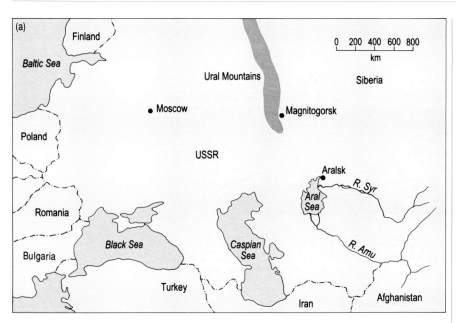

▲   *Figure 5.2*
(a) Location of
Magnitogorsk and the Aral
Sea in the Soviet Union.

(b) The diminishing extent
of the Aral Sea
(*predicted extent).

The Aral Sea

The Aral Sea, in the Central Asian region of Kazakhstan, is more than 1500 kilometres from Moscow. The Aral is an inland salt sea, with an area approximately the same as Tasmania. It has two principal feeder sources, the river systems of the Syr and the Amu (see Figure 5.2a). In the 1970s, under Brezhnev, the rivers were diverted to provide irrigation for cotton and rice, and by 1990 the volume of water flowing into the Aral was estimated to be down by over two-thirds. This has had a dramatic effect on the size of the sea: see Figure 5.2(b). The most pessimistic predictions are that the sea will disappear altogether by the year 2000. Its very existence is threatened because of the predominance of centralised planning over local interests, and two decades of official silence as the waters receded.

The reorientation of agricultural production has led to unforeseen and catastrophic consequences for the local ecology. The actual diversion of the rivers upstream to irrigate the semi-arid lands has proved to be both wasteful and inefficient: some 40% of water is lost in the sand before it reaches the crops. The drastically increased application of pesticides and fertilisers is adding to the pollution of a sea which is already high in salt. The combination of receding waters and high pollution levels has led to the destruction of the fishing industry in settlements bordering the Aral, with only four out of thirty-eight species of fish surviving.

In the 1960s the town of Aralsk was a thriving port. Today its central economy is destroyed. It is suffering a severe water shortage, the incidence of typhoid is twenty-nine times the national average, and over 80% of the children have some illness or dietary disorder. The infant mortality rate is 59 in every 1000, and more than 15 000 people have left the town altogether.

Environmental changes brought about by centralised planning have left the region, which once flourished agriculturally, impoverished, and have dramatically altered the social and economic conditions of the local people. It seems as if the consequences of such major interference were

◄   The desertification of the Aral Sea: (top) fishing boats left high and dry by the receding shoreline of the Aral Sea; (below) once a prosperous agricultural area, there is now an acute shortage of water.

never even considered: the priority, in line with Marxist orthodoxy, was to increase productivity. So far little or nothing is being done locally to tackle the problem, even though there are signs of some structural changes nationally. Moscow is a long way away, and cooperation and help from outside could be a matter of too little, too late. The question of whether the loss of the Aral Sea will have long-term effects on the climate has yet to be addressed.

Magnitogorsk

Stalin's steel city of Magnitogorsk is also some 1500 kilometres from Moscow, just to the east of the Ural Mountains, in Bashkiv province: see Figure 5.2(a). It is one of over a hundred cities in the Soviet Union cited as 'ecologically dangerous'. One massive production plant, the Combinat, accounts for some 10% of the total output of Soviet steel, with a technology largely unchanged since the Second World War. According to statistics compiled by a local newspaper in 1988, the Combinat has been responsible for putting into the atmosphere the equivalent of 800 000 tonnes of pollutants per annum. One of the consequences of this is reported to have been a very high incidence of lung cancer and bronchial disease amongst the inhabitants. The problem is that the livelihoods of most families in Magnitogorsk are bound up with the steel works. Of the population of some 450 000 over 63 000 work at the Combinat, which continues to be a product of the central administration's 'command system'. As one steel-worker has explained: 'We have got to live here; what else can we do?' All the iron ore is now imported, for which the state pays, but the state cannot afford the pollution control.

There is a need for a radical reconstruction to produce cheaper steel more efficiently and with less harmful effects, but that will require a large investment as well as the political will. The bankruptcy of the Soviet economy and the cost of importing new technology paid for in hard currency add to the difficulties. There is certainly a new awareness of environmental pollution here, but the trade-off between the cost of cleaner air and economic performance and the impact on employment is the dilemma for perestroika. It is by no means a unique dilemma – Sheffield thirty years ago was called the 'most polluted city in Europe' – but it is afforded especial significance here by the sheer magnitude of the problem.

Activity 3

Note down your conclusions from this case study. Do you think that all forms of centralised planning are condemned by these examples? Or is it the almost blind pursuit of a particular dogma and ideology that is to blame?

Pressure to modernise industry in the 'new' eastern Europe of the 1990s is coming from the west as well as from within these countries. But is the market economy, the hallmark of an unbridled capitalism, really what eastern Europe needs or wants? Investment in modern facilities could promise a cleaner environment, but an influx of western credit could also place many new pressures on already severely damaged environments. The recently constituted 'European Bank of Reconstruction and Development of Eastern Europe' is in the vanguard of this newest wave of economic assistance. There are clearly great opportunities for capital investment on a large scale which will almost certainly provide large dividends. Will the Bank ensure that environmental protection and restoration are amongst its primary objectives, in helping to ensure sustainably effective economic development for the future? We should remain sceptical, for the signs are not all that encouraging, not if we have regard for the current multilateral lending practices of the developed world, and the concern shown for environmental protection globally.

◄   *A paper plant on the River Duina, Archangel in the Soviet Union.*

By way of contrast we now examine what many consider to be the greatest global environmental catastrophe so far – the destruction of the tropical rainforests – and the different set of economic and political circumstances and relationships that is causing this destruction. In this second case study the themes of greed, consumerism, neo-colonialism and poverty are to the fore. While you are reading this case study, consider what processes come to light and what or who are the principal agents of this destruction.

3.3   *Deforestation in the tropics*

There is nothing new in cutting down trees to provide a resource for human sustenance and survival. There is also nothing new in the wholesale destruction of forests; we need look no further than the forest clearances in Britain. *Simmons* (1990) details the extent of human exploitation of forests.

The tragedy of the tropical rainforests is the scale and rate of their destruction, with little attempt being made to address the needs of a sustainable regime. The destruction is total: whole ecosystems are being destroyed, with an increasingly critical impact in relation to global warming. The 'Rainforest Fact File' (*The Guardian*, 8 December 1989), reproduced as Figure 5.4, provides a useful summary of the state of affairs as it existed at the beginning of the decade, and Figure 5.3 shows how environmental pressure groups like Friends of the Earth are attempting to convey the message of a global catastrophe.

Understandably, many environmentalists are taking a highly alarmist stance in relation to the threat, speaking unequivocally of 'an ecological disaster unprecedented in human history' (Porritt, 1990). Estimates about the scale of destruction vary greatly, however. Alarming the destruction undoubtedly is, but for our purpose we need to be clear about its causes, and who is primarily responsible. What we see, in effect, is a picture of short-term 'winners' and long-term 'losers'.

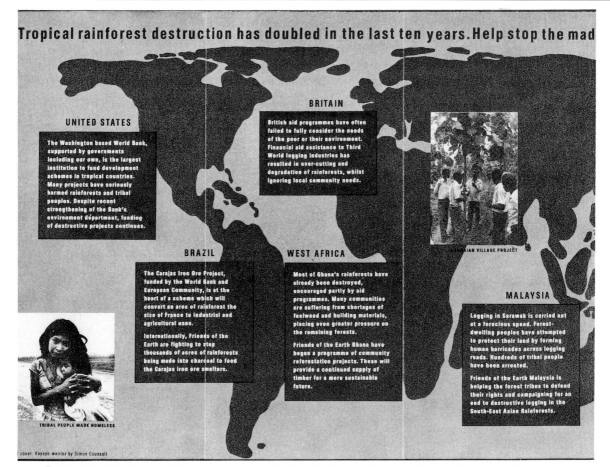

Tropical rainforest destruction has doubled in the last ten years. Help stop the mad

BRITAIN

UNITED STATES

British aid programmes have often failed to fully consider the needs of the poor or their environment. Financial aid assistance to Third World logging industries has resulted in over-cutting and degradation of rainforests, whilst ignoring local community needs.

The Washington based World Bank, supported by governments including our own, is the largest institution to fund development schemes in tropical countries. Many projects have seriously harmed rainforests and tribal peoples. Despite recent strengthening of the Bank's environment department, funding of destructive projects continues.

GHANAIAN VILLAGE PROJECT

BRAZIL

WEST AFRICA

MALAYSIA

The Carajas Iron Ore Project, funded by the World Bank and European Community, is at the heart of a scheme which will convert an area of rainforest the size of France to industrial and agricultural uses.

Internationally, Friends of the Earth are fighting to stop thousands of acres of rainforests being made into charcoal to feed the Carajas iron ore smelters.

Most of Ghana's rainforests have already been destroyed, encouraged partly by aid programmes. Many communities are suffering from shortages of fuelwood and building materials, placing even greater pressure on the remaining forests.

Friends of the Earth Ghana have begun a programme of community reforestation projects. These will provide a continued supply of timber for a more sustainable future.

Logging in Sarawak is carried out at a ferocious speed. Forest-dwelling peoples have attempted to protect their land by forming human barricades across logging roads. Hundreds of tribal people have been arrested.

Friends of the Earth Malaysia is helping the forest tribes to defend their rights and campaigning for an end to destructive logging in the South-East Asian Rainforests.

TRIBAL PEOPLE MADE HOMELESS

cover: Kayapo warrior by Simon Counsell

▲   *Figure 5.3   World map of tropical rainforest destruction from a Friends of the Earth pamphlet.*

Amongst the short-term winners are many of the developed nations. Japan is currently the world's largest market for tropical hardwoods, using it mainly for concrete shuttering whilst building; there is beginning to be a move to at least re-use it for this purpose. With just 2% of the world's population, Japan takes some 40% of the mahogany from the rainforests. Huge multinationals, like Mitsubishi, are orchestrating massive logging operations in Malaysia, Indonesia, Thailand and Burma, and in the forests of Central Africa and the Amazon. The largest funding institution for development schemes, the World Bank based in Washington, is a central target of the lobbying campaign by environmental groups like Friends of the Earth. Many projects in developing countries, funded by the world's financial institutions, have aided and abetted the process of destruction, often because of the burden on these countries imposed by crippling debt repayments.

Amongst the long-term losers are the peoples whose livelihoods and very means of existence depend upon the rainforests: the Penan tribes of Sarawak, the Orang Jaku tribes in the Malaysian peninsula, the Yanomami and Sirawe tribes of Brazil, are four examples: see Figure 5.5. In the 1950s four-fifths of the Pacific Island of Haiti were covered by forests. By 1990 this had been reduced to one-twentieth, through logging and charcoal burning. Now there is very serious soil erosion, and Haiti's six million

ness before it's too late.

JAPAN

Japan is the largest market for tropical hardwoods in the developed world. Huge companies such as Mitsubishi, better known for selling cars, are logging rainforests throughout South-East Asia. As these forests are exhausted, Japan is turning its attention to Amazonia and Central Africa.

WE CANNOT CHANGE OUR LIFE LIKE OTHER'S RACES.

RAINFOREST FACT FILE

● Tropical rainforests play a critical role in regulating the climate and what is called the greenhouse effect. They act as the earth's lungs by producing vast quantities of oxygen and using up carbon dioxide during photosynthesis.

● Burning the forests sends at least two billion tonnes of carbon dioxide per year into the air. This increases global warming. The practice of burning fossil fuels currently adds around 5.6 billion tonnes to this per year.

● Forest cover is disappearing at a rate of more than 200,000 acres a year in Brazil, Colombia, Indonesia, Mexico, Thailand, Ivory Coast, Ecuador, Nigeria, Peru and Malaysia. All these countries lie wholly or mainly in the Tropics.

● Constant media references to tropical rainforests suggests that all forests in the tropics are rainforests and consist of an extremely complex and fragile web of flora and fauna. This is not true. Not all moist tropical forests are evergreen, nor are all tropical forests moist.

● Commercial logging is directly responsible for only 20 per cent of the deforestation in tropical rainforests. But related activities, including road building and damage to other trees as logs are pulled clear, increase the toll.

● More critically, road construction in logging areas opens up huge tracts of forest to the landless poor who then move in to practise a version of the traditional method of cultivation that has been carried on for years. However these "shifting cultivators" do not leave the forest soil long enough for it to recover its fertility before returning to clear the trees and farm again.

● Radical environmentalists say that commercial development of the forests is the root of the destruction. The World Bank says that lack of commercial development, by creating armies of landless poor, is to blame.

● Drier and more open tropical forest formations, together with the shrubland into which they merge (and which falls under the definition of forest) are even more acutely threatened and their shrinkage should give cause for concern

● Since 1945 40 per cent of the world's rainforests have been destroyed. As a result, over 50 species of plants and animals become extinct every day.

● Rainforests cover only 6 per cent of the total land surface but contain at least 50 per cent of all species of life on earth.

▲   Figure 5.4

people are amongst the poorest in the world. Ultimately, it can be argued, we are all losers if we can countenance the daily extinction of over fifty species of plants and animals.

It is too easy, though, to see the process of deforestation in terms of simple cause and effect. This can mask what for many concerned environmentalists is the crux of the conflict, that on the one hand forests *must* be utilised and produce an economic return in order to survive, and on the other that utilisation can mean destruction. A heavy burden of responsibility does rest upon the developed world, with its emphasis on consumerist values. It is equally easy to underplay the role of the governments and other agencies in the developing countries themselves.

To understand further some of the complexities involved it is informative to look at the example of Brazil. For many environmentalists the Amazon rainforest presents the greatest of all ecological challenges. The rate of forest destruction in Brazil is currently estimated to be in the region of 42 000 square kilometres a year – that is an area greater than the size of the Netherlands: see Figure 5.6. Only about one-fifth goes for commercial logging, the remainder being cleared and burned. The burning (through the *quiemadas* – giant forest fires: see the photo on the back cover) releases some 470 million tonnes of carbon dioxide annually into the atmosphere.

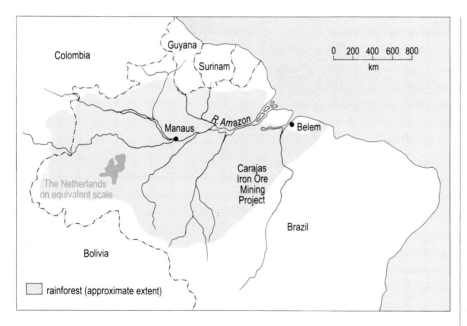

▲ *Figure 5.5   A plea from the Penan forest peoples of Malaysia and (right) Penan from all over Sarawak came to organise blockades against the timber companies.*

◄ *Figure 5.6*
The Amazonian rainforest, Brazil.

To appreciate the roles of the various 'actors' involved in the current drama, we need to go back a quarter of a century, to the setting up of 'Operation Amazon', by the generals in power in Brazil during the years of military dictatorship. The objective of Operation Amazon, to be centred in Manaus, was to 'flood the Amazon with civilisation', by attracting multinationals to invest in the region, and to encourage peasant 'settlers' to

◀ *The Carajas iron ore project in Brazil.*

come to Amazonia purportedly to ease population pressure in Brazil's overcrowded coastal periphery. It also provided an easy means for cattle ranchers (*fazendeiros*) to establish land and property rights in the forest. This colonisation process was given full government support. Since Operation Amazon was launched, land speculation has resulted in more than 60 million hectares passing into private ownership, mostly concentrated in the hands of a few major land-owners. Yet the big ranches, operating at a 'carrying capacity' of less than one animal per acre, have been an economic as well as an ecological disaster, and have only survived because of huge government subsidies, guaranteeing large profits for the land-owners. There has been an unholy alliance between successive governments and the powerful cattle ranchers union, the UDR. So huge sums of money have at the same time been fuelling the national debt, lining the pockets of the new land-owners, and producing forest destruction on a massive scale.

Side-by-side with this land speculation have come vast commercial projects, created under the auspices of Operation Amazon, and financed largely by international finance. Major logging centres have been established as roads have opened up the forests. In Paragominas, the 'saw-mill capital of the world', 500 mills handle 5000 trees a day. A by-product of the logging is charcoal burning, which has become the new boom industry, principally to provide fuel for the smelting of pig iron. Iron ore is present in the Amazon in large quantities, and mining companies have moved in with massive investments. The largest scheme is the Carajas Iron Ore project, jointly financed by the World Bank, the European Community and Japan. This will convert an area of forest the size of France to industrial and agricultural use, with the production of pig iron for export to make cars in Japan and the European Community.

This type of development is being used to pay the interest on Brazil's world record foreign debt. Involved in the chain of destruction are dozens of developed countries who are helping to foot the bill through the aid financing of the World Bank and the IMF, and through the investments of multinationals.

The ecological devastation is matched by the suffering of the people: the indigenous Indian tribes who have lived for generations on a

◀ *A Yanomami girl with a severe skin disorder, believed to be mercury poisoning, and a man receiving medication on a drip, in Poraima, Brazil. The arrival of settlers has brought many health problems to the indigenous population.*

sustainable basis off the fruits of the forest, and the landless 'settler' peasants whose dreams of owning land have been thwarted since they cannot afford to buy, and squatting is outlawed – by the *fazendeiros*. They are forced to eke out a meagre subsistence, working for poor wages for the new industrialists, and cutting and burning further tracts of the forest to work the land for the sparse crops it will support. The plight of the Indians is worse: theirs is a cruel story of lost lands and dwindling culture. As contact with outsiders increases so too does the incidence of introduced diseases, and there is little or no support from the state health services.

All of which sounds very depressing. It is easy to lose one's objectivity when assessing the consequences on this scale of so-called development. Yet our main purpose has been to highlight the processes involved, the interconnections between the developed and the developing world. There are indications that the Brazilian state is beginning to take steps to control the rate of development. Pressure from international environmental pressure groups and a change of government (in 1990) is producing some results. The Government Environment Office, IBAMA, now mounts annual forest monitoring by helicopter in an attempt to prevent unlicenced burning. Fines are levied on the worst offenders. But the power of the fazendeiros through the UDR and of vested commercial interests remains very strong; and the current state President reportedly is a close associate of the *fazendeiros*.

Activity 4

Where do you see solutions to this major problem coming, from, and what form could/should they be taking? Compare your answer with the one given at the end of the chapter.

3.4   The growth of global environmental concern

The two case studies were chosen to focus attention on the
environmentally harmful effects at a global level of two contrasting
economic systems. In the Soviet Union and in eastern Europe the effects of
decades of a totalitarian regime wedded to a centrally planned economy
were examined. Now that regime is crumbling, and the market economy is
set to spread into new territory. Yet we have also seen the equally
damaging impact that unrestrained capitalism can have – with the help of
governments in both the developed and developing world – in the case of
the tropical rainforests.

These last two sections pick up the strands of thinking outlined in the
first part of the chapter and use them both to help understand some of the
ideals and political implications of the 'new' environmentalism, and to
show how the concept of sustainable development has achieved its current
prominent position on the global political agenda. This provides a basis for
discussing what might be achievable for the future, and will enable us to
re-examine the major environmental problems discussed earlier in the
book, in the context of what an 'ethic of sustainability' might mean in
political, economic and social terms.

We have already seen that there is nothing new about environmental
concern. What marks out the modern environmentalist movement is the
formation in the late 1960s and early 1970s of distinctive pressure groups,
like Friends of the Earth (formed in 1970) and Environmental Defense and
Environmental Action in the United States, which openly preached more
direct political involvement. As already noted, their message echoed the
thinking of radicals like Morris and Kropotkin of almost a century before:
that the only way to prevent environmental and ecological catastrophe was
to change fundamentally the values of industrialism and industrialised
societies. Why had that message taken so long to surface in radical,
political form? As much as anything it was to do with a growing awareness
and anxiety about 'the *limits* to the ability of the Earth to sustain the present
levels of economic and population growth, consumption of resources, and
the destruction of the ecosphere through pollution and agricultural
methods'. It was a critical concern about the 'tragedy of the commons' (see
the Introduction to this book) as predicted by Garrett Hardin (1968) and
others, and it was a concern being expressed almost exclusively by the
developed nations.

The early 1970s witnessed a veritable explosion of literature in the
'ecodoom' mould: *The Population Bomb, The Environmental Crisis, Economic
Growth and Environmental Decay, How to be a Survivor, Blueprint for Survival*.
The latter carries the somewhat Utopian vision characteristic of much of
the writing of this genre:

> We have seen that [humankind] in our present society has been
> deprived of a satisfactory social environment. A society made of
> decentralised, self-sufficient communities, in which people work near
> their homes, have the responsibility of governing themselves, of
> running their schools, hospitals and welfare services, in fact of
> constituting real communities, would we feel be a much happier
> place. Its members, in these conditions, would be likely to develop an
> identity of their own, which many of us have lost in the mass society
> we live in. They would tend once more to find an aim in life, develop
> a set of values, and take pride in their achievements as well as in
> those of their community.   (Goldsmith *et al.*, 1972)

There are echoes of Kropotkin in this statement, and of a significant number of individuals in today's 'green movement' also. This mode of thinking found economic expression in E. F. Schumacher's famous text *Small is Beautiful* (1973). His emphasis on decentralised, self-sufficient communities carries with it the implicit warning that it is economic growth that is the root cause of all our current problems: the breakdown of ecosystems, the depletion of resources, the cause of pollution, the disruption of contemporary society. Indeed, some texts went further to mount an all-out attack on the evils of economic growth, although in Schumacher's thoughtful analysis we do find a real concern about the development of appropriate economic growth for the third world. It would be misleading here to classify all such critical texts produced at this time as being purely idealistic.

These protestations of impending crisis due to unlimited growth and consumerism found international recognition in the 1972 publication of *The Limits to Growth*, produced by the so-called Club of Rome, an informal, 'non-political', international group of scientists, humanists, economists, educators, bankers and industrialists, who shared 'a deep concern about the problems threatening human society'. The fundamental problem, they explained, was that growth of world population and of industrial output were both **exponential**: see Box 5.4.

The stage had been reached where such increases exceeded the capacity of the world industrial systems to support them. Catastrophe by the year 2000 was seen as inevitable unless action was taken immediately. The 'solution' was seen in terms of working towards a stable world population and a **steady-state economy**, rather than any form of **technological fix**: technology could not be expected always to come up with solutions to problems, and that in the long run the aim should be a world economy which does not have growth as its primary objective, as capitalism does. The tenor of the Limits to Growth message is encapsulated by the remarks of the then UN Secretary General, U Thant:

> I do not wish to seem overdramatic, but I can only conclude from the information that is available to me as Secretary General, that the Members of the United Nations have perhaps ten years left in which to subordinate their ancient quarrels and launch a *global partnership* to curb the arms race, to improve the human environment, to defuse the population explosion, and to supply the required momentum to development efforts. If such a global partnership is not forged within the next decade, then I very much fear that the problems I have mentioned will have reached such staggering proportions that they will be beyond our capacity to control.   (Meadows *et al.*, 1972)

The Club of Rome's project found political support in another international initiative of 1972, the UN Conference on the Human Environment in Stockholm. Amongst the 150 proposals presented at the conference, the following three recommendations provide a flavour of the expression of concern about global environmental issues:

- Governments should be especially mindful of activities in which there is an appreciable risk of effect on climate, and carefully evaluate the likelihood and magnitude of climatic effects, and disseminate their findings before embarking on such activities.
- The Secretary General should take steps to ensure that continuing surveillance of the world's forest cover is provided for

Box 5.4   Exponential growth rates

In an *exponential process*, the rate of change of some quantity is proportional to the quantity itself. So, if a population is said to be growing exponentially, the rate of population increase itself becomes greater the more individuals there are in the population.

Figures 5.7 and 5.8 show exponential growth rates for world population and economic growth in selected countries, respectively. If the quantity (population numbers or industrial output) is plotted against time, a characteristic J-shaped curve should result.

The crucial point being argued was that resources could not sustain such growth and catastrophe would inevitably ensue unless urgent steps were taken to check growth.

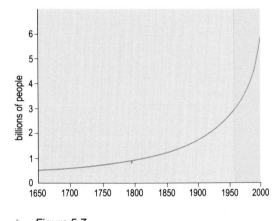

▲   *Figure 5.7*
The exponential growth of the world's population. (Green tone indicates United Nations' projections.)

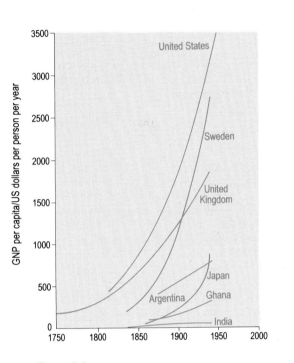

▲   *Figure 5.8*
Economic growth rates: differences in exponential growth rates are widening the gap between rich and poor countries.

through the establishment of an appropriate monitoring system, and the Food and Agriculture Organisation (FAO) should co-ordinate an international programme for research and exchange of information on forest fires, pests and diseases.

● The attention of governments should be drawn to the need for action in the following priority areas: the launching or further development of national population policies dealing with the growth and distribution of population in relation to the role, location and size of human settlements and in keeping with a *rational* use of resources.

(United Nations, 1972; emphasis added)

The Conference had an impact in terms of initiatives set in motion, with subsequent international conventions, like the Law of the Sea conferences and the Montreal Protocol, establishing some limits and controls in the use and exploitation of global resources, as discussed in earlier chapters. Twenty years on, though, many of the conference recommendations continue to have a decidedly hollow political ring about them. The Conference and the Limits to Growth project (particularly the latter) also

had an impact on the collective psyche of the supporters of continuing technological advancement and economic growth as the only way of dealing with the world's problems. These interests launched a vigorous counter-attack along the lines that the claims of the environmentalists were grossly exaggerated and out of all proportion to reality. It is to these arguments that we now turn because they lead us, conveniently, to a consideration of the current debate about sustainable development.

3.5   *From Limits to Growth to the Brundtland Report*

It is important to realise in this present context that throughout history ideas about 'growth' have been greatly influenced by prevailing political ideologies and social attitudes. Criticism of the Limits to Growth philosophy has come from both the left and the right of the political spectrum. The technologically optimistic 'technocentric' view rests on the premise that the Limits to Growth protagonists have deliberately focused on the gloomiest evidence, and have laid the blame for our environmental problems squarely at the door of modern science and technology, rather than acknowledging that scientific knowledge and technology may offer the greatest promise for their amelioration and cure. The school of 'technological optimists' has consistently seen 'growth' and 'improvement' as complementary objectives. Note here two statements from an ardent opponent of the 'eco-doomsters', John Maddox in *The Doomsday Syndrome* (1972): 'There is a good chance that the problems of the 1970s and 1980s will not be famine and starvation but, ironically, of how best to dispose of food surpluses in countries where famine has until recently been endemic.' This positive position related directly to the 'success' of the so-called 'green revolution' in improving plant yields (see *Grigg* (1991) and *Woodhouse* (1991)), and in bringing closer the realisation of the hope that increases in food supplies would *soon* outstrip population growth throughout the world. Similar optimism was displayed by Maddox on the question of energy supplies:

> All fears of fuel shortages should in any case have been dispelled by the coming nuclear power, which has already broadened the range of choice . . . The prospect, always unrealistically dramatic, of a crippling scarcity of energy has been exorcised by a single technological development.

For the moment I will leave you to draw your own conclusions on these two statements. We will be dealing later with the substantive issues raised by them in the context of the agenda put forward by the Brundtland Commission.

Clearly, perspectives vary according to the amount of emphasis placed upon the interchangeability of the concepts of 'growth', 'development' and 'improvement'. For optimists like Maddox the terms are mutually interdependent. For most environmentalists 'growth' and 'improvement' are certainly not synonymous, and 'development' has to be seen in a radically different way.

Activity 5

Think about the interrelationship between the three terms: growth, development, improvement. Can you detect both strengths and weaknesses in the 'ecocentric' (ecology-centred) views of the Limits to Growth followers, and the 'technocratic' view of the technological optimists? What other critical perspectives could be developed here? Compare your answer with that given at the end of the chapter.

There is a major school of thought which is not anti-growth, nor anti-industrialisation, but which is critical of both the **ecocentric** and **technocentric perspectives**. We have met this already in historical guise, but its usefulness as an explanatory focus for contemporary issues should also be considered. Neo-Marxist (contemporary Marxist) analysts such as Michael Redclift continue to argue their case on the exploitative nature of capitalism being at the root of current environmental crises, but they take the analysis further to consider the relationship between capitalism, underdevelopment and environmental impact.

Interestingly enough, neo-Marxist thinkers agree with other environmentalists that industrial societies are heading for disaster if radical steps are not taken to avert crisis. However, they have been highly critical of the Limits to Growth philosophy, particularly because of its 'neo-Malthusian' overtones. Recall that Malthus stated that population cannot exceed resources and that famine or disease provide natural checks on population growth (*Findlay*, 1991). Contemporary Marxists contend that *The Limits to Growth* is essentially about dealing with rapid increases in population, and that the logic behind the Malthusian Principle is that some form of pre-emptive or even coercive action is needed to control population and thereby conserve resources. Neo-Malthusians take an eco-centred view, emphasising the limits of Nature for ideological reasons: that is they focus on population growth as the main 'problem' for developing countries (as opposed to the developed countries), and they fail to address *distributive issues*. In short, they fail to recognise 'the role of international economy in structural underdevelopment' (Redclift, 1987). So this is taking a stage further the discussion we had earlier about imperialism and neo-colonialism. (Refer back to Sections 2.5 and 2.7 to check the essential elements of that discussion.)

The main point of the argument is that the developed countries, because they are 'resource-hungry', have a vested interest in drawing attention to resource scarcities, since these put at risk *their* economic development. The 'technological fix' argument looks good for the developed world when it is the developed world that benefits, but – the argument continues – only a fundamental restructuring of the international economy can help relieve many of the resource pressures experienced by the developing countries. It could be said, in its defence, that at least *The Limits to Growth* addresses this issue implicitly, as this extract from one of the conclusions illustrates:

> It is possible to alter these growth trends and to establish a condition of ecological and economic stability that is sustainable far into the future. The state of global equilibrium could be designed so that basic material needs of each person on earth are satisfied and each person has an equal opportunity to realise his/her individual human potential.   (Meadows *et al.*, 1972)

The problem with this type of polemic, as the more radical commentators see it, is that the sentiments expressed are all very well, but they do not touch political economic realities. The ecocentric approach tends to 'depict the ecological crisis as larger than politics, larger even than capitalism' (Redclift, 1987). Here is another quote from Michael Redclift's challenging analysis of sustainable development: 'The appeal to balance, to good husbandry, to the defence of species, appears to put Nature before People; but it does so in a way that reduces the role of human beings in their own development' (Redclift, 1987). Redclift takes the analysis further: 'Sustainable development is the objective of many perspectives on the environment, but the role of the *market* in defining the various outcomes is considered in few of them' (emphasis added). For critics like Redclift the ecocentric view may make objections to the market as a principle of economic organisation, but there is scarcely any attempt to establish how the objectives of **'zero-growth'** can be legitimised or brought nearer under a capitalist model of economic reorganisation.

3.6   Summary

The aim of these last two sections has been to cast some light on the developing concern for global environmental issues. By emphasising 'from Limits to Growth to the Brundtland Report', my intention has been to focus attention on fifteen years of thinking between the publication of the two reports in 1972 and 1987 respectively. I have tried to show how ideas have developed in this time, and how certain themes re-emerge. The question posed is: how can we progress the debate about sustainable development, given the various contradictions which are apparent after examining the contrasting responses to global environmental problems? These contradictions relate to the debate about *growth* and *development*. We have been considering three contrasting sets of arguments:

● *The ecology-centred, 'ecocentric', perspective*, developed in *The Limits to Growth* and elsewhere, with its neo-Malthusian undertones, which focuses on the relationship between rapid population growth, industrial expansion and resource use. It advocates radical economic change, a refutation of the whole 'growth' ethos, a movement to a steady-state economy wherein resources are used and distributed more equitably (although it fails to say how much equity of distribution is to be achieved). In its rejection of economic growth it echoes the sentiments of a number of traditions of thought, from the romantic movement to the radical socialism of William Morris and the anarchism of Kropotkin and his followers, as well as embracing contemporary radicalism. It does see essential change coming locally through decentralised, self-regulating communities. It does not suggest how we are to progress effectively from the dominating ideology of capitalism with its emphasis on a free market economy, in order to reach such seemingly Utopian objectives.

● *The technology-centred, 'technocentric', perspective* which sees sustained growth and scientific and technological advancement as the only way of dealing with global development and environment issues. The way forward for the developed and the developing countries, West and East, North and South, is to embrace the continuing logic of natural interdependency and advancement afforded by free market economics, with checks and balances being provided by government intervention where necessary. For it is only too clear in the 1990s that this model of development – the capitalist model – retains its dominance over all others. It would appear that the newly liberated countries of eastern Europe are eager to adopt the political economic values of the west, and many of the developing countries have similar aspirations. This may be the 'new' political economic reality for the next century.

● *The neo-Marxist critique*, which offers a fundamental *structural* analysis of the relationship of economic dependency between developed and developing nations. Of the three perspectives this is the only one which stresses the role of international economy in structural underdevelopment and uneven development. As such it arguably provides a challenging critique of the concept of development as seen through the workings of the market economy. This perspective is not anti-growth, but it is anti-capitalist and anti-consumerist. The limitations of this perspective are less a matter of the insights afforded by its explanatory breadth and depth, than in its realistic application. Indeed, we are witnessing a retreat from Marxist-inspired regimes throughout the world.

These three contrasting perspectives will provide a framework for undertaking a critical evaluation of the concept of sustainable development in the final chapter, focusing in particular on the potential contradictions which are inherent in the concept.

References

ALLEN, J. (1981) 'Race and class', Unit 11 of D102 *Social Sciences: a foundation course*, Milton Keynes, The Open University.

BROWN, S. (1990) 'Humans and their environments: changing attitudes', Ch. 7 in Silvertown, J. and Sarre, P. (eds).

ENGELS, F. (1970) *Selected Works of Marx and Engels*, London, Laurence and Wishart.

FINDLAY, A. (1991) 'Population and environment: reproduction and production', Ch. 1 in Sarre, P. (ed.).

GOLDSMITH, E. *et al.* (1972) *A Blueprint for Survival*, Harmondsworth, Penguin.

GRIGG, D. (1991) 'World agriculture: productivity and sustainability', Ch. 2 in Sarre, P. (ed.).

HARDIN, G. (1968) 'The tragedy of the commons', *Science*, Vol. 162, pp. 1243–8.

HOBSBAWM, E. (1968) *Industry and Empire*, Harmondsworth, Penguin.

MADDOX, J. (1972) *The Doomsday Syndrome*, Harmondsworth, Penguin.

MEADOWS, D. *et al.* (1972) *The Limits to Growth* (A Report for The Club of Rome's Project on the Predicament of Mankind), London, Earth Island.

PORRITT, J. (1990) *Where on Earth are we Going?*, London, BBC Publications.

PRYDE, P. R. (1972) *Conservation in the Soviet Union*, Cambridge, Cambridge University Press.

REDCLIFT, M. (1984) *Development and the Environmental Crisis*, London, Methuen.

REDCLIFT, M. (1987) *Sustainable Development: exploring the contradictions*, London, Methuen.

SARRE, P. (1990) 'Environmental issues in Cumbria', Ch. 1 in Silvertown, J. and Sarre, P. (eds).

SARRE, P. (ed.) (1991) *Environment, Population and Development*, London, Hodder and Stoughton/The Open University (Book Two in this series).

SCHUMACHER, E.F. (1973) *Small is Beautiful: economics as if people mattered*, London, Abacus.

SILVERTOWN, J. (1990) 'Inhabitants of the biosphere', Ch. 3 in Silvertown, J. and Sarre, P. (eds).

SILVERTOWN, J. and SARRE, P. (eds) (1990) *Environment and Society*, London, Hodder and Stoughton/The Open University (Book One in this series).

SIMMONS, I. (1990) 'The impact of human societies on their environments', Ch. 5 in Silvertown, J. and Sarre, P. (eds).

THOMPSON, E.P. (1976) *William Morris*, London, Pantheon Press.

UNITED NATIONS (1972) *Only One Earth*, The United Nations Conference on the Environment, Stockholm, London, Earth Island.

WILLIAMS, R. (1982) *Socialism and Ecology*, SERA publications.

WORLD COMMISSION ON ENVIRONMENT AND DEVELOPMENT (1987) *Our Common Future* (The Brundtland Report), London, Oxford University Press.

Further reading

MCLAREN, D.J. and SKINNER, B.J. (eds) (1987) *Resources and World Development*, Dahlem Workshop Reports, Chichester, John Wiley and Sons.

PEARCE, D., MARKANDYA, A. and BARBIER, E. (1990) *Sustainable Development: economics and environment in the third world*, Edward Elgar Publications.

PORRITT, J. and WINNER, D. (1988) *The Coming of the Greens*, London, Fontana.

Answers to Activities

Activity 1

The ideas that we can draw out from the United States experience are certainly diverse. The appreciation that the US conservation movement embraced divergent thinking is also relevant to an assessment of the concept of sustainable development. The implication of the use of terms like 'conservation' and 'sustainable development' is that some sort of consensus exists as to their meaning and importance. As the case study has shown, this is far from being so.

Scientific management, economic exploitation, collective ideals, government intervention, an obligation to posterity, a belief in the 'ethic' of preservation (even if it means financial loss) – these are some of the divergent themes that we can derive from the USA at the beginning of the twentieth century. A particular consequence of the scientific management approach allied to political involvement at both a federal and a state level, has been the development of specific resource agencies in the United States having delegated, executive powers to determine the planning and management of particular resources. One example would be the management of National Parks: here you could contrast Yosemite National Park in California with the Lake District in the United Kingdom.

Activity 2

Marx, Engels, Morris and Kropotkin were all critics of the system of industrial capitalism, but for quite different reasons.

Marx and Engels were concerned above all about capitalism's inequitable use of resources and the unjust and unequal distribution of its benefits between different social classes. They asserted that poverty could only be tackled by achieving greater productivity within a socialist system of production and development.

The legacy of Marxist-inspired, centrally planned economies are discussed in Section 3.2 and the contemporary application of neo-Marxist ideas are explored in Section 3.5.

Morris was particularly concerned about the productive processes of capitalism, about their essentially destructive nature, and he emphasised needs above market principles. He tended to look backwards to a pre-industrial age, rather than ahead to how his ideas might challenge the existing economic order. In contemporary form his ideas of putting human needs first, and of valuing quality of production rather than quantity of output, could become a powerful cornerstone for a set of principles about sustainable development. The values and aims of his Arts and Crafts Movement have tended to find contemporary support amongst the wealthier middle classes who are looking for alternatives to the rampant consumerism of the late twentieth century.

Kropotkin was one of the earliest radical thinkers to link ecological and political lines of thought. His ideas on the decentralisation of the processes of production, and a social co-operation were certainly progressive, and have been taken up by contemporary writers like Schumacher.

The message of the pressure groups which started in the 1960s and '70s – such as Friends of the Earth – reflected the thinking of radicals like Morris and Kropotkin in that they all believed that the fundamental values of industrialism had to be changed if environmental and ecological catastrophe were to be averted.

Activity 3

Certainly the ideological context is important. 'Production at any costs', however inefficient and damaging, has undoubtedly been the servant of a doctrinaire master. The adherence to orthodox Marxist thinking has been unswerving, but arguably misguided, taken out of its historical context. The process of democratisation now sweeping the former Soviet bloc should at least ensure that 'production for production's sake' is committed to the wastebin of history. There is now ample evidence to show that the centrally planned economies have been at least as damaging to the environment as market economies. In the case of the latter there has been both pollution control legislation, of varying degrees of comprehensiveness, and extensive modernisation to industrial plant. On the other hand it is a sobering commentary on the effectiveness of pollution legislation to note that, for example, after the passing of the Clean Air Act in the United Kingdom in 1956 the story goes that polluting industries, particularly in the Black Country, took it in turns to pay the fines because it was cheaper than cleaning up their act!

Activity 4

We will be looking shortly in more general terms at the challenges for a sustainable future. As you will now appreciate if you did not before, the issue of the destruction of the tropical rainforests is a complex one. Here are some of the ideas which have been put forward about possible solutions, to which we shall refer again subsequently:

● Waiving the third world debt (to which there would have to be considerable strings attached – how could developing countries be made accountable for their actions in the environment? What sanctions could be operated?)

● Boycotting tropical hardwoods (Friends of the Earth already run an international campaign to encourage precisely this, but what about the major markets like Japan?)

● Ensuring social and political rights for the displaced forest peoples.

● Setting up an international convention for tropical forests in a similar manner to those which already operate for the oceans and the ozone layer.

● Seeing the forests as a *sustainable resource*, in terms of their *total economic value*: this would include both 'use' and 'non-use' values. Direct use values include watershed protection and carbon fixation; non-use values relate to the value of conserving tropical forests regardless of any direct use in the present. (This is taken up in the next chapter.)

The challenge for sustainable development in the rainforests is to 'solve' the conflict between resource exploitation, spurred on by the lure of short-term economic and political gain, and resource conservation with its message of long-term 'wise' economic use and management.

Activity 5

A strength of the ecocentric view is that a concern for human progress and a concern for 'nature' must be intrinsically linked. Growth, development and improvement are not necessarily interrelated. Indeed, for the more radically minded 'growth' and 'improvement' imply a contradiction in terms.

A weakness rests in the political realisation of these views. How is the necessary radical change going to occur, given the dominance of the capitalist economic system?

A strength of the technocentric view is that industrial capitalism is a remarkably resilient and adaptable form of development. For the technological optimists, growth, development and improvement are closely interrelated.

A weakness of this view is that it has yet to be demonstrated that technology can indeed 'solve' the major environmental problems of the world. Why are these problems getting worse?

A third major perspective is the neo-Marxist, and this is developed in Section 3.5.

1   Introduction and objectives

The last chapter looked at global development issues in both an historical and a contemporary context. The objective was to raise questions about the processes of development, seen in terms of industrialisation and economic growth, within contrasting ideological contexts – capitalist and Marxist – in order to provide a framework for analysing the concept of sustainable development. The objectives of this final chapter, which is again in two parts, are:

- to discuss and to analyse the concept of sustainable development in order to understand the extent to which it might be possible to achieve the sustained use of resources globally in ways which lead to greater equity in terms of their distribution and use, and

- to evaluate the concept critically using three contrasting perspectives to probe the feasibility of actually achieving a sustainable future.

Some of the questions this chapter will be addressing are: What is sustainable development? What is it seeking to achieve and how? In whose interest is it being promoted, and whose responsibility is it to try to implement it? Can this be undertaken within either a market economic system (capitalist), or some form of centrally planned system, or is there some other way?

At the end of Chapter 5, I provided a summary of three contrasting perspectives which could be used to evaluate the concept of sustainable development: an ecocentric view, a technocentric view (based upon market economic principles) and a neo-Marxist view. These will be taken up in this chapter.

The first part of the chapter discusses the development of the ideas of sustainability within the context of the Brundtland Report and outlines the challenge for sustainable development (in Section 2.1), assesses the Brundtland agenda in terms of what are seen as being the major problems to be confronted and tackled (in Section 2.2) and examines in detail three substantive policy issues – population and human resources, food security and energy (in Sections 2.3 to 2.5).

The second part of the chapter – Section 3 – takes a critical look at sustainable development by putting the Brundtland Report into global perspective and appraising it critically, then focusing on contrasting approaches to sustainable development taking in turn an ecology-centred approach, a market-based approach and a neo-Marxist approach. Section 3.6 summarises the strengths and weaknesses of these competing perspectives.

Section 4 then looks at the practical implications for sustainable development at a local level in Thailand and India. The chapter concludes with a forward-looking challenge – 'Towards a sustainable future?' – and questions whether we are really in a position to be able to 'choose the future'.

2   Sustainable development: an agenda for action?

2.1   The Brundtland Report: the context

There have been other important international conventions between *The Limits to Growth* (1972) and the report of the World Commission on Environment and Development (see Box 6.1) which have tackled the issues of sustainability and the linkages between North and South. Two in particular are worthy of note, since both led to the publication of significant reports: the *World Conservation Strategy* (1980) – reference is made to this in *Grigg* (1991) – and the Brandt Report on *North and South: a programme for survival and common crisis* (1983), which in a number of ways formed the basis for the Brundtland Report upon which we are now focusing. However, it is in the latter that we encounter for the first time the concept of sustainable development being advanced to emphasise the links between development and environmental problems, and to promote political and economic change locally, nationally and globally to tackle these problems: see Box 6.1.

In stressing *need* and focusing on *world poverty* the Report is clearly acknowledging the crucial linkages that exist between the developed and the developing world, between North and South, that involve critical economic and strategic issues: see Box 6.2. Chapter 5 looked in some detail

Box 6.1

The United Nations World Commission on Environment and Development chaired by Gro Harlem Brundtland, the present (1991) Prime Minister of Norway, presented its report in 1987. Its published title is *Our Common Future*, but it is most commonly referred to as the Brundtland Report. Since it appears regularly in Chapter 6, we shall refer to it as 'the Report' following the initial reference.

Although stated in Chapter 5, the Brundtland definition of sustainable development is worth repeating here:

Sustainable development is development that meets the needs of the present without compromising the ability of future generations to meet their own needs. It contains within it two key concepts:

● the concept of needs in particular the essential needs of the world's poor, to which over-riding priority should be given;

● the idea of limitations imposed by the state of technology and social organisations on the environment's ability to meet present and future needs.

▲   *Gro Harlem Brundtland.*

at this relationship as it has developed historically. In *Sustainable Development* (1987) Michael Redclift highlights some of the contemporary consequences of the North–South relationship:

- The existence in the EC of food mountains which can have a dramatic impact on the environment in the South: for example, the increase in European production of sugar beet, allied to trade protection policies, had a dramatic impact on traditional sources of supply of sugar cane; the increase in supply with a static demand depresses commodity prices, and the effect can be to force people off the land and into the cities (see also *Gilbert*, 1991).

- The dispersal of food-grain surpluses from the North to the South in the past.

- The penetration of the South by new agricultural production technologies (under the rubric of the 'green revolution'), which have served to shift agriculture in many areas away from traditional, environmentally sustainable systems towards greater specialisation and economic dependency (see *Woodhouse*, 1991).

Box 6.2

The terms 'South', 'third world', 'developing countries' and 'less developed countries' appear as interchangeable terms throughout the four books of the series. There is no overall agreement as to the most appropriate term to use, the choice often coming down to a matter of style or author preference, or the need to vary terminology because of repetition or to emphasise different stages of development. Readers should refer to the discussion in *Findlay* (1991, p. 4) and *Gilbert*

(1991, pp. 256–7) for further elaboration of this debate.

The frequent references to the 'South' and the 'North' in this chapter relate to the terminology employed in the Brandt Commission on North–South issues which produced its report *Common Crisis* in 1983, and was the forerunner to the Brundtland Report of 1987, which continued the use of the terms. Figure 6.1 shows Brandt's 'North–South' divide.

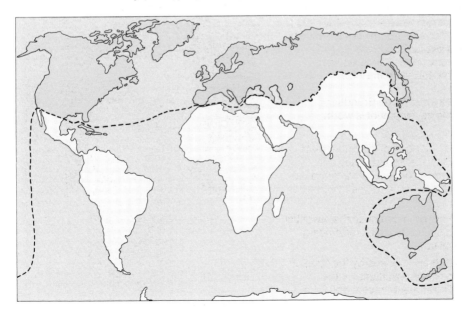

◀   *Figure 6.1*

- The existence of enormous external debts which have to be repaid by increasingly specialised exporting of cash crops and forest products (a point taken up in Section 2.2).

What we see here is the capitalist model of development as a model of *economic dependency*, with all its political implications of neo-colonialism and imperialism, to which reference has been made in the previous chapter.

I have chosen to focus specifically on the Brundtland Report because it has been widely regarded as making a significant advance on previous international responses on environment and development. As chair of the United Nations Commission Gro Harlem Brundtland has expressed her conviction quite clearly that the free market principles which effectively govern international economic relations would be inappropriate and prejudicial to the interests of better environmental management in the South. (This issue is taken up in Section 3.4.) Explicit in the Report is the recognition that change can only be achieved as a result of political action over the environment, clearly a highly controversial and contested arena. How far the Report represents a basic challenge to the system of industrial capitalism is what we are concerned to find out here.

For its agenda the Brundtland Commission chose a broad-based definition of sustainable development, relating it to human needs, as we have already seen. This might have both beneficial and less encouraging implications: beneficial because it focuses on the concept of need, less encouraging because the broader the terms of reference the wider the scope for political interpretation and manoeuvre. Certainly the term sustainable development can mean all things to all people, capable of diverse interpretations, a point stressed in the last chapter. There are many value positions and assumptions underlying the concept of sustainable development. Pearce (1989) is keen to distinguish **economic growth**, with its relatively crude index of measurement, Gross National Product (GNP), from **economic development**, with its implicit promise of improvement, although he accepts that 'development' is an inherently value-laden term. Robert Chambers, who contributed to the Brundtland Commission on the issue of food security, talks in terms of **sustainable livelihoods**. Sustainable refers to the maintenance or enhancement of resource productivity on a long-term basis. Michael Redclift argues that:

> Sustainable development, if it is to be an alternative to unsustainable development, should imply a break with the linear model of growth and accumulation that ultimately serves to undermine the planet's life support systems. Development is too closely associated in our minds with what has occurred in western capitalist societies in the past, and a handful of peripheral capitalist societies today.   (Redclift, 1987, p. 4)

You should make a particular note of these various interpretations now as I will be returning to them in the second part of the chapter (Section 3.1–3.6).

2.2   *The Brundtland Report: the agenda*

The General Assembly of the United Nations set up the World Commission on Environment and Development as an independent body in 1983, requesting that it formulate 'a global agenda for change.' These were its terms of reference:

● To propose long-term environmental strategies for achieving sustainable development by the year 2000 and beyond.

● To recommend ways concern for the environment may be translated into greater co-operation among developing countries and between countries at different stages of economic and social development, and lead to the achievement of common and mutually supportive objectives that take account of the interrelationships between people, resources, environment and development.

● To consider ways and means by which the international community could deal more effectively with environmental concerns.

● To help define shared perceptions of long-term environmental issues and the appropriate efforts needed to deal successfully with the problems of protecting and enhancing the environment, a long-term agenda for action during the coming decades, and aspirational goals for the world community.

The Commission had members from 22 nations – Norway, Italy, Germany, Japan, USA, Canada, Yugoslavia, Hungary, USSR, China, Sudan, Saudi Arabia, Zimbabwe, Ivory Coast, Algeria, Nigeria, Mexico, Colombia, Brazil, Guyana, India and Indonesia – the intention being to have more than half the representatives from developing countries. The point about representation is a highly pertinent one. Previous international initiatives on global environment and development issues have all come from the developed world: the Stockholm Conference (1972), the World Conservation Strategy (1980), the Brandt Report (1983) to instance three. The Brundtland Commission is no exception here in that it is an initiative which owes its inspiration to the North. However, it does represent significant progress in terms of *process*, by ensuring the fullest possible participation from representatives of developing countries. How far the Report reflects the developed world's view on global development and environment and how far it is a reflection of third world concern is a matter for subsequent evaluation. The Commission certainly received many hundreds of submissions from governments, environmental agencies and individuals globally, at a series of 'hearings' from 1984 to 1987. The final report, *Our Common Future*, has been regarded by many observers as the most important document of the 1980s on the future of the world.

The Report saw the issue of environment and development in terms of a series of *interlocking crises*: an environmental crisis, a development crisis, an energy crisis. We have already discussed the essential elements of these interlocking crises:

● *Population growth*: UN projections on the 'stabilisation' of global population vary between 8 billion and 14 billion sometime next century; the developing countries will account for more than 90% of the increase from the current figure of something over 5 billion.

● *Economic activity* and *technological improvement*: industrial production globally, the Report calculates, has grown by more than fifty times during the past century, and four-fifths of this growth has occurred since the end of the Second World War.

● *Resources*: growth on this scale (remember that *The Limits to Growth* talked in terms of *exponential* growth rates as was explained in Box 5.4) has taken its toll on the world's stock of finite resources, and this growth has become increasingly *inequitable*. The developing countries of necessity have to operate in a world where the *resources gap* between the industrial nations and the developing world is widening. As we saw in the case study of deforestation in the tropics, it is the industrial world which dominates in the rule-making of some key international bodies – the IMF and the World Bank, for example – and it is the industrial world which has already exploited the greater part of the Earth's *ecological capital*. As Brundtland states: 'This inequality is the planet's main *environmental* problem; it is also its main *development* problem' (1987, p. 6).

A major feature of this inequality is that while new technology, the mainspring of economic growth and development, might offer alternatives or options in terms of the more efficient use of resources, and in particular in the use of *renewable resources*, the industries which are now the most 'resource-hungry' and which are potentially the most polluting – particularly heavy manufacturing capacity like iron and steel – are those which are growing in the developing countries, where, as the Report states, 'there is both more urgency for growth and less capacity to minimise damaging side-effects'. At the same time, there are no guarantees for the developed world that new technology will not bring with it yet more harmful side-effects – as has happened with the growing hole in the ozone layer.

The Report aptly summarises the impact of these changes in global economic relationships:

> These related changes have locked the global economy and global ecology together in new ways. We have in the past been concerned about the impact of economic growth upon the environment. We are now forced to concern ourselves with the impacts of ecological stress – degradation of soils, water regimes, atmosphere and forests – upon our economic prospects. We have in the more recent past been forced to face up to a sharp increase in economic interdependence among nations. We are now forced to accustom ourselves to an accelerating ecological interdependence among nations. *Ecology and economy* are becoming ever more interwoven – locally, regionally, globally – into a seamless net of causes and effects.   (p. 5; emphasis added)

The Report focuses on the recent series of crises in Africa as one of the most tragic illustrations of the ways in which economics and ecology can interact destructively and, indeed, catastrophically. Following is a summary of the main analytical points which should provide an insight into how the Brundtland Report identifies major policy issues that need to be addressed.

Activity 1

How do you think the interaction of economics and ecology has produced crises in Africa? What are the key element in the process? (You may wish to recall earlier discussions here: for example *Findlay* (1991) on the crisis of famine in Ethiopia.) Compare your answer with the ideas developed below.

The first point to make here is a general one. Although during the 1960s and 1970s a good number of developing countries experienced encouraging trends of growth in national income, which at least kept pace with population growth, during the 1980s economic growth in most developing countries came to a halt. Problems escalated to embrace not

▲   *This area of Burkina Faso was heavily wooded ten years ago.*

just economic factors, but political and ecological ones as well. Population growth continued to outstrip economic growth, especially in many countries of Central Africa and the Sahel, and more than two-thirds of the developing countries actually experienced sharp falls in per capita income, by as much as 25% in some cases.

In Africa, specifically, the crisis has been triggered by a recurring factor, drought, although the more fundamental causes lie deeper, within the context already described. They can be linked to both national and international factors. In terms of national policies too little attention too late has been paid to *local initiatives* to the needs of 'small-holder agriculture' in relation to the threat of rapidly increasing populations. At an international level the majority of African nations suffer from **structural underdevelopment**, hopelessly tied in to a global economic system that takes more out of a poor continent than it puts in.

On a global scale the cumulative debt of developing countries has now reached roughly $1000 billion (about 8% of the total world economy, estimated to be of the order of $13 000 billion, or roughly equivalent to total annual global military expenditure at the end of the 1980s). The interest payment on this debt amounts to some $60 billion a year. We saw in Chapter 5 that Brazil is one of the countries with a massive problem about debt payment.

Table 6.1   Long-term debt and financial flows in developing countries, 1982–88 /billions of dollars

	1982	1983	1984	1985	1986	1987	1988
Debt outstanding	562.5	644.9	686.7	793.7	893.8	996.3	1020
Debt service	98.7	92.6	101.8	112.2	116.5	124.9	131
Principal payments	49.7	45.4	48.6	56.4	61.6	70.9	72
Interest payments	49.0	47.2	53.2	55.8	54.9	54	59
Net flows	67.2	51.8	43	32.9	26.2	15.9	16
Net transfers	18.2	4.6	−10.2	−22.9	−28.7	−38.1	−43

Source: Figures from World Bank, in *Scientific American*, September 1989.

Activity 2

Study Table 6.1. How do the debt figures and financial flows
indicated here reflect the worsening financial situation of developing
countries? What is happening to the cumulative debt of developing
countries, and to the transfer of capital from the developed countries?
You should focus, in particular, on the figures related to outstanding
debt, interest payments, net flows and net transfers.

Since 1984 there has actually been a *net outflow* of capital from the
developing to the developed countries, and this had grown to $43 billion in
1988. (The net transfer is calculated by subtracting the interest payments
from the 'net flow' of capital. The net flow of capital into the developing
countries includes new loans. The debt service is the combination of
principal payments and interest payments.)

In Africa the impact has been disastrous, because many African
countries were amongst the least developed in the world:

> Debts they cannot pay force African nations relying on commodity
> sales to over use their fragile soils, thus turning good lands into
> desert. Trade barriers in the wealthy nations – and in many
> developing ones – make it hard for Africans to sell their goods for
> reasonable returns, putting yet more pressure on ecological systems.

Aid from donor nations has not only been inadequate in scale, but too often has reflected the priorities of the nations giving the aid, rather than the needs of the recipients.   (Brundtland Report, 1987, p. 6)

The fact is that the production base of the majority of countries in the developing world is suffering both from *local failures* and from the workings of the *international economic system*. With rising poverty, pressures on environmental resources have increased, because more people have been forced to rely directly upon them (again we saw this in Brazil with the landless peasants in Chapter 5). In many countries economic growth depends principally upon their stocks of environmental resources, or **environmental capital**: soils, forests, fisheries, species, water. The long-term economic development of these countries depends upon maintaining and sustaining the use of these resources, but some developing countries have depleted virtually all of their ecological capital and are on the verge of **environmental bankruptcy**: remember the example of Haiti in Chapter 5, Section 3.3 and such also is the case in Central Africa. Figure 6.2 shows how the resource dependence of the economies of selected developing countries (both low-income and middle-income) is apparent in the percentage of their total exports that are *primary products* – fuels, minerals, metals and agricultural products. In many cases the percentage has fallen

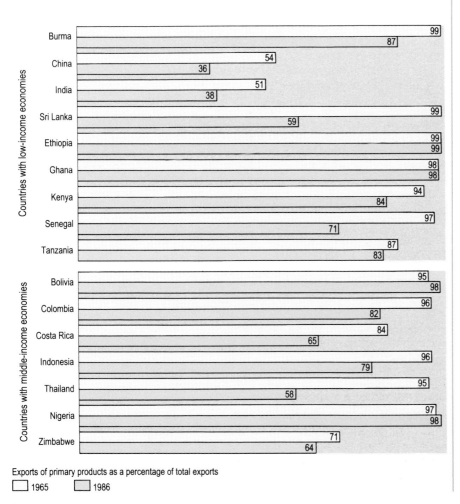

Exports of primary products as a percentage of total exports
☐ 1965   ☐ 1986

◄   *Figure 6.2*
Resource dependence of selected developing countries in 1965 and 1986: exports of primary products as a percentage of total exports, by value.

over the past two decades, which, where this is a result of diversification (such as Thailand to an extent), is a good thing, but in most of these countries it is a result of mineral resources being depleted or the fall in prices of the world markets of cash crops such as coffee and of some metals and minerals. The effect of the latter two events is a dramatic fall in the flow of export capital into these countries, at the same time as the prices of goods which they want to import continue to rise, a combination which can put great stress on already struggling economies.

Perhaps most crucially of all environmental destruction and decline is an increasing source of political unrest and international tension in Africa, Latin America and Asia. Within ever-deepening crisis are the seeds of threat to national security. The destruction of the Amazonian rainforest is not only of international concern, but increasingly is a source of internal conflict, illustrated by the murder in 1989 of Chico Mendes, leader of the rubber tappers union in the Amazonian state of Acre, and a vocal opponent of the large land-owning and ranching interests there.

Unfortunately, despite the likely long-term effects on food production, the ecological problems facing many third world countries are still not seen as the main priority. Here is a stark observation from the Report:

> The recent destruction of much of Africa's dryland agricultural production was more severe than if an invading army had produced a scorched-earth policy. Yet most of the affected governments still spend far more to protect their people from invading armies than from the invading desert . . . The arms race – in all parts of the world – pre-empts resources that might be used more productively to diminish the security threats created by environmental conflict and the resentments that are fuelled by widespread poverty.   (1987, p. 7)

Such is the impact of interlocking crises assessed by the Brundtland Commission.

Having established such a depressing backdrop for its deliberations, the Commission proceeded to take a very positive stance on policies for sustainable development, although with the inevitable rider that 'in the final analysis sustainable development must rest on *political will*' (my emphasis). It considered what it termed the 'institutional gaps' which would have to be filled at national and international level to obtain the necessary integrated approach to the global environment and development challenge. Major institutional development and reform is *the* challenge to political will, and we will be assessing some of the specific recommendations later. In particular, this assessment will focus on the role of international economy, institutional and legal change, and a call for action.

Before this, however, I intend to take a closer look at some of the substantive policy issues involved. The Commission focused on *six* interrelated areas:

- population and human resources
- food security
- energy and the choices for environment and development
- the loss of species and ecosystems and ensuring resources for development
- industry and producing more with less
- human settlements and the urban challenge.

We will be looking at the first three in more detail.

2.3   Population and human resources

> Development will stabilise population, but will development come
> before population growth and harsh technologies do irremediable
> damage to the planet's life support capacity?   (Nathan Keyfitz, 1989)

As was implied in the previous chapter, the control of population growth is
amongst the most politically and morally sensitive of all issues. Since
Malthus wrote his *Essay on the Principles of Population* in 1798, the debate
about the relationship between population and development has swung to
and fro like a pendulum. In recent times we have noted the impact of the
'Limits to Growth' thesis in the early 1970s. From thence it receded as a
major global issue for a decade or more as the green revolution and some
indication of sustained industrial growth in the developing world seemed
to avert the problem; ultimately it proved to be no more than a false dawn.
The 1980s saw 'Thatcherism' and 'Reaganomics' colour the western world
with all sorts of promises associated with the revival of laissez-faire values
and a major world recession presented the developed world with more
'immediate' problems to face.

This debate has resurfaced as a fundamental issue. The Report is quite
categorical:

> Present rates of population growth cannot continue . . . Each year the
> number of human beings increases, but the amount of natural
> resources with which to *sustain* this population, to improve the
> quality of human lives, and to eliminate mass poverty remains
> finite.   (1987, p. 95)

However, the neo-Malthusian arguments about population reduce the
discussion to a question of *a single cause and effect*. Yet the population issue
is not just about numbers and the Brundtland Report clearly recognises
this: it is equally about human progress and human quality. Threats to the
sustainable use of resources come as much from *inequalities* in people's
access to resources and from the ways in which they use them as from the
sheer numbers of people. An additional person in the North uses far more
resources than an additional person in the South. So, **patterns of
consumption** are just as important as numbers of consumers when the

relationship between population, environment and development is explored. Most calls for control come from the industrially developed North, yet not one first world government has established a population policy of its own. In 1990 more than 70 governments in the South were committed to the cause of population planning, albeit with a very varied pattern of commitment. *Findlay* (1991) has already discussed in some detail patterns of population change over time related to fertility and mortality rates, so here I will confine my comments to some key issues raised by the Report about control and global stabilisation and to three illustrative examples.

There are considerable differences in the momentum of population growth among countries in the South, in particular, as shown in Figure 6.3. Long-term UN predictions, based on current trends, show that – at a global level – if 'replacement-level fertility' (that is, an equilibrium is reached between the number of live-births and the mortality rate per annum) is reached:

- in 2010, global population will stabilise at 7.7 billion by 2060
- in 2035, population will stabilise at 10.2 billion by 2095
- only in 2065, global population in 2100 would be 14.2 billion.

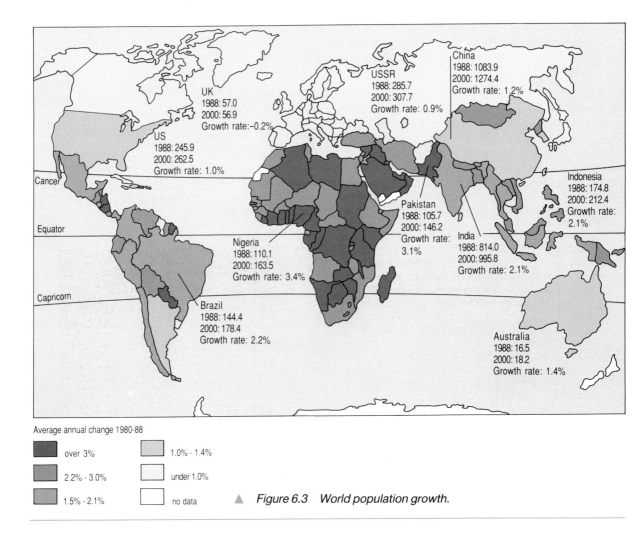

Average annual change 1980-88

- over 3%
- 2.2% - 3.0%
- 1.5% - 2.1%
- 1.0% - 1.4%
- under 1.0%
- no data

▲ Figure 6.3 World population growth.

From the aforegoing discussion two parallel 'themes of action' appear to be emerging, the one explicit, the other implicit: countries in southern Asia, Africa and Latin America have to look at the effectiveness of population policies, and the industrialised nations have to look to their patterns of consumption. We will be confronting the latter in due course, but I want to look briefly now at three examples of population policies, in Boxes 6.3, 6.4 and 6.5, and then at some recommendations from the Report.

Box 6.3

Kenya is the world's fastest growing nation, with a current population growth rate of 3.5%, and a total population estimated (in 1990) to be in excess of 22.5 millions. The total fertility rate (TFR) (that is the number of live births) has declined from 8 per woman in the 1970s to 6.7 in the early 1990s. This has been regarded as 'a substantial decline in fertility' by the Kenyan government, but is unlikely to impress the country's foreign creditors. Internally, the problem is not seen as one of numbers per se, but of a disequilibrium between population growth and resources to sustain it. To make population planning acceptable, it is argued, and to counterbalance the highly sensitive issue of 'dictating family size', economic growth must accompany reduced rates of population increase. In any event there are serious cultural, moral and religious barriers to implementing a country-wide programme of control, and Kenya is certainly not alone in its predicament. For one thing the Catholic Church forbids the use of contraceptives, and there are over 5 million Catholics in Kenya. The government recognises national family planning, and the long-term demographic objective is to achieve a growth rate of 2.5% by the year 2000. That is still a relatively high figure. A Malthusian perspective might emphasise that AIDS could have a potentially devastating impact on population in developing countries, particularly those in Africa.

Box 6.4

Outside China, India had the first systematic population programme in the world, but one which has come in for some criticism, principally because of the emphasis on sterilisation. In fact the great majority of families participating in this scheme have completed their families anyway, according to authoritative sources. The Indian government currently spends around $500 million a year on family planning and welfare, but without a great deal of political commitment. Even so, India's current population is in the region of 835 million, of whom an estimated 300 million are living below what is in any case a very low poverty line. Most predictions forecast a population of around one billion by 2000.

There have been improvements. The life expectancy at birth for the average Indian is now nearly 60, whereas it was only 20, according to the census of 1921. Infant mortality has declined markedly, but the figures continue to mask incidences of **total deprivation** (a phrase used by the Report to emphasise the worst forms of poverty). In some remote rural areas the mortality rate has reached 240 per thousand. The signs for the future do not appear to be that optimistic. The current rate of increase (the growth rate) is 2.15% and 40% of the population is under 14. Table 6.2 provides some comparative statistics for life expectancy and infant mortality in major regions of the world.

▲   *A Harijan family in Marharashtra village.*

Table 6.2   World health indicators by major region, 1950–85

Region	Life expectancy at birth (years)		Infant mortality rates (deaths per 000 live births)	
	1950–55	1980–85	1960–65	1980–85
World	49.9	64.6	117	81
Africa	37.5	49.7	157	114
Asia	41.2	57.9	133	87
South America	52.3	64.0	101	64
North America	64.4	71.1	43	27
Europe	65.3	73.2	37	16
USSR	61.7	70.9	32	25
Oceania	61.0	67.6	55	39

Source: Brundtland Report, based on data in World Resources Institute/International Institute for Environment and Development, *World Resources 1986* (New York: Basic Books, 1986).

Box 6.5

Indonesia is the fifth most populous country in the world, with nearly 175 million people in 1988, and a growth rate of 2.1%.

In 1970 Indonesia started an official family planning programme. This comprised a network of village centres acting as foci for general health and welfare issues and education and for the distribution of contraceptive devices. Authoritative sources claim that Indonesia's campaign has met with 'notable success'. In twenty years the fertility rate has been reduced from 5.6 to 3.4 children per woman. In 1972 some 40 000 couples practised birth control; in 1989 more than 18.6 million did so. In the same period infant mortality has been reduced by over 40%. The 'success' is due to a mixture of strong government, community support and education, and the emphasis on *local* initiatives.

▲   *A travelling clinic in Java, Indonesia, paying an annual visit to weigh babies and give contraceptive advice to the women.*

As a general point on these three case studies, it should be noted that all information on population control programmes in developing countries is taken from 'official' sources. It is the author's own experience that many women in developing countries, particularly in Latin America, and not primarily by reason of religion, are deeply suspicious and resentful of national population programmes. They see them as coercive, and closely linked to the imperialist and neo-colonialist undertones of the international economic order.

In its recommendations the Report leaned heavily towards responsibilities in the developing countries themselves:

> The critical issues are the balance between population size and available resources, and the rate of population growth in relation to the capacity of the economy to provide for the basic needs of the population, not just today but for generations.   (1987, p. 105)

The goals of sustainable development and lower fertility levels, according to the Report, are intimately linked and mutually reinforcing. But policies must be about more than controlling numbers: quality of life, health, social welfare and education must be given equal weight.

Developing countries are being asked to manage their population growth in an integrated approach to development, which means also managing its distribution and its mobility. This has particular implications for the continuing process of rural-urban migration and for the dominance of cities like Mexico City (see *Gilbert*, 1991). There needs to be a commitment to rural development, which in turn means encouraging locally based initiatives.

Explicit in the Report is the need for all developed and developing countries to see population in terms of an *asset* rather than as a *liability*: the Report states that it is people who are the ultimate resource of a country. This means focusing on improving health and broadening education. In particular, it means 'empowering the most vulnerable groups', like the threatened tribes in the tropical rainforests.

> The environment is the business of everybody, development is the business of everybody, life and living is the business of everybody. I think the solution will be found in encouraging mass environmental literacy, so that there can be democratic and literate decisions, because if decisions are taken by a few without the incorporation of the opinion of the masses, the NGOs [non-government organisations] especially included, the likelihood is that the situations will not succeed. They will be imposed from above, the people will not respond positively to them, and the project is lost before it is launched.   (Joseph Ouma, Statement to the WCED, Nairobi, September 1985; Brundtland Report, 1987, p. 107)

2.4   Food security

> In the context of basic survival, today's needs tend to overshadow consideration for the environmental future. It is poverty that is responsible for the destruction of natural resources, not the poor.   (Geoffrey Bruce, WCED Hearing, Ottawa 1986)

Policies formulated to achieve **food security** must take account of certain *external factors* which have a bearing on all sectors of economic life in any given society. By food security we mean the provision of enough food to feed the world's population, on a sustained basis, whilst at the same time minimising environmental change.

It is a fact that growth in world cereal production has progressively outstripped world population growth, although admittedly not without some environmental cost. This is clearly shown in Figure 6.4. It is also a fact that in 1990 there were more people in the world who did not get enough food than there were in 1980. Current estimates put the number of people who do not eat enough to lead productive working lives in excess of 730 million, or about 15% of the present world total. Globally, however, there is the potential to grow enough food to feed everyone. The problem is that it is often not available in the right places. Achieving food security means achieving sustainable development with increasing **equity**, that is with the increasingly equitable distribution of food supplies to balance demand.

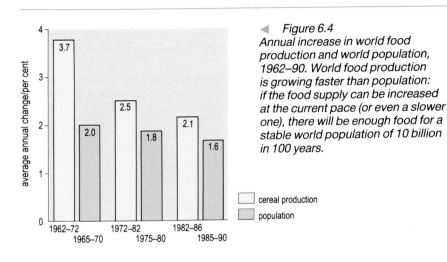

◀   Figure 6.4
Annual increase in world food
production and world population,
1962–90. World food production
is growing faster than population:
if the food supply can be increased
at the current pace (or even a slower
one), there will be enough food for a
stable world population of 10 billion
in 100 years.

Q   I used the term 'external factors' in a previous paragraph. Can you
     suggest what external factors should be taken into account in drawing
     up policies to achieve food security?

A   There are at least three sets of interrelated factors which are critical
     here:

     • the growth and regional distribution of world population

     • the growth and regional distribution of levels of income

     • the political climate internationally, especially as it affects trade at a
     global level, and also internal to nations.

     (You might choose to include a fourth set of factors, under the heading
     of global climatic change. This is certainly not insignificant, but is
     arguably more problematic. You can see Chapter 2 for a detailed
     analysis of this issue.)

Table 6.3 provides a useful summary of projections for cumulative
population totals in developed and developing countries to the year 2075.
As we discussed in the previous section estimates for growth in developing
countries vary considerably, but even taking the more conservative figures
of Keyfitz (1989) gives us a percentage increase of population in the
developing countries from 73% to 83% over a one-hundred year period
(1975–2075). Many forecasters are agreed that world population figures
should stabilise at around the 10 billion mark by 2100, that is twice the
current total, although as we saw previously these figures are speculative.
Even so, the implications in these figures for agricultural production and
distribution should be readily apparent.
     Predictions concerning income distribution are more difficult to make
with accuracy. Figure 6.5 gives some comparative projections of per capita
income, assuming a 2% average annual growth rate. This assumption is
based upon figures for the sustained increase in GNP (Gross National
Product) of the poorer countries, as shown in Table 6.4, and the reasonable
judgement that the developing countries will continue to press for
economic advance. The point about these projections in relation to
agricultural production is that in the developed countries increases in
income will add little to the increased demand for world food commodities.
By contrast, in the poorest countries increases in income will stimulate

Table 6.3   World population projections to 2075/millions

	Year	Developed countries[1]	Developing countries[2]	Percentage in developing countries
Barrie[3]	1850	302	869	74
	1900	510	1098	68
	1920	605	1255	67
	1930	677	1391	67
	1940	729	1565	68
	1950	751	1764	70
	1960	854	2144	72
Keyfitz[4]	1975	1092	2844	73
	2000	1274	4619	78
	2025	1380	5984	81
	2050	1415	6782	83
	2075	1434	7012	83
World Bank[5]	1982	1106	3413	76
			4835	
			8313	

Notes:
[1] USA, Canada, western Europe, USSR, eastern Europe, Japan, Australia, New Zealand.
[2] All those not listed in 1.
[3] Barrie, W.D. (1970) *The Growth and Control of World Population*, London, Weidenfeld and Nicolson.
[4] Keyfitz, N. *et al.* (1981) 'Estimates of population 1975–2075', in *CO$_2$ Assessment Program Contribution Nos 82–6*, Institute for Energy Analysis, Oak Ridge, TN.
[5] World Bank (1982) *World Development Report*, New York and London, Oxford University Press.

Source: Clark, W.C. and Munn, R.E. (1987) *Sustainable Development of the Biosphere*, Cambridge, Cambridge University Press, p. 106.

Table 6.4   Sustained increase in GNP of the poorer countries

	Per capita GNP in 1960 (1982 $)	Average annual growth 1960–82 (%)
China	106	5.0
Sri Lanka	182	2.6
Pakistan	207	2.8
Thailand	300	4.5
Egypt	317	3.6
The Philippines	447	2.8
South Korea	468	6.6

Notes: The list is not exhaustive of countries in the poorest group that achieved an annual per capita GNP growth of at least 2% from 1960 to 1982.

National income accounting systems, from which the above and all other per capita GNP estimates are derived, do not include the social and environmental costs of income growth. If they did, estimates of growth might be lower.

Source: Clark, W.C. and Munn, R.E. (1987) *Sustainable Development of the Biosphere*, Cambridge, Cambridge University Press, p. 107.

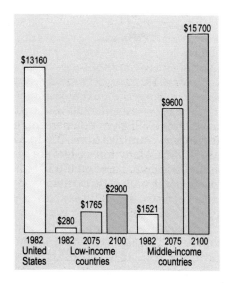

▲   Figure 6.5
Projected per capita income in the United States and in developing countries, 1982–2100 (US $). The projections assume a 2% average annual growth.

relatively large increases in the demand for basic foods. In short, there is a direct correlation between increased income and increased demand for food in the least developed countries.

Agricultural development in many developed countries has been amazingly successful if measured in terms of a capital-intensive enterprise seeking to maximise its output. The existence of huge surpluses has become an increasing feature of capitalist agricultural production in the first world. This has been achieved through major incentive schemes, incorporating massive economic subsidies – the product of political intervention – and the harnessing of the latest technology. It has also been achieved at some environmental cost (*Grigg*, 1991). In the previous chapter we saw how, in a centrally planned economy, political domination in the Soviet Union to increase agricultural productivity also had major environmental consequences.

In many developing countries we can see the reverse of the problem. There has been insufficient support, certainly little incentive for the small producer, and often inadequate technology. The result has been food deficits, and yet there has still been an environmental cost. Many farmers have been forced on to marginal land, and have contributed to the process of deforestation, leading to soil erosion and land degradation. Some countries, particularly in Asia, have improved productivity, by using new plant varieties dependent on higher inputs of fertilisers and pesticides (*Woodhouse*, 1991). But is the importation of methods and technologies from the developed world the answer?

The rhetoric of agricultural development and improvement at a global level is straightforward enough. Agricultural development has to be seen as a *social process* wherein a fundamental social objective must be the movement toward 'a more equitable treatment of the disadvantaged'. The technology exists and the potential is there for feeding 10 billion people by 2100. There could be a political commitment to lift trade barriers and to lessen the protectionist stance taken by some nations in relation to others. This is particularly relevant to the relationship between the developed and the developing world. For those of a somewhat sceptical nature all this may seem like a quantum leap of faith. The present reality is of major food shortages and famine in the poorest nations on Earth. It is of massive deforestation, already bordering on the catastrophic, of soil loss, of resource depletion and environmental damage generally. (See Plate 9.)

The Report recognises all of this. The challenge for the policy-makers is to balance supply with demand, to ensure that even the poorest of the poor can obtain food. This is the fundamental objective of food security. The Report advocates the importance of taking a global perspective: 'When it comes to farming, countries are at their most conservative, continuing to think mainly in local or national terms, and concerned, above all, to protect their own farmers at the expense of competitors' (1987, p. 132). Lifting protectionist barriers and changing trading patterns to shift food production towards food-deficit countries will take some effort of political and economic will, but this is what the Report recommends. In a series of further and detailed proposals the Report deals in turn with:

● *Sustaining the resource base*, involving increased public interventions by governments and resource agencies to provide the necessary framework for implementing specific policies concerned with land use, water management, alternatives to chemical fertilisers and pesticides, forestry and agriculture. Here is what Brundtland has to say on the issue of forest resources:

Programmes to preserve forest resources must start with local people who are both victims and agents of destruction and who will bear the burden of any new management scheme. They should be at the centre of integrated forest management, which is the basis of sustainable agriculture . . . Prices for forest products need to reflect the *true resource value* of the goods.   (1987, pp. 136–7; emphasis added)

(I referred to the concept of 'resource value' in Chapter 5 and it will be discussed in more detail in Section 3.4 below.)

● *Productivity and yields,* where improvement will best be achieved by strengthening the technological and human resource base for agriculture in developing countries. Brundtland talks about the importance of 'blending traditional and modern technologies offering possibilities on a sustainable basis'. The issue of biotechnology and the role of the multinationals in the continuing green revolution is viewed cautiously in the Report. Particular emphasis is given to what is a major issue – the critical role of women in agriculture: 'Women should be given the same educational opportunities as men . . . Women should be given more power to take decisions regarding agriculture and forestry programmes' (1987, p. 140).

● *Equity* for Brundtland is perhaps the greatest challenge of sustainable agriculture in the developing world. Food security is not just a question of raising food production, but of ensuring that the rural and urban poor do not go hungry during the short term or midst a local food scarcity. All this requires the systematic promotion of equity in food production and distribution. This will require major initiatives in the areas of land reform, programmes for integrated rural development, and distribution systems for coping with fluctuations in food availability.

2.5   Energy

Energy efficiency can reconcile environmental concerns with economic development for all nations. It can stretch energy supplies, slow climatic changes, and buy time to develop alternative energy resources.   (John Gibbon *et al.*, September 1989)

The Brundtland Commission states that there are a number of key elements of energy sustainability that have to be reconciled:

● sufficient growth of energy supplies to meet human needs (which means accommodating a minimum of 3% per capita income growth in developing countries)

● energy efficiency and conservation measures, such that waste of primary resources is minimized

● public health, recognising the problems of risk inherent in energy sources

● protection of the biosphere and prevention of more localised forms of pollution.

Reddish (1991) has argued that energy has been used and continues to be used in most parts of the world in an unsustainable manner. To remind you of patterns of energy consumption, the consumption of energy per

person in market economies is more than 80 times greater than, say, in
sub-Saharan Africa. About 25% of the world's population consumes over
75% of the world's primary energy: see Table 6.5. The Report estimates
that if per capita use remained at the same levels as today, by 2025 a global
population of say 8.2 billion (based on current UN projections at the 'less
optimistic' end of the scale) would need approximately 14 terawatts of
energy (that is 14×10^7 kilowatts) – over 4 TW in developing countries and
over 9 TW in industrial countries – an increase of 40% over 1980
consumption figures. However, if energy consumption per capita became
uniform worldwide at current industrial country levels, by 2025 some 55 TW
of energy would be required. That figure is simply alarming, although it is
highly unlikely to prove realistic.

The following provides an indication of the scale of the problem being
faced:

> We cannot conceive of development without changes in the extent or
> nature of energy flows. Because it is so fundamental, every one of
> those changes of flows has environmental implications. There is *no
> such* thing as a *simple energy choice*. They are all complex. And they all
> involve trade-offs. However, some of the choices and some of the
> trade-offs appear to be unequivocally better than others, in the sense
> that they offer more development and less environmental
> damage.   (David Brooks, Friends of the Earth, Ottawa, May 1986;
> Brundtland Report, 1987, p. 173; emphasis added)

Of particular significance in this respect are the domination of the energy
market by oil, and the domination of energy consumption by the United
States. In 1988 oil accounted for some 38% of commercial energy
consumption. Dependence on oil from the Middle East puts pressure on

Table 6.5   Global primary energy consumption per capita, 1984

World Bank GNP economy category	GNP per capita	Energy consumption (kW per capita‡)	Mid 1984 population (millions)	Total consumption (TW)
Low income	260	0.41	2390	0.99
Sub-Saharan Africa	210	0.08	258	0.02
Middle income	1 250	1.07	1188	1.27
Lower middle	740	0.57	691	0.39
Upper middle	1 950	1.76	497	0.87
Sub-Saharan Africa	680	0.25	148	0.04
High-income oil exporters	11 250	5.17	19	0.10
Industrial market economies	11 430	7.01	733	5.14
East European non-market economies		6.27	389	2.44
World		2.11*	4718	9.94

Notes:
‡kW per capita is kW years/year per capita.
*Population-weighted average energy consumption (kW/capita) for first three main categories
  is 0.654 and for industrial market and east European categories is 6.76.

Source: The Brundtland Report (1987): based on World Bank, *World Development Report
1986*, New York, Oxford University Press, 1986.

the economies of both the industrialised and the developing world. In 1987 the US imported over $40 billion worth of oil (approximately equivalent to one-third of their trade deficit). The sheer scale of the United States' energy consumption indicates that the US could have a major impact on global carbon emissions by developing more efficient cost-effective technologies. Transportation, particularly private car usage, in the US is a huge consumer of energy: in 1991 in Los Angeles the 12 million inhabitants had between them 8 million cars. Compared to the industrialised world, the developing world's share of energy consumption is relatively small, but demand is growing rapidly. The main problem is its inefficient use. With help the developing countries could apply technical solutions that would promote economic growth while keeping energy-demand growth relatively low.

The Report requires a collective effort from both the North and the South to develop opportunities for efficient resource use in their economies. The Report details a number of key issues, now briefly summarised. Perhaps most urgently it focuses on the continuing dilemma of the heavy reliance on *fossil fuels* and the increasing risk of global warming: 'No nation has the political mandate or the economic power to combat climatic change alone.' It urges the development, as soon as possible, of internationally agreed policies for the reduction in emission of the greenhouse gases and the adoption of strategies needed to minimise damage, and to cope with the climatic changes and rising sea-level. It is worth noting at the time of writing (1990) that an international conference is due to be convened in Geneva to discuss the possibilities of reaching just such an agreement.

Progress can be made now in increasing and extending the recent steady gains in energy efficiency and shifting the mix more toward renewable sources of energy. The Report also documents the urgent need to reduce industrial air pollution and to minimise the damage from the long-range transport of air pollution. It recognises that the exact causes of the damage are hard to prove, although much research has already been carried out in Scandinavia, for instance, on increasing levels of acidity

◄   Indra Prastha coal-burning power station on River Yamuna, Delhi, India. Reliance on fossil fuels, with increasing demand for energy in the third world, will add to the risk of global warming.

produced by 'acid rain', but it states categorically that 'reduction strategies are certainly within reach and economic'. They ought to be viewed as 'a cheap insurance policy compared with the vast amount of potential damage these strategies avoid'.

The Commission produced a whole series of recommendations on the continuing unsolved problems of nuclear energy. In particular, it stressed the need for *international co-operation and agreement* on a number of specific items including:

- the transboundary movement of all radioactive materials, including fuels, spent fuels and other wastes, by land, sea or air
- internationally accepted standards for waste repositories
- a code of practice on liability and compensation
- the reporting of routine and accidental discharges from nuclear installations.

> The generation of nuclear power is only justifiable if there are solid solutions to the presently unsolved problems to which it gives rise. The highest priority must be accorded to research and development of environmentally sound and economically viable alternatives [like wind power, see *Reddish* (1991)], as well as on means of increasing the safety of nuclear energy.   (Brundtland Report, 1987, p. 189)

It is worth noting here that a 1990 United Nations report, commissioned from a group of experts, argues in favour of expanding nuclear power generation globally, to reduce dependence on power stations burning fossil fuel as a way of tackling global warming!

The critical issue of the vanishing resources of wood fuels is also tackled in some detail. In 1980 the Food and Agriculture Organisation estimated that some 1.3 billion people lived in *wood-deficit areas*, that is areas where there are insufficient supplies of timber to satisfy the demand for fuelwood. If over-harvesting continues at 1990 rates, then some 2.4 billion people may be living in such areas by 2000. As the Report emphasises, these figures reveal great human hardship, and the fuelwood crisis, although related, is *not* the same as deforestation. Urgent strategies are needed to ensure not just replanting but the *equitable distribution* of fuelwood supplies. It is quite apparent that a greater understanding is required of the fundamental role that fuelwood plays in many rural areas, in local economies, and of the social relations governing its production and use.

The Report concludes its consideration of energy with a heavy emphasis on three crucial areas:

- realising the untapped potential of renewable energy, which could in theory provide 10–13 TW annually
- maintaining the momentum of energy efficiency
- ensuring effective energy conservation measures.

> It is clear that a *low energy path* is the best way towards a sustainable future . . . A safe, environmentally sound and economically viable energy pathway that will sustain human progress into the distant future is clearly imperative. It is also possible. But it will require new dimensions of political will and institutional co-operation to achieve it.   (1987, pp. 201–2; emphasis added)

For further discussion of renewable energy sources and of **low energy paths**, see *Reddish* (1991).

2.6   Summary: a prescription for change?

I have chosen to look in detail at what seems to me are the three really crucial policy areas: population, food and energy. This is certainly not to deny the great importance of the others – ecosystems, industry and the urban challenge – and you may query my choice. Of course, all these policy issues are interrelated, and this is really the essential point to underline, about seeing sustainable development as a *total concept*. This is indeed the approach taken in the Brundtland Report. Sustainable development is seen as an overarching concept, as a desirable policy objective, arising out of a positive but critical analysis of development processes. It is essentially a *prescriptive approach*, where the responsibility for action and change is placed firmly in the hands of governments, agencies and individuals.

I hope it has come across that the Brundtland Commission has phrased its recommendations in terms of broadly stated policy objectives, often in a generalised, almost all-embracing, type of format. It has emphasised the absolute priority for a global, international response, allied with essential institutional and legal changes; equally, it has stressed the crucial

---

Box 6.6   Strategic imperatives

1   *Reviving growth*   Sustainable development must address the issue of poverty, as poverty increases pressure on the environment. The very logic of sustainability, of sustainable development, implies an internal stimulus to growth in the developing countries.

2   *Changing the quality of growth*   This means making 'growth' less materialistic, less energy-intensive and more equitable in its impact. Economic and social development have to be 'mutually reinforcing'.

3   *Meeting essential human needs*
More food, not just to feed people but to attack undernourishment; basic housing, fresh water supply, health, energy. The need for energy cannot be universally met unless energy consumption patterns change.

4   *Ensuring a sustainable level of population*
The challenge is to tackle the highest rates of population growth, especially in Africa. This is linked to improving the quality of life, raising incomes and working for a more equitable distribution of population between rural and urban areas.

5   *Conserving and enhancing the resource base*
There is a moral as well as an economic argument here. Included are agricultural resources (land, soil, water), forestry, fisheries and energy. There is a pressing need for efficient, low-waste technologies.

6   *Reorienting technology and managing risk*
The implications of 1–5 above are for the reorientation of technology in two principal ways – the capacity for innovation needs to be greatly enhanced in developing countries, and technological development generally must pay greater attention to environmental factors. This is closely linked to the issue of 'risk management', wherein environmental impact has to be effectively minimised.

7   *Merging environment and economics in decision-making*   Economics and ecology should not be seen in opposition but as interlocking. Sustainable development requires the unification of economics and ecology in international relations.

To achieve 1–7 the Report sees the following as essential requirements:

• A *political system* that secures effective citizen participation in decision-making.

• An *economic system* that is able to generate surpluses and technical knowledge on a self-reliant and sustained basis.

• A *social system* that provides for solutions for the tensions arising from disharmonious development.

• A *production system* that respects the obligation to preserve the ecological base for development.

• A *technological system* that can search continuously for new solutions.

• An *international system* that fosters sustainable patterns of trade and finance.

• An *administrative system* that is flexible and has the capacity for self-correction.

importance of local, community-based initiatives. It has repeatedly underlined that a primary goal of sustainable development is greater *equity*, both among nations and within nations. But how is it all to happen? The Report deals in generalisations here rather than with specific technical or methodological issues. Sustainable development is seen as a process for harmonising resource use, investment, technological development and institutional change. In short, it is a 'grand design' for global action and change. Box 6.6 gives a summary of what the Commission describes as its 'strategic imperatives' for sustainable development.

Activity 3

What is your reaction to these strategic imperatives? Try to make some connections between the far-reaching 'requirements' of the Commission, and the discussion in Section 3 of Chapter 5 on contrasting ways of seeing growth, development and improvement. I give my reaction in Section 3.1 below. In terms of contrasting ways of seeing growth development and improvement I will be developing the ecology-centred, market-based and neo-Marxist perspectives.

---

3   Sustainable development: a critical appraisal

3.1   Brundtland in perspective

The chapter so far has looked at how the Brundtland Report defines the concept of sustainable development, what it sees as the major policy issues underpinning the concept, and which have to be addressed if sustainability is to be achieved in terms of resource use globally, the more equitable distribution of resources, and safeguarding the environment for future generations. I have emphasised that the Report is an *agenda*, not a blueprint for action. Even if a consensus can be reached about what sustainable development is, and what has to be done, *how* is it going to be achieved?

I wonder if your initial reaction was like mine when I first read *Our Common Future* and in particular the Strategic Imperatives, outlined in Box 6.6: surely this requires nothing short of the radical restructuring of the whole global economic system to achieve sustainable development on these terms, to really get to grips with the fundamental objectives of dealing with the problems of *need* and *equity*. Yet the Report's forthright approach is deserving of our most serious attention. It provides clear evidence for the links between *poverty* and *environment* in developing countries: and that a group of 'mainstream' politicians should have helped put such a document as the Brundtland Report together is a mark of the seriousness with which the discussion has been voiced at an international level.

However, isn't it all too optimistic, too ambitious, too far-reaching? Well, it is only an agenda, and it does leave the door open for action, but we need to take a harder look here. Brundtland appears to be saying a number of things that are inherently contradictory. The entire credibility of the Report would seem to hinge on the premise that major economic growth can be achieved in ways that sustain and even enhance environmental capital. Development, Brundtland emphasises, is the best way of achieving population control, and growing populations in the developing world should be sustained at economic levels 'above the minimum' to satisfy fundamental need, because improvement of *quality of life* is also a basic tenet of the thesis. This means an increase in consumption patterns for many countries, but not in the materialist mode of the industrialised world. So, in other words, development for the, as yet, underdeveloped nations has to be different from that experienced in the past, and the developed countries have got to change their consumerist habits!

Are growth and development synonymous in the Report, then? Is economic growth an adequate measure of development? When the Report refers to sustainability, what is it that is to be sustained – levels of production or levels of consumption, or both, but on a far more equitable basis? This is a very significant distinction, because what makes development *unsustainable* now at a global level are the patterns of consumption in the developed world, as we have already discussed. Yet the main focus for development is necessarily production rather than consumption. Again, at what level is sustainable development aimed: local, national or global? Brundtland tackles major environmental issues like global warming, the management of the oceans, and transnational pollution, but it also stresses sustainability at the level of the individual farmer in remote rural areas. The problem is that what is sustainable at one level might not be at another.

So is the Report offering us a *consensus view* of sustainable development where no consensus exists? Can sustainable development be concerned with meeting human needs, maintaining economic growth and conserving natural capital at one and the same time? Does it mean all things to all people? We saw earlier how the concept has been variously interpreted. Interpretations, and the policies which may follow, will vary according to the 'starting-point for investigation' – an essentially ecological approach would differ substantially from an economic one – and according to *ideological differences*: an ecologist from the Green Party, say, would almost certainly offer a radically different point of view from an economist in the cabinet of a Conservative government in the UK in the 1990s. How do these different approaches help to shed light on the apparent contradictions which are contained in the Report, and which indeed are inherent in the very term sustainable development?

3.2   Contrasting approaches to sustainable development

In theoretical terms the three contrasting approaches to development and environment issues – the ecology-centred perspective, the technology-centred perspective and the neo-Marxist critique, which I discussed in Chapter 5 (Sections 3.5 and 3.6) and to which I referred in the introduction to this chapter – offer very different options for the future. In the following three sections I will be taking each in turn in an attempt to probe the *underlying assumptions* of the concept of sustainable development. Which

approach most appropriately addresses the 'real' issues? Which seeks to
expose most effectively the gap between *rhetoric* and *reality*? Which affords
the most practicable and feasible basis for moving forwards to a
'sustainable future'? Do these approaches cover *all* the possibilities? This
last is, of course, a highly pertinent question. They clearly do not, cannot,
account for all possible points of view or value positions. What they
provide are what we might call three major, contrasting 'schools of
thought' on global development and the environment, that appear to offer
the greatest prospect for practical progress in achieving sustainable
development. They are all rooted in history, as was stressed in Chapter 5,
and being schools of thought there is within each a considerable variety of
ideas which themselves may often appear to be in conflict, although there
are certain *fundamental beliefs* in each around which a consensus could be
said to exist.

In evaluating each I will attempt to underline where such a consensus
occurs and what are the strengths and weaknesses of each approach. As I
stated in the introduction to Chapter 5, my own value positions may
become apparent in this process, and I will explain as far as possible why I
am persuaded by the comprehensiveness and logic of one set of arguments
over another. You may not agree, of course, and it will be up to you to
justify your own position. This is, after all, the essence of discussion and
debate in the social sciences. Approached constructively it is a way of
achieving progress, optimistically with the objective of reaching some sort
of consensus about the most appropriate course of action to follow.

There is a further basic point we need to recognise, to which I have
already made some reference (in Section 2.2). It is that each of these
approaches essentially reflects the values and assumptions of the
developed world – they each contain ideas dominantly influenced by
western intellectual thought. *Brown* (1990) has shown how the traditions of
Stewardship, Romanticism, Utilitarianism and Imperialism have
influenced contemporary attitudes to environment, and it is a theme
pursued in Chapter 5. So we need to be aware of this in considering each
approach, and to ask to what extent each takes account of a 'third world'
perspective. This is clearly a major issue. A writer from a developing
country may well have approached these last two chapters in quite a
different way.

With these methodological points in mind, let us turn to an evaluation
of the three approaches: ecology-centred, market-based technology-
centred and neo-Marxist.

3.3   *An ecology-centred approach*

In the previous section the point was made that each major school of
thought may contain a wide variety of sometimes conflicting views. This is
particularly so with the ecology-centred approach. The implication is of an
overall consensus – indeed this is the impression with which I left you in
Chapter 5 – but this can mask often quite marked political differences.
Fundamentally, to recap, an 'eco-centred' approach requires that a concern
for human progress and a concern for nature must be intrinsically linked.
This is indeed a principal underpinning of the contemporary Green
Movement. Part of the quotation with which Chapter 5 started states that
'the Green Movement seeks to *re-establish connections* that have become
fractured between people and their surroundings' (*The Guardian*,
5 February 1990). This translates into a critical evaluation of development

as seen essentially in terms of economic growth (as discussed in Chapter 5, Sections 3.5 and 3.6); both the ends and the means of 'development' have to be questioned. There can be no 'technical' solutions to environmental problems that arise as a result of economic development. In this sense, there is a general consensus in this school of thought that would be critical of the Brundtland Report's approach to sustainable development, indeed of the whole concept itself. How can any forms of development, couched dominantly in economic terms, be 'sustainable'? For although the Report is seriously concerned to address such fundamental issues (for ecologists) as the severe damage to ecosystems and loss of species, the eco-centric view points to the outright contradiction that economic growth and environmental conservation can be seen to be mutually compatible.

It is in the pursuit of the objectives for radical change, explicitly demanded by an ecology-centred approach, that we can find the seeds of controversy and conflict. It is manifest in the debate about *political ends* and *means*. In Chapter 5 I traced the historical roots of the 'anti-growth' philosophy, stressing their often rich diversity from the Romantic movement, to the Utopian socialism of William Morris, to the populism of Peter Kropotkin and others. A general point to emphasise here is that in almost every period since the Renaissance the development of revolutionary thought has been influenced by a branch of science, often in combination with some form of philosophical thinking. Kropotkin was certainly one of the earliest of radical thinkers to link ecological ideas with political and economic processes, and his intellectual heirs have had a significant influence in the Green Movement.

The appeal to populism, local action and practical solutions, which is one of the hallmarks of green thinking, owes much to Kropotkin's writings. It comes through in different ways in the contributions of E. F. Schumacher in *Small is Beautiful* (1973) and of Vandana Shiva, author of *Staying Alive* (1988), which is unequivocally concerned with poverty and survival in the third world, written by a citizen of the third world. In the former the emphasis is on the *person* not the *product*, and a system of **intermediate technology** is envisaged. Schumacher defined this as 'technology with a human face', where technology is redirected so that it serves humankind instead of destroying us; this leads to 'production by the masses instead of mass production' and organisation is based upon small working units and communal ownership (Schumacher, 1973, pp. 132–3).

Now here is the crucial point about this discussion. There are many who are indeed searching for a 'greener politics', using the rich traditions of thought already noted, together with the essential scientific underpinnings provided by ecological analysis, to work for a practical means of integrating what have been quite divergent branches of scientific thinking: ecology and economics. To achieve this inevitably calls for political change, but change sought progressively using populist support and local action. Importantly and vitally, this process must involve third world participation.

However, there is also a yet more controversial seam of thought, within what has been termed **deep ecology** (see Box 6.7), that owes less to ecological thinking as such, and more to the political imperatives that are taken to be inherent in the rejection of economic growth. It runs from the somewhat Utopian visions of writers like Goldsmith to the more sinister forms of 'eco-orthodoxy' which puts the natural world first, and sees humankind as a species which is 'terminally culpable for the wanton destruction of nature' (*The Guardian*, 5 February 1990). It is almost entirely an expression of 'green concern' from the developed world. Unlike the

Box 6.7   Deep ecology

Deep ecology is the name given to a particular philosophical position developed by a number of writers based in California, Scandinavia and Australia. It is essentially abstract and idealistic in its roots, with the underlying conviction being that human beings should seek to emphasise their inherent unity with other living beings and processes. In this, deep ecology is biocentric, rather than anthropocentric, meaning that the whole of nature is more important than the human race. This is in stark contrast to dominant western culture which has seen nature as exploitable, something to be tamed and conquered (discussed in Section 2.2 of Chapter 5). It is 'deep' as opposed to 'shallow', the latter defining – as far as ecologists are concerned – the position of most environmentalists in the west.

Brundtland Report, it does not address the structural inequalities between North and South. It does not deal with the essential issue of human need. It does not tackle the fundamentals of the 'struggle to survive' from the perspective of the least developed countries in the world. In this context, consider two previously quoted (in Chapter 5) extracts, the first from Gro Harlem Brundtland:

> It is both futile and indeed an insult to the poor to tell them that they must remain in poverty to protect the environment.

And the second from the editorial, 'In search of a greener politics':

> [There] is an authoritarian streak that springs directly from the hopeless utopianism of deep ecology, which leads seamlessly from telling the underdeveloped world that it is forbidden the benefits of an industrialised society, through population control to eugenics. At best middle-class self indulgence, at worst it opens up a potential nightmare vision of repression.   (*The Guardian*, 5 February 1990)

Here is the greatest challenge for the ecology-centred approach, and arguably also its greatest dilemma. It offers a rich diversity of ideas, many of which can provide a practical basis for tackling some of the pressing problems of global resource use and distribution, focusing in particular on third world issues and stressing *local* participation and action. It also provides for the more extreme forms of political argument which are undemocratic, and have given rise to the term 'eco-fascism'. Somehow, the eco-centred approach must reconcile the short-term demands of politics and economics with long-term *ecological imperatives*, within an essentially pluralist political context.

3.4   Market-based approach

Professor David Pearce's book *Blueprint for a Green Economy*, which he co-wrote with Dr Arich Markandya and Dr Edward Barbier, was originally prepared as a report for the United Kingdom Department of the Environment in 1989. Labelled the 'Pearce Report' it received widespread coverage for its 'practical, down-to-earth approach to sustainable development' in terms of economic appraisal. It has been hailed variously as 'setting a new agenda for environmental protection' and as 'providing an economics of hope for the world around us'. As a perspective, it is far removed from that of deep ecology.

The report was commissioned by a government eager to see whether sustainable development was actually feasible or practicable. In the event the product has given an unequivocal 'thumbs up' to the concept, arguing that the great environmental problems of our time can indeed be solved. In the wake of the seemingly enlightened 'green think' which coloured the Conservative administration in 1989 – a 'green awakening' for the 1990s? – Professor Pearce was made economics adviser to the then Environment Secretary, Christopher Patten.

In essence the Pearce Report takes a neo-classical economic approach, in that it builds a positive and optimistic model for sustainable development by implying that everything can be given a **market value**. In this respect it both takes the Brundtland Report a stage further and also criticises the Commission's inconsistency in being able to say precisely what it means by sustainable development. (Remember that Brundtland is critical of using market forces alone for achieving sustainability.) Pearce is quite consistent in asserting that economics does throw light on the meaning of sustainable development as a 'practical, feasible concept'. Figure 6.6 provides a simplified illustration of the approach.

D is the demand for the 'services' of a natural environment. According to basic laws of supply and demand, if there was a price for such services then the demand would be greater the lower the price. An example here might be an entrance fee to a National Park (in the USA if not in the UK). *S* is the supply of 'services', and is shown as a vertical curve, because supply is assumed to be fixed. If there was a *market* in the environment in question price would settle at the 'equilibrium price' P^1, and the amount of environment used up would be Q^1.

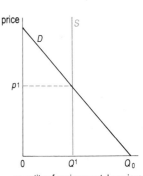

▲   *Figure 6.6*
Environmental problems arising from the absence of markets.

Q What would the absence of a market mean? What is the significance here of Q_0? A zero-priced resource will be *over-used* in both economic and environmental terms. Also, can we be sure that even a price P^1 will prevent the environment from being degraded over time?

A The absence of a market in the environment means that the price is zero – no value at all is placed upon it – and the amount consumed is Q_0. Too much of the environment is consumed. This should establish the importance of valuing the economic functions of environment. The equilibrium price P^1 does not guarantee that the environment will not become degraded over time. Safeguarding the environment cannot be left to market mechanisms alone. This discussion is pursued below.

The argument rests on the importance of valuing the economic functions of the environment. Environmental problems are perceived as being essentially economic problems: 'they are manifestations of the failure of market systems to allocate resources efficiently'. The Pearce Report looks to the changes which would be made to the nature of economic development, in the light of the requirements of sustainable development, which could lead to a progressive eradication that avoids the worst consequences of development (in line with the Brundtland Report's thinking), and by adjusting prices for environmental costs, so that in effect everything has a 'value', whether or not it is actually used or indeed useable as a resource. (We have already met the concept of **resource value** in the case study of the tropical rainforests: see the answer to Activity 4 in Chapter 5.)

Pearce has developed an economic formula to demonstrate the importance of using monetary measures to value environment. In effect he is refining the traditional economists' approach to 'cost-benefit analysis' by 'adding' certain values and developing the simplified view shown in Figure 6.6. He starts with the concept of **user value**: this incorporates both *actual use* and the more complex (in terms of measurement) **option use** – an expression of preference, a willingness to pay to conserve now and to use later, or indeed to conserve in perpetuity. Thus he affirms:

total user value = actual use value + option use value

To this Pearce adds the yet more complex concept of **intrinsic value** or **existence value**, that is the value we might assign to a given resource merely because it exists. We end up with the following formula for total economic value:

total economic value =
actual use value + option use value + existence value

To abbreviate here the analysis presented in the report, Pearce argues that using basic economic concepts, such as those outlined above, sustainable development involves valuing the environment 'properly', so that the next generation is able to inherit a stock of both manufactured and natural capitals, no less than the stock inherited by the previous generation. This broad concept of 'wealth bequest' (whose *raison d'être* sounds not dissimilar to the 'conservationist ethos' preached by Pinchot and others in the American Declaration of Resource Conservation discussed in Box 5.1) has to take account of avoiding 'irreversible losses of environmental assets', which is seen as a constraint on the operation of free market forces. Pearce argues that sustainable development must accept some trade-offs between narrowly construed economic growth and environmental quality, meaning that the economic value of environmental cost, if there is one, has to be understood. This implies then that society is given a choice, with all options costed. There do, however, appear to be real problems with this approach when we consider the 'management of the commons'. How are 'environmental costs' to be allocated here?

At any rate, the clear message from the Pearce Report is that environmental improvements are equivalent to economic improvements, if 'quality of life' is beneficially affected. Pearce and his colleagues have certainly taken up one of the Brundtland Report's 'imperatives' – that environment and economics should be merged in decision-making. Given the political will, fiscal policies could be devised which levied taxes on energy, resources and pollution that could have a significant effect on patterns of consumption in the developed world. The employment of 'market incentives' to encourage 'good environmental practice', as has been attempted recently in a limited fashion for farming in the United Kingdom, could also be a step in the right direction. In the case of Environmentally Sensitive Areas, a value is placed on particular areas of landscape to be managed for conservation rather than agricultural purposes, and the farmer receives a return from the government in lieu of the income forgone by using less intensive methods (*Blunden*, 1991). Internalising the costs of pollution so that the polluter pays is a further mechanism for improving market imperfections in relation to environmental costs. On the issues of global warming, the Pearce approach would see market-based approaches as a necessary part of any attempt to reduce the greenhouse effect, with the most attractive options involving the encouragement of energy efficiency.

All seems possible, yet so much rests on political will and government intervention into a dynamic economic system whose overriding motor

drive is the desire to maximise profits. Whether industrial democracies will be able to overcome the political constraints on bending the market-system towards long-term sustainability is *the key* question here. If the amount of money given by governments into the United Nations Environment Programme's Environment Fund since it was established at the Stockholm Conference in 1972 is anything to go by – just $30 million a year and often less – then perhaps we have to remain sceptical about their *real* commitment to sustainable development.

This also raises the problem, highlighted in the previous section, that while political and economic issues are essentially viewed in the short term, environmental ones have to be seen in the long term. Can individual firms, the multinationals and indeed nation-states 'risk' their competitiveness in increasingly international markets by being environmentally friendly, for the sake of long-term economic and environmental survival? The implications are marked, not just for industry in the first world, where technological improvement and capital-intensive development can help to reduce environmental impact, but more significantly in eastern Europe and the Soviet Union, where there is already a huge bill to be paid for modernisation, and in many of the developing countries, where 'state of the art' technology may simply be beyond reach by reason of cost.

Perhaps not surprisingly, given the expressions of concern in the previous two paragraphs, the Pearce Report, in taking a market-oriented (if not a 'pure market') view, has itself become the centre of controversy and criticism. John Bowers (in *The Guardian*, 1990), on behalf of the British Association of Nature Conservationists, challenges the proposition that you can put a *realistic value* on the environment and on environmental effects. 'How do you value the greenhouse effect?', he asks. The consequences of such global environmental issues have not been foreseen due to lack of scientific knowledge, so how can the market allocate costs on the basis of information that does not even exist? Bowers also attacks Pearce's revitalised ideas on cost-benefit analysis. The assumption in the Report is that decisions on specific cases would be made somehow 'independently'. The reality, Bowers argues, is that decision-making is never independent or impartial: 'The environment suffers because of the institutional failure of public sector decision-making.'

On a broader level Bowers argues that continuing growth and sustainability are not always compatible:

> If sustainability is to be accepted then the poor, both in the Third World, and lower income groups in developed countries, must be protected . . . Substantial sacrifices will be required by the wealthy who consume the lion's share of the world's resources.

This line of criticism is taken further by Michael Redclift, who points out that the Pearce approach works better for developed than developing countries. He sees Pearce as seeking 'intellectual purity rather than political reality', because he has undertaken the discussion of sustainable development 'within a framework of "value-free" academic enquiry' which make no assumptions about who benefits or who loses, or recognises that structural linkages among nations at different levels of development can result in a politically and culturally biased view of what is sustainable. The issue of equity is 'the driving force behind indiscriminate resource degradation in developing countries', but such considerations are not high on the Pearce agenda of looking at total user value and total economic value.

3.5   *Neo-Marxist approach*

We have already encountered elements of the type of critique developed by more radical writers like Michael Redclift (in, for example, *Sustainable Development: exploring the contradictions* (1987)). It is rooted in an analysis of *historical processes* and is centrally concerned with the contradictions within sustainable development imposed by the *structural inequalities* of the global economic system. In particular, it focuses attention on the *economic dependence* of the less developed countries on the developed (a theme introduced in Chapter 5, Section 2.5). People in the South 'are being thrown against the contradictions of development in their struggle to survive'. This is where Redclift points to shortcomings in the Brundtland Report in not taking the analysis far enough. The dominance of a particular economic system, capitalism, is explicitly recognised, but there are major assumptions made about the ability of that system to accommodate the sort of changes required by that Report. Herein lies the major contradiction. Its recommendations, on a *radical* interpretation, are not much short of revolutionary, or put another way, from a radical point of view it will require nothing short of a revolution in political and economic terms to achieve the stated objectives. Radical change is being advocated, but the Report does not say how it is to be achieved. That is up to government. It is scarcely surprising that the Report did not go as far as this. We are, after all, talking about an approach that offers a fundamental challenge to structures within the global economy, and that attacks the processes of imperialism and neo-colonialism that I discussed earlier. As the last chapter also noted, it does not take issue with the concept of economic growth as such.

Let us take two instances here. The Brundtland Report, as I commented in a previous section, is remarkably guarded on the role of the multinational or transnational corporations (TNCs), yet their role in development, as we have already seen in the case study of the tropical rainforests, is highly contentious. They are viewed by many critics as being irresponsible in the way they put profits before nature conservation, and, indeed, before human livelihoods. This is particularly so with the role of the TNCs specialising in biotechnology, engaged in 'agribusiness' in the developing world. **Biotechnology** is used to refer to the modern techniques of increasing food production, both in the input sector (that is in the use of seeds, fertilisers and pesticides) and in technologies used after harvesting (particularly in food processing). The development of so-called 'miracle seeds' was at the heart of the green revolution in the third world. Critics saw this as producing even greater dependence on the rich nations, and particularly on the giant chemical industries who were capitalising on the 'biotechnological revolution'. Here is a provocative quote from a well-known writer on development issues, and particularly on the debt crisis, Susan George, in which she encapsulates the role of such TNCs:

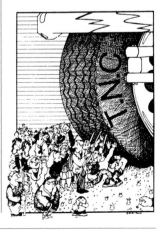

> Present-day biotechnology is the result of the work of thousands of people who patiently built the foundations, the walls and raised the roofbeams of an enormous edifice. Now that these labours are over, corporations new and old are crowding and jostling each other on the building site to put the final slates on the roof and call the whole place theirs.   (George, 1984)

The implication of this statement is that the 'green revolution' has enabled the TNCs to extend their already powerful influence to further integrate global agricultural production into their main fields of interest, and has enhanced the dependence of the third world on the industrialised nations.

The role of the TNCs and the issue of debt are interrelated in that they are both symptomatic of a model of development that puts the making of profits and the expansion of world trade firmly in the driving seat, according to the neo-Marxist view. This is certainly a complex area, and I can do little more here than to indicate to you the essence of the argument. (Note that I have already addressed the question of debt in Section 2.2 above.) World debt and the price of oil are inextricably linked together. The debt crisis arose following the massive increases in oil prices by the OPEC countries in 1973/74. At the time it was profitable to lend money because interest rates in real terms were low compared with world inflation. Accordingly the banks in the North lent considerable sums of money to the developing countries, in particular, to enable them to 'adjust' to the effects of oil price rises.

The crisis was exacerbated at the end of the 1970s when oil prices rose sharply again. This time interest rates were much higher, and credit was not so freely available, even though the debtor countries needed to borrow more. The apogee of the crisis occurred in 1982 when the debt in Mexico 'went through the roof' leaving that country effectively bankrupt. The IMF, the World Bank and other lending institutions were 'forced' to assemble a huge 'debt rescue package'. This package included a strict **structural adjustment policy**. Bluntly, what this means for developing countries is that in order to qualify for further loans and continuing membership in the international community, they must adhere to the policies of the North and followed prescribed routes in relation to development. In real terms the

▲   The headquarters of the International Monetary Fund in Washington, DC, opened in 1973.

impact has been crippling for millions in the developing world in terms of falls in living standards, and highly damaging for already fragile environments, as we have seen in the examples earlier in Brazil and Africa. Many developing countries are struggling merely to pay the interest on their debts, and since 1984 there has been a net outflow of capital from the South (shown in Table 6.1). Clearly, it is more complicated than this, as the case study of Brazil indicated. Corrupt governments in the South have misused or expropriated funds intended for the alleviation of poverty. Nevertheless, what we need to be clear about here are the underlying processes which bring about structural inequalities and lead to underdevelopment. Michael Redclift summarises it thus:

> Indebtedness is not a curiosity of bad economic management, it is a symptom of a deeper malaise that equates 'development' with the conversion of natural resources into consumable products, many of which we produce but cannot sell. Indebtedness makes claims on the environment which are unsupportable and unsustainable. It is part of the motor of destruction that we see both in the developed world and in less developed countries, and to which an alternative is urgently required . . . World trade can be expanded without net benefits accruing to poorer trading 'partners'. *The IMF exists to ensure that trade and economic growth are maintained, whatever the social and environmental consequences.*   (1987, p. 72; emphasis added)

I have used the examples of debt crisis and the TNCs to highlight the argument about structural interdependencies and inequalities which exist between the North and the South, as these point to inconsistencies and contradictions in the approach to sustainable development taken by the Brundtland Report.

The strength of the neo-Marxist analysis is that it seeks to explain in a comprehensive fashion the nature of economic dependence of the developing world on the industrialised nations, and its consequences in terms of uneven development. It challenges the assumption of the Report that sustainable development is an achievable goal, but it also leaves questions unanswered. What are the political implications of such an approach? The political and economic consequences of following through a Marxist-type analysis are radical indeed. If a Marxist-inspired approach is that worthwhile, then why are we seeing so many countries, certainly in the second world withdrawing from totalitarian regimes supposedly built upon Marxist doctrine? Isn't Marxism outmoded and indeed irrelevant to the consideration of global issues for the twenty-first century?

3.6   Summary

Activity 4

Go back over the last three sections, and also refresh your memory of Sections 2.5 and 2.6 of Chapter 5. Consider briefly each of the approaches in turn in terms of their apparent *strengths* and *weaknesses* in analysing the concept of sustainable development, and in putting forward practical policy options for the future. Compare your answer with that given in the following paragraphs.

PUNCHLINE
by **CHRISTIAN**

A FEW YEARS AGO MY GOV'T COULDN'T PAY BACK THE BILLIONS OF DOLLARS OF LOANS IT OWED TO WESTERN BANKS.

YEARS OF EXPLOITATION AND ABUSE AND TODAY WE'RE ABLE ONLY TO PAY BACK THE INTEREST ON OUR LOANS!..

AS A RESULT, THEY WERE FORCED TO CLOSE DOWN OUR HOSPITALS, OUR SCHOOLS, THEY SMASHED OUR UNIONS.

..WHAT WORD CAN POSSIBLY DESCRIBE SUCH A HORRIFIC TRAGEDY?!

RECOVERY...

Sections 3.2 to 3.5 have, I hope, been challenging and provocative. The aim has been to build upon the discussion in Chapter 5 Sections 3.4–3.6, and to subject the Brundtland Report, and in particular the concept of sustainable development, to a cross-examination. The approaches have offered contrasting analyses from quite different starting-points. If you can cast your mind back to Section 3.1 of Chapter 5, I talked there in terms of the confrontation of two contrasting ideologies – capitalism and Marxism – and posed the question as to whether either could provide a political economic context for achieving a sustainable form of development. This may have sounded like some great intellectual battleground in which two opposing giants are locked in protracted conflict. Indeed, some social scientists have chosen to approach the question of global economic relationships in these terms.

What I have sought to achieve is a more 'open-ended' analysis in the sense that behind the dogma may lie opportunities for change. What the Report appears to be providing is a challenge to capitalism, to the market-based approach, from within capitalism itself, *given the political will*. What Pearce and others are saying is that the system (industrial capitalism) is sufficiently flexible to allow for such change, based upon market principles. Historically, capitalism has demonstrated its capacity to adopt to changing circumstances. The only way to proceed, the argument continues, is to enable technological innovation, guided by the political will, to combat the growing threat to the environment in *all* parts of the globe.

The neo-Marxist response does not appear that flexible, but you need to assess the logic of the argument carefully. Fundamentally, the capitalist system has to be changed, because at the root of all environmental problems lie the destructive seeds of consumerism, greed and inequality that are spawned and allowed to flourish within it. But the answer scarcely lies in the second world where the popular clamour has been for a shift from 'socialist' growth to 'market-oriented' growth. We have to ask what realistic agenda for action might arise from the neo-Marxist position.

Within the ecology-centred approach we have encountered progressive thinking, radicalism and political uncertainty. The argument for 'low input' technology and local initiatives is an attractive one, particularly for the developing world: the no-growth solution is not. Yet the implications for the former are unclear in political terms, if you accept the structural neo-Marxist explanation of economic dependence within a dominant global political economic context that is capitalist. How is change to occur? The appeals to populism, to local action and participation sound encouraging, but how realistic are they in the political climate of the 'real' world?

The practical implications of sustainable development need to be understood at all levels – national, global and local. Earlier in this chapter some of the implications for population control policies in three developing countries were considered. Chapter 4 examined the political problems associated with the drawing up of international conventions, for 'managing the global commons'. The next section takes a brief look at some local initiatives for achieving a sustainable means of existence in the developing world.

4   *Sustainable development in practice*

The Brundtland Report made numerous references to the importance of local, community-based initiatives, in relation to achieving the objectives of sustainable development. Yet its overall tenor is global, dealing with issues of population, industrial development, energy and resources at a 'macro-level'. A report by the Food and Agricultural Organisation (FAO) to the Commission argues that analysis and policy should begin with people, rather than 'things' or 'issues', with the poor and especially the rural poor. There is an echo here of an ecology-centred approach, and particularly of Schumacher, emphasising people before products. The integrating concept the Report emphasised was that of 'sustainable livelihoods', a brief definition of which I provided in Section 2.1:

> Livelihood is defined as adequate stocks and flows of food and cash to meet basic needs. Security refers to secure ownership of, or access to, resources and income-earning activities, including reserves and assets to offset risk, ease shocks and meet contingencies. Sustainable refers to the maintenance or enhancement of resource productivity on a long-term basis.
> (Chambers, 1988, p. 1)

There is much agreement that poverty and environmental degradation are often interlinked. It is a matter of a struggle to survive. The problem with many 'aid' programmes is that they have more often than not caused serious environmental damage and severely disrupted the lives of local people (as we saw in Brazil, for example). Projects have been imposed from above by groups of 'professionals' who have tended to misunderstand the problem, and mis-specify the solution. Frequently, technical solutions have failed, as in many soil and water conservation projects, because the views of the people have not been sought, and education has not been part of the programme.

The Greening of Aid (1988), based on the FAO report, is an attempt to demonstrate how aid, properly administered at a local level, involving the participation of the community, can begin to achieve some of the objectives of sustainability in the least developed 'resource-poor' areas of the world, where 'grand designs' may not. By means of a series of 33 case studies, detailing actual projects in Africa, Asia and Latin America, *The Greening of Aid* provides practical evidence of how improving the livelihoods of the poor is an essential aspect of sustainable development in reducing the pressures on natural environments.

The emphasis in all the projects is on sustainability through self-help, allied to a 'learning-process' approach, putting people's priorities first and securing rights and gains for the poor, like common property resources. Such an emphasis does require the commitment of governments, and the sensitive response of the non-government organisations (NGOs), including the aid agencies. So the effective development of sustainable livelihoods is necessarily linked to a flexible and responsive *institutional framework* (another prerequisite underlined in Brundtland).

Resource-poor and ecologically vulnerable people, and the environments in which they live, need new forms of development that enable them to gain a secure and decent living for themselves and their children, where they are and with the resources they can command. It is by starting with the priorities of the poorer, and enabling them to gain the livelihoods they want and *need*, that both they and sustainable development can best be served.

(Chambers, 1988, p. 15)

The following case studies provide illustrations of two projects in northern Thailand, and in Haryana State, India.

Box 6.8
Lampang Applied Nutrition Programme

The principal objective of this project, started in the Lampang Province of northern Thailand (see Figure 6.7) in 1982, is the improvement of the nutritional status of the 86 000 people living in the Ngao and Sobprap districts. The project has been co-ordinated by the Meals for Millions/Freedom From Hunger Foundation (MFM) in co-operation with the Thai Ministry of Public Health. The success of the venture, measured in terms of its long-term effectiveness to foster sustainable development in this area, has rested on the limited intervention from outside (foreign financial assistance has been relatively small), and local control over the day-to-day management programme. MFM fieldworkers have promoted technical skills, and a 'bottom-up' approach. What the programme has achieved is the promotion of an intensive agriculture, based on highly nutritious soya beans which improve soil quality, encourage long-term cultivation in situ, and discourage 'slash and burn' techniques. It has emphasised the management of contaminents in the area's agroecosystem in a number of ways:

● by using organic means to increase soil fertility

● by supporting sanitation projects and environmentally sound means of waste disposal

● by introducing simple techniques for storing and preserving food and water.

In this way 'the interrelationship between improving nutrition and protecting the environment from human use has led to a programme that is environmentally sustainable'. Also the vital role played by women in agricultural development has been emphasised in this programme.

   The costs of the project have been modest. Between 1982 and 1986 some $600 000 were

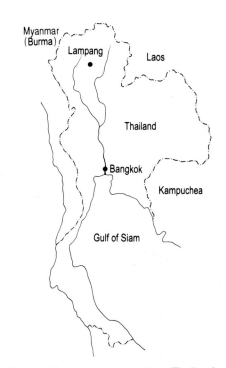

▲   *Figure 6.7   Lampang, northern Thailand.*

spent, of which $175 000 came from the Thai government. The benefits have been realised beyond Lampang province: Thai government ministries have begun to adopt the applied nutrition activities independently. Whereas in 1982 the Thai government's rural development efforts were essentially 'top-down' in character, the ANP 'has successfully demonstrated a more participatory development strategy'.

Box 6.9   Sustainable Energy Project, Haryana State

This project was initiated on an experimental basis in 1984 by the Tata Energy Research Institute, New Delhi. (The Institute is partially funded by the Tata Industrial Group, one of the largest corporations in India.) The aim has been to demonstrate the practical achievements of work in the field on local renewable sources of energy, focusing on one village Dhanawas, with the long-term objective of spreading the ideas to other villages in the state. (See Figure 6.8.)

Participation by the villagers is a cornerstone of the initiative, in what is a bottom-up process. All work is undertaken in complete co-operation with the village council, employing the equitable concept of common property resources, and to date (1990) at no cost to the inhabitants. Funding comes jointly from TERI, the FAO and the Indian government. The principal features of the project are:

● The establishment of a seven hectare plantation on what were very poor saline soils supporting only scrub vegetation. The policy is for long term improvement of soil quality, using hardy nitrogen-fixing species like acacia and mesquat which can be used as fuelwood on a sustainable basis. All trees are held as a common property resource.

▲ Figure 6.8
Haryana State.

● The setting up of *biogas* makers, which use a mixture of dung and water. The capacity of the unit is 2 cubic metres per day, which is sufficient for about 5 hours cooking on modern cookstoves or 10 hours of lighting. The plan is to introduce enough of these to enable the village to become self-sufficient in renewable sources of fuel, reducing the consumption of fuelwood in conventional cookstoves in the process. (See Plate 12.)

● The development of a *gasifier*, using a mixture of shredded mustard stalks, dung and water, which are made into pellets and then converted into gas. The equipment is capable of generating the

equivalent of 5 kilowatts of electricity with an 80%/20% gas/diesel mix. (See Plate 13.)

● The use of solar-powered water heaters, of which there are two at present.

The project is about using intermediate technology to promote the efficient use of renewables, thus cutting the cost of conventional fuel consumption in rural areas. It is seen by TERI as going hand in hand with education and development. The problem is that Haryana State is amongst the most agriculturally productive states in India, and the inhabitants of Dhanawas have been willing to participate because their village is 'richer' than most. Poorer villages have other priorities, like access to safe water and income generation.

These projects demonstrate what can be achieved locally with a small budget in terms of aid, and with the political co-operation of a national government. It puts some perspective on the willingness of Thailand's and India's politicians to give practical meaning to the idea of sustainable development for local communities and to encourage local participation. At the same time, such local initiatives are taking place within a context of continuing pressure for economic growth nationally, particularly in the case of Thailand, which in the 1990s has one of the world's fastest-growing economies. Is this, then, something of a contradiction, or does it imply that although sustainable development, as seen by the Brundtland Report, encourages us to 'think globally', the only effective way to achieve progress is to 'act locally'?

5   Towards a sustainable future: whither green politics?

We seem to have come a long way from ideas about conservation in the USA, the industrial revolution in the UK and its impact on the minds of thinkers like Marx, Morris and Kropotkin, to discuss issues of sustainability in Thailand and India, taking in the destructive nature of communism 'behind the Iron Curtain', and the destructive nature of capitalism in the tropical rainforests. In terms of 'choosing the future', I hope that the foregoing discussion has actually established in your mind some potential options for the future, whether feasible, realistic or otherwise.

The aim of these two chapters has been to try to introduce themes of *critical enquiry* and of *political economic realism* on the major issues of global environmental concern. I have asked you to reflect critically on contrasting ways of seeing the relationship between environment and development from the controversial 'anti-growth' arguments of 'deep' ecology, through the market-oriented 'optimistic' perspectives of neo-classical economists like Pearce, to the neo-Marxist analysis of economic dependency of writers such as Michael Redclift. In particular, I have emphasised the importance of *historical processes* in relation to current thinking on how ideas have developed and why. While stressing the political and economic implications of relationships between development and environment, I have tried to show that concern for the environment means taking account also of *social processes*. This was well illustrated, for example, in the case study on the tropical rainforest in the last chapter and in the local examples discussed above.

I stressed in Section 3.2 that my own *value positions* could well come across during the course of discussion. The emphasis on *local action* and low-impact technology within an ecology-centred approach has considerable appeal (as demonstrated in the previous section) but I remain sceptical about this as an overriding context for tackling global environmental problems because it does lack political and economic realism. I also reject the 'no growth' school of thinking, and see certain positions within deep ecology as being at best naive and at worst arrogant and politically unacceptable. I question the market-based approach, because I am certainly not convinced that global environmental issues can be 'solved' within a framework of the dominant political economy of capitalism, although I accept, as does the Brundtland Report, that we have to work within this framework because there is, currently, no other; and there is within capitalism the *potential* flexibility to adapt to the requirements of an economically and environmentally sustainable system. This means acknowledging and coping with the contradictions. In terms of its explanatory strengths I am persuaded by a neo-Marxist approach, because it offers a challenging and relevant analysis of the fundamental aspects of economic dependency in global development. It points out what are the inevitable contradictions within the concept of sustainable development. Moreover, it does put, in theory at least, people and poverty and the consideration of equity and inequalities above the issues of the market place. But then so do the approaches of writers like Schumacher and Shiva (as shown in Section 3.3).

That, you may rightly argue, is the 'luxury' of taking an *academic approach*, but we must also search for *relevance* in our enquiry. Theory has to relate to practice, and here is the real problem for both the deep ecologists and the neo-Marxists. I have taken, as far as I am able here, a long hard look at the proposals of the World Commission on Environment and Development, the Brundtland Report, and its implications for achieving sustainable development. Despite its contradictions and its tendency to compromise, it does set out a forthright agenda. It does meet its terms of reference. So what more should we ask or expect? What happens now is up to people. Writes Lloyd Timberlake, (1988):

> Sustainable development is ultimately a *local activity*. Governments do not *do* development: people do . . . Sustainable development cuts across sectoral boundaries; governments do not. Governments will have to be pushed, goaded, advised, pressurised and encouraged by non-governmental organisations and by non-governmental people.

I think there is hope in the movement (politically) of people, locally, regionally, nationally. We only have to look at what has been happening at the start of the decade in eastern Europe to appreciate that.

On the other hand, is that a sufficiently challenging note on which to leave this discussion, or is it evading some fundamental issues of political economy? Global environmental concerns must impinge upon national aspirations and goals, crucially so in the developed world, if a sustainable future for all the peoples of the world is to be anything other than hollow rhetoric. In 1990 the United States, for example, is dragging its heels on the issue of drawing up even an initial international agreement to tackle global warming. The basic issue about patterns of production and consumption in the industrialised North has got to be confronted. There has to be change, and action has to be taken sooner rather than later. The industrialised countries have to clear up their own mess first before expecting the developing nations to do likewise.

At the World Commission on Environment and Development Conference in Bergen in May 1990 Gro Harlem Brundtland stated:

> The Earth is one, but the World is not . . . There will be no sustainable development in the world if this takes place only in the North. There can be no sustainable development as long as poverty is a scourge from which more than one billion people suffer.

She reasserted the emphasis of the 1987 Report on the need for growth, but qualified this by arguing that:

> We need a stronger sense of environmental responsibility both in public policies and planning, *and* in corporate boardrooms. Long-term sustainability has yet to reach the same importance as short-term profitability as a measuring rod for corporate success. Business must be profitable to survive, but it also must face the call to become sustainable to enable us all to survive.   (at Bergen, 1990)

At Bergen, a forum for 34 industrialised countries of the North, there were tens of thousands of words written and spoken in a similar vein. A 'Joint Agenda for Action' was agreed upon, which in terms of its rhetoric certainly developed the thinking of the 1987 Brundtland Report. Yet the response of the critics, from environmental groups like Greenpeace and from youth organisations, was: 'Words, more words – still no action!'

RECYCLING CITY · UK 2000 PROJECT

sponsored by British TELECOM

C A R D I F F

In all of this discussion we cannot ignore the perspective from the developing countries. Indeed, quite the opposite has to be the case. Many observers from the third world continue to argue that the West has an immense *historical debt* to pay. The consequences of following the 'conventional path' of economic development over 200 years of history have been disabling and dependency-creating for much of the developing world. These are manifest in rising debt, in structural adjustment programmes, in trade protectionist policies. They see the role of science and technology not as 'liberator' but as 'destroyer'. They point to the huge annual expenditure on armaments, a continuing growth industry which for them epitomises the worst face of free-market capitalist enterprise. Here, there is some sign of hope in the changing political picture with the 'end' of the Cold War, which could see funds being diverted away from military expenditure into the so-called 'Peace Dividend'. Yet many, many questions remain unanswered for the third world citizen who does not have enough to eat, and no permanent place to live.

> Modern technology has made it possible to deliver a bomb across the world in minutes. Women in rural areas of Asia and Africa still walk several hours a day for the family's water supply.
>
> (Quaker Movement, 1989)

As a postscript I would like to leave you with this extract from Raymond Williams' paper on *Socialism and Ecology* (1982), to which I referred in Chapter 5. I find this both challenging and provocative.

Box 6.10
Raymond Williams: A new politics (1982)

For any ecologist this is a special challenge. It is too easy, in the rich industrial north, to say that we have had our industrial revolution, we have had our advanced industrial and urban development, and we have known some of its undesirable effects, and so we are in a position to warn the poor countries against going down that same road. We have indeed to try to share that whole experience of indiscriminate production. But we must do it in a kind of good faith which is in fact rare. It must not become an argument for keeping the poor countries in a state of radical underdevelopment, with their economies in fact shaped to keep supplying the existing rich countries. It must not become an argument against the kind of sensible industrialisation which will enable them, in more balanced ways, to use and develop their own resources, and to overcome their often appalling problems of poverty. The case, that is to say, has to be made from a position of genuinely shared experience and from a deep belief in human equality, rather than from the overt or, even more dangerous, covert prejudices of the developed northern societies.

Bringing these issues together, then we can see that in local, national and international terms there are already kinds of thinking which can become the elements of an ecologically conscious socialism. We can begin to think of a new kind of social analysis in which ecology and economics will become, as they always should be, a single science. We can see the outline of political bearings which can be related to material realities in ways that give us practical hope for a shared future.

Yet none of it is going to be easy. Deep changes of belief will be necessary, not just conveniently, where they are in fact impossible, among the existing power elites and the rich classes of the world, but in all of us who are now practically embedded in this general situation. We are bound to encounter the usual human reluctance to change, and we must accept the fact that the changes will be very considerable and will have to be negotiated rather than imposed.

References

BRANDT, W. and SAMPSON, A. (eds) (1980) *North–South: a programme for survival* (The Brandt Report), Cambridge, Mass., MIT Press.

BROWN, S. (1990) 'Humans and their environment: changing attitudes', Ch. 7 in Silvertown, J. and Sarre, P. (eds) *Environment and Society*, London, Hodder and Stoughton/The Open University (Book One of this series).

BLUNDEN, J. (1991) 'Competing demands in the countryside: a United Kingdom case study', Ch. 5 in Sarre, P. (ed.).

CHAMBERS, R. (1988) 'Sustainable rural livelihoods', Ch. 1 in Conroy, C. and Litvinoff, M. (eds).

CLARK, W.C. and MUNN, R.E. (eds) (1986) *Sustainable Development of the Biosphere*, Cambridge, Cambridge University Press.

CONROY, C. and LITVINOFF, M. (eds) (1988) *The Greening of Aid: sustainable livelihoods in practice*, London, Earthscan.

FINDLAY, A. (1988) 'Population and environment: reproduction and production', Ch. 1 in Sarre, P. (ed.).

FOOD AND AGRICULTURE ORGANISATION (1984) *Land, Food and People*, Rome.

GEORGE, S. (1988) *A Fate Worse than Debt*, Harmondsworth, Pelican.

GIBBON, J.H. *et al.* (1989) 'Strategies for energy use', *Scientific American*, September, pp. 86–93.

GILBERT, A. (1988) 'Urban problems in the third world', Ch. 7 in Sarre, P. (ed.).

GOLDSMITH, E. *et al.* (1972) *A Blueprint for Survival*, London, Tom Stacey.

GORZ, A. (1980) *Ecology as Politics*, London, Pluto Press.

GRIGG, D. (1991) 'World agriculture: productivity and sustainability', Ch. 2 in Sarre, P. (ed.).

KEYFITZ, N. (1989) 'The growing human population', *Scientific American*, September, pp. 71–77A.

MEADOWS, D.H. *et al.* (1972) *The Limits to Growth* (A Report for the Club of Rome's Project on the Predicament of Mankind), London, Earth Island.

PAKKASEN, P. (1988) *Leading Issues in Thailand's Development Transformation 1960–1990*, Bangkok.

PEARCE, D. *et al.* (1989) *Blue Print for a Green Economy*, London, Earthscan.

PHANTUMVANIT, D. (1987) *Thailand: natural resources profile*, Bangkok.

QUAKER MOVEMENT (1989) *Peace and Disarmament*, (pamphlet).

REDCLIFT, M. (1987) *Sustainable Development: exploring the contradictions*, London, Methuen.

REDDISH, A. (1991) 'Sustainable energy futures', Ch. 5 in Blunden, J. and Reddish, A. (eds) *Energy, Resources and Environment*, London, Hodder and Stoughton/The Open University (Book Three in this series).

SCHUMACHER, E.F. (1973) *Small is Beautiful: economics as if people mattered*, London, Abacus.

SCIENTIFIC AMERICAN (1989) *Special Issue on Sustainable Development*, September.

SARRE, P. (ed.) (1991) *Environment, Population and Development*, London, Hodder and Stoughton/The Open University (Book Two in this series).

SHIVA, V. (1988) *Staying Alive: women, ecology and survival in India*, London, Zed Press.

TIMBERLAKE, L. (1988) 'The Brundtland Report: an opportunity for NGOs?', speech at conference, Brussels, 27–29 April, organised by the International Institute for Environment and Development.

UNITED NATIONS COMMISSION (1983) *Common Crisis, North–South: cooperation for world recovery*, The Brandt Commission, Cambridge, Mass., MIT Press.

UNITED NATIONS WORLD COMMISSION ON ENVIRONMENT AND DEVELOPMENT (1987) *Our Common Future* (The Brundtland Report), Oxford, Oxford University Press.

WILLIAMS, R. (1982) *Socialism and Ecology*, London, SERA.

WOODHOUSE, P. (1991) 'Farming a wetland ecosystem: rice cultivation in Asia', Ch. 3 in Sarre, P. (ed.).

WORLD CONSERVATION STRATEGY (1987) *World Conservation Strategy*, International Union for the Conservation of Nature and Natural Resources, Gland, Switzerland.

Further reading

CADMAN, D. and PAYNE, G. (1989) *The Living City: towards a sustainable future*, London, Routledge and Kegan Paul.

PEARCE, D. (1989) *Sustainable Development*, London, IIED.

SARRE, P., SMITH, P. M. and MORRIS, E. (1991) *One World for One Earth: overcoming environmental degradation*, London, Earthscan/The Open University.

TIMBERLAKE, L. and HOLMBERG, J. (1991) *Defending the Future: a guide to sustainable development*, London, Earthscan.

Appendix

The following is the full text of the leader article which appeared in
The Guardian on 5 February 1990. Part of this article is quoted in Chapter 5
and it is reproduced here in order to present in full the views expressed in
that editorial.

In search of a greener politics

As EUROPE'S political barriers come down, there is suddenly a sense of a common human destiny, of people making elementary connections in place of the artificial boundaries of ideology and repression. It is no coincidence that this revolution has emerged alongside a world-wide concern with environmental degradation. Indeed, a significant impulse behind change in eastern Europe has been fury at the physical ruination of the environment. The Green movement seeks to re-establish connections that have become fractured between man and his surroundings. So does Green philosophy provide the framework for a completely new order that will save the world?

Environmental concern operates on different levels. It is local: the traffic gridlock around London; the sulphurous smogs from eastern European chimneys; Chernobyl; Bhopal; or the deadly spume of chemicals in the Adriatic. It crosses national boundaries through acid rain and the destruction of species in pursuit of profit. And environmentalism is above all stratospheric. It predicts imminent catastrophe through global warming caused by too much carbon dioxide being pumped into the atmosphere. Green politics says that mankind's greed and selfishness are to blame and that the consumer society and economic growth itself must be halted if the very planet is not to perish.

We find many reverberations but also much misapprehension among these observations and prescriptions. We believe that man bears a moral responsibility both for the survival and well-being of his own kind and for his surroundings. He bears it because he is a rational being, a fact which elevates him above the flora and fauna and simultaneously endows him with a duty towards the natural world. Environmentalists cover a broad spectrum of opinions, and must be credited with raising awareness of the consequences of man's actions to the top of the political agenda. But much Green philosophy appears to downgrade mankind to a species of no greater worth than any other and which is terminally culpable for the wanton destruction of nature. Implicit — although doubtless inadvertent — is the assumption that saving the whale matters more than preventing a pogrom. Indeed, man's inhumanity to man hardly gets a mention in eco-orthodoxy. Associated with this latent misanthropy is an authoritarian streak that springs directly from the hopeless utopianism of deep ecology, which leads seamlessly from telling the underdeveloped world that it is forbidden the benefits of an industrialised society, through population control to eugenics. At best middle-class self-indulgence, at worst it opens up a potential nightmare vista of repression.

At the same time, the burgeoning apocalypse industry is busily fleecing those very consumers upon whom such books pronounce their anathema. This modern version of catastrophe theory is intellectually dishonest and thus will undermine the real need for action. This literature predicts global warming, pins its cause on rising carbon dioxide levels and pronounces the undiluted disaster of its effect, all as an utter certainty stamped and approved by science. This is false. Scientists agree that there is an accelerating rise in carbon dioxide levels. But they don't know the consequences of the rise and the role other factors may play in warming the atmosphere. (For example, the regular El Nino movements of Pacific Ocean currents, which occurred in 1982/83 and 1986/87, are thought to have contributed significantly to the very warm years 1983, 1987 and 1988.) Moreover, so far from the ice caps melting, recent satellite surveys indicate that the Greenland ice sheet is thickening; and the ½° rise in global temperature since the beginning of the century is thought to be within the normal range of variations. The fact is that scientists simply don't know enough to support the wilder predictions now being made. Does this mean the world should do nothing about carbon dioxide emissions? Absolutely not. The risk of unacceptable damage from even a small increase in warming is simply too great to permit inertia. It is important that politicians like Mrs Thatcher are given no excuse to weasel out of such action, which is why the dishonesty of those who preach apocalypse now plays absolutely into her hands.

Acknowledgements

Grateful acknowledgement is made to the following sources for permission to reproduce material in this book:

Covers

Front cover, clockwise from top right: Roy Lawrance; Ron & Valerie Taylor/Ardea; © Greenpeace/Midgley; Charles Mason/Colorific!; © Jeremy Hartley/Oxfam; Simon Fraser/Science Photo Library; Paul M.Smith; Dr. David Snashall; © François Gohier/Ardea; *centre:* © Ann Purcell/Colorific!; *back cover:* H.Girardet/The Environmental Picture Library.

Colour plate section

Plates 1 and 2: Reproduced with permission of the Earth Observation Satellite Co. (EOSAT), Lanham, Maryland, USA; *Plates 3 and 4:* Figures 7.13 and 5.6 (a,b,c) from J.T. Houghton, J.T. Jenkins and J. Ephraums, *Climate Change: the IPCC scientific assessment*, Cambridge, Cambridge University Press, © WMO/UNEP/IPCC, 1990; *Plate 5:* National Aeronautics and Space Administration; *Plate 6:* Philippe Plailly/Science Photo Library; *Plate 7:* Simon Fraser/Science Photo Library; *Plate 8:* 'Coalbrookdale by Night' by Philip James de Loutherbourg, 1801, National Museum for Science and Technology; *Plate 9:* Jeremy Hartley/ OXFAM; *Plates 10 and 11:* Simon Fraser/Science Photo Library; *Plates 12 and 13:* Paul M. Smith.

Figures

Figures 1.2, 1.3, 1.4: pp. 14, 15, 17, 43 from S. Smith, *Discovering the Sea*, Trewin Copplestone Books Ltd, London, 1982, a division of Longman Group Ltd, and Sceptre Books, Hodder & Stoughton Ltd; *Figures 1.5, 1.6, 1.7, 1.9, 1.17, 1.19, 1.21, 1.22:* Figures 2.5, 2.13, 9.6, 9.7a & b, 9.8, 11.15, 11.17 in P.S. Meadows and J.I. Campbell, *An Introduction to Marine Science*, Blackie & Son Ltd, 1988; *Figure 1.8:* 'The main oil transport routes by sea in 1980', in 'Oil pollution control in the East African region', *UNEP Regional Seas Reports and Studies*, No. 10, 1982, © UNEP/IMO, 1982; *Figure 1.11:* illustration by Allen Bechel in S.J. Holt, 'The food resources of the ocean', in *Scientific American*, September 1969; *Figure 1.14:* 'Exclusive economic zones', *Leaflet – Focus 68*, The Department of Energy and Marine Technology Directorate Ltd, 1988, reproduced with permission of HMSO; *Figures 1.15, 1.16:* C. Sanger, pp. 57,179, *Ordering the Oceans: the making of the Law of the Sea*, Zed Books and University of Toronto Press, 1986; *Figure 1.20:* adapted from Figures 12:4, 12:5 in G.L. Small, *The Blue Whale*, Columbia University Press, New York, 1971; *Figures 1.23, 1.25:* adapted from Figures 2.4, 2.1 in 'Pattern of residual near-surface currents' from *The North Sea Forum Report*, The Council for Environmental Conservation (Co ENCO), 1987. Reproduced with permission of Ciba-Geigy Plc; *Figure 1.24:* R. Milne, *New Scientist*, p. 53, 19 November 1987, IPC Magazines Ltd, World Press Network, 1990; *Figure 2.1: (top left and bottom left) The Observer*, 26 November 1989, 25 February 1990, © The Observer; *Figures 2.3 (b) (c):* R.G. Fleagle and J.A. Businger from *An Introduction to Atmospheric Physics*, © Academic Press, 1963; *Figures 2.7, 2.10, 2.11, 2.12, 2.13:* J. Gribbin, *Hothouse Earth*, Figures 2.3, 3.3, 1.1, 5.2, 5.1, Bantam Press, a division of Transworld Publishers Ltd, 1990/Bantam Books, a division of Bantam Doubleday Dell Publishing Group, Inc., 1990, © John and Mary Gribbin, 1990, and by permission of Murray Pollinger; *Figure 2.18:* Figure 10, p.128 in J.F.B. Mitchell, 'The greenhouse effect and climate change', *Reviews of Geophysics*, Vol. 27, No. 1, February 1989. Reproduced from Figures 14, 15, pp. 781, 782 in Schlesinger and Mitchell, 1987. © 1989 The American Geophysical Union; *Figure 2.20:* Figure 21, p.788 in M.E. Schlesinger and J.F.B. Mitchell, 'Climate model simulations of the equilibrium climatic response to the increased carbon dioxide', *Reviews of Geophysics*, Vol. 25, No. 4, May 1987, © 1987 The American Geophysical Union; *Figures 2.14, 2.16, 2.17, 2.19, 2.22:* adapted from SCOPE 29, *The Greenhouse Effect, Climatic Change, and Ecosystems*, edited by B. Bolin *et al.*, John Wiley & Sons, Chichester, UK, 1986; *Figures 3.2, 3.4, 3.8, 3.9, 3.14, 3.16, 3.17, 3.18, 3.19, 3.22, Box 3.1:* Diagrams from SORG (UK Stratospheric Ozone Review Group), 1987, 1988, 1990. Reproduced with permission of HMSO; *Figure 3.10:* K. Warr, 'The path to ozone loss', p.37, *New Scientist*, 27 October 1990, IPC Magazines Ltd, World Press Network 1990; *Figures 3.11, 3.21:* M.B. McElroy and R.J. Salawitch, *Science*, p. 764, Vol. 243, 10 February 1989, p. 927, 21 November 1986, American Association for

the Advancement of Science, © AAAS; *Figure 3.13:* R.P. Wayne, *Chemistry of Atmospheres,*
Figure 4.19, p.159, The Clarendon Press, 1985; *Figure 3.20:* Figure 1, p. 326 from Elwood, *et al.,*
'Relationship of melanoma and other skin cancer mortality to latitude and ultraviolet radiation
in the US and Canada', *International Journal of Epidemiology,* Vol. 3, 1974, by permission of
Oxford University Press, 1974; *Figure 4.1 (and Figure 2.15):* J.T. Houghton, J.T. Jenkins and
J. Ephraums, *Climate Change: the IPCC scientific assessment,* Cambridge University Press, 1990.
© WMO/UNEP/IPCC, 1990; *Figures 4.6, 4.7(b), 4.11, 4.15:* Intergovernmental Panel on Climate
Change: Working Group Three Report, *Formulation of Strategies,* June 1990, © WMO/UNEP/
IPCC, 1990; *Figures 4.9, 4.12:* M. Grubb, 'Fossil carbon emissions per unit RGNP', p.18,
Figure 5b, 'Fossil carbon emissions' p. 15, Figure 2a, *The Greenhouse Effect: negotiating targets,*
The Royal Institute of International Affairs, 1989; *Figure 5.1:* P. Harrison, Map 3 'The colonial
past', from *Inside the Third World,* Penguin Books, 1987. Copyright © P. Harrison, 1987;
Figure 5.2(b): Michael Smith, 'The changing profile of the Aral Sea', p.13, *Geographical Magazine,*
March 1990; *Figure 5.3:* Friends of the Earth; *Figure 5.4:* 'Rainforest Fact File', *The Guardian,*
8 December 1989. Copyright © Guardian Newspapers Ltd, 1989; *Figure 5.5 (left):* Friends of the
Earth; *Figure 5.7:* D.J. Bogue, *Principles of Demography,* John Wiley & Sons, 1969; *Figure 5.8:*
S. Kuznets, *Economic Growth of Nations,* Harvard University Press, 1971. Reprinted with
permission of Harvard University Press. Copyright © Harvard University Press, 1971;
Figure 6.2: from illustration by Ian Worpole (adapted from the World Bank *World Development
Report 1988),* in J. McNeill, 'Strategies for sustainable economic development', *Scientific
American* (international edition), September 1989; *Figure 6.3:* from graphic by Paddy Allen from
World Bank data, from *The Guardian,* 23 February 1990. Copyright © Guardian Newspapers,
1990; *Figure 6.4:* P. Crosson and N. Rosenberg, 'Strategies for agriculture' from *Scientific
American,* September 1989; *Figure 6.5:* W.C. Clark and R.E. Munn, 'Per capita income in the
USA and developing countries', from *Sustainable Development of the Biosphere,* Cambridge
University Press, 1987. Permission to reproduce from International Institute for Applied
Systems Analysis, Austria; *Figure 6.6:* D. Pearce, A. Markandya and E.B. Barbier, *Blueprint for a
Green Economy,* Earthscan Publications Ltd, 1989. Copyright © David Pearce, Anil Markandya,
Edward B. Barbier, 1989.

Tables

Table 5.1: E. Hobsbawm, *Industry and Empire,* p. 115, Penguin Books, 1969. Copyright ©
E. J. Hobsbawm, 1968, 1969; *Table 6.1:* an illustration by Johnny Johnson from J. McNeill,
'Strategies for sustainable economic development', *Scientific American* (international edition),
September 1989; *Tables 6.2, 6.5: Our Common Future,* by The World Commission on
Environment Development, published by Oxford University Press, 1988. Copyright © World
Commission on Environment and Development, 1987; *Tables 6.3, 6.4:* W.C. Clark and R.E.
Munn, *Sustainable Development of the Biosphere,* pp. 106, 107, Cambridge University Press, 1987.
Permission to reproduce from International Institute for Applied Systems Analysis, Austria.

Photographs and cartoons

p.23: David Parker/Science Photo Library; *p.26:* Popperfoto; *p.33:* Topham Picture Library;
p.36: Simon Fraser/Science Photo Library; *p.42:* Paddy/Clyde Sanger/Zed Press, London, and
The University of Toronto Press, Toronto, 1986; *p.52:* Graham Burns/Environmental Picture
Library; *p.53:* Mary Evans Picture Library; *p.57:* Rapho/M.Fraudreau/Science Photo Library;
p.63: Peter Dunne/The Times; *p.66: (top left)* Pete Fryer/Environmental Picture Library,
(top right) © Greenpeace, (bottom) David Parker/Science Photo Library; *p.85:* Mary Evans
Picture Library; *p.87:* Fred Espanak/Science Photo Library; *p.89:* © British Antarctic Survey;
p.91: Adam Hart-Davis/Science Photo Library; *p.92:* Peter Menzel/Science Photo Library;
p.103: Barnaby's Picture Library/Oliver; *p.121: (left)* National Cavity Insulation Association
Ltd, *(right)* Vanessa Miles/The Environmental Picture Library, *(centre)* © Eric Brissaud/
Gamma/Frank Spooner Agency; *p.141:* Frank Lane Picture Agency/photo by Alfred Saunders;
p.142: © Pete Addis; *pp.143, 144:* © British Antarctic Survey; *p.145: (left)* NASA/Science Photo
Library, *(right)* © British Antarctic Survey; *p.146:* NASA/Science Photo Library; *p.153:* James
Stevenson/Science Photo Library; *p.154:* Courtesy Professor Alan Teramura; *p.157:* John
Storey/*World Medicine; p.161 :*© Hector Breeze/Guardian Newspapers Ltd; *p.162: (top)*
Associated Press, *(below)* © Greenpeace; *p.164:* © David Austin/*New Scientist; p.187:* Simon
Fraser/Science Photo Library; *p.189:* Peter Dickerson/Susan Griggs Agency; *p.190:* © David

Austin/*New Scientist*; *p.191:* Adam Hart-Davis/Science Photo Library; *p.192:* © Greenpeace/ Midgley; *p.193:* © Carlos Reyes/Andes Press Agency; *p.197:* Scott Willis/*San José Mercury News*. Copyright © Scott Willis/Copley News Service; *p.211:* Furness Museum, Barrow; *p.213: (both)* Mary Evans Picture Library; *p.216: (both)* Mansell Collection; *p.217:* Crown Copyright/ Trustees of the Victoria and Albert Museum; *p.218:* Mansell Collection; *p.223:* Graphic by WiP (a Polish anarchist group); *p.225: (both)* Vladimir Siomin/Comptoir Photo/Rapho/Network; *p.227:* © Greenpeace/Morgan; *p.230:* © Third World Network Features and Consumers' Association of Penang; *pp.231, 232:* Susan Cunningham; *p.236:* from *Green Cartoons for Care*, Earthscan, 1990; *p.244:* Norwegian Embassy Press and Information Service; *p.249:* Jeremy Hartley/Oxfam; *p.250: IIDC Campaign Newsletter*, No. 14, October 1988/89; *p. 253:* YDC International Secretariat, Amsterdam; *p.253:* © 1986 Chicago Tribune; *p.255:* Maggie Murray/ Format; *p.256:* Jenny Matthews/Format/IPPF; *p.263:* Mark Edwards/Still Pictures; *p.269:* Lucy Arnold; *p.274: ICDA News*, March 1984; *p.275:* International Monetary Fund; *p.276:* Punchline by Christian, *New Internationalist*, © Christian 1986.

Text

Extract in Chapter 5, whole article in Appendix: 'In search of a greener politics', *The Guardian*, 5 February 1990. © Guardian News Services Ltd, 1990; *Box 6.10:* R. Williams, pp. 6, 20 from pamphlet: 'Socialism and Ecology', Socialist Environment and Resources Association, 1982.

Index

(Page numbers in *italics* refer to figures, tables and photographs.)